MTP International Review of Science

Biochemistry Series One

Consultant Editors

H. L. Kornberg, F.R.S. and
D. C. Phillips, F.R.S.

Publisher's Note

The MTP International Review of Science is an important new venture in scientific publishing, which is presented by Butterworths in association with MTP Medical and Technical Publishing Co. Ltd. and University Park Press, Baltimore. The basic concept of the Review is to provide regular authoritative reviews of entire disciplines. Chemistry was taken first as the problems of literature survey are probably more acute in this subject than in any other. Physiology and Biochemistry followed naturally. As a matter of policy, the authorship of the MTP Review of Science is international and distinguished, the subject coverage is extensive, systematic and critical, and most important of all, it is intended that new issues of the Review will be published at regular intervals.

In the MTP Review of Chemistry (Series One), Inorganic, Physical and Organic Chemistry are comprehensively reviewed in 33 text volumes and 3 index volumes. Physiology (Series One) consists of 8 volumes and Biochemistry (Series One) 12 volumes, each volume individually indexed. Details follow. In general, the Chemistry (Series One) reviews cover the period 1967 to 1971, and Physiology and Biochemistry (Series One) reviews up to 1972. It is planned to start in 1974 the MTP International Review of Science (Series Two), consisting of a similar set of volumes covering developments in a two year period.

The MTP International Review of Science has been conceived within a carefully organised editorial framework. The overall plan was drawn up, and the volume editors appointed by seven consultant editors. In turn, each volume editor planned the coverage of his field and appointed authors to write on subjects which were within the area of their own research experience. No geographical restriction was imposed. Hence the 500 or so contributions to the MTP Review of Science come from many countries of the world and provide an authoritative account of progress.

Butterworth & Co. (Publishers) Ltd.

BIOCHEMISTRY SERIES ONE

Consultant Editors
H. L. Kornberg, F.R.S.
Department of Biochemistry University of Leicester and
D. C. Phillips, F.R.S., *Department of Zoology, University of Oxford*

Volume titles and Editors

1 **CHEMISTRY OF MACRO-MOLECULES**
Professor H. Gutfreund, *University of Bristol*

2 **BIOCHEMISTRY OF CELL WALLS AND MEMBRANES**
Dr. C. F. Fox, *University of California*

3 **ENERGY TRANSDUCING MECHANISMS**
Professor E. Racker, *Cornell University, New York*

4 **BIOCHEMISTRY OF LIPIDS**
Professor T. W. Goodwin, F.R.S., *University of Liverpool*

5 **BIOCHEMISTRY OF CARBO-HYDRATES**
Professor W. J. Whelan. *University of Miami*

6 **BIOCHEMISTRY OF NUCLEIC ACIDS**
Professor K. Burton, F.R.S., *University of Newcastle upon Tyne*

7 **SYNTHESIS OF AMINO ACIDS AND PROTEINS**
Professor H. R. V. Arnstein, *King's College, University of London*

8 **BIOCHEMISTRY OF HORMONES**
Professor H. V. Rickenberg, *National Jewish Hospital & Research Center, Colorado*

9 **BIOCHEMISTRY OF CELL DIFFER-ENTIATION**
Dr. J. Paul, *The Beatson Institute for Cancer Research, Glasgow*

10 **DEFENCE AND RECOGNITION**
Professor R. R. Porter, F.R.S., *University of Oxford*

11 **PLANT BIOCHEMISTRY**
Professor D. H. Northcote, F.R.S., *University of Cambridge*

12 **PHYSIOLOGICAL AND PHARMACO-LOGICAL BIOCHEMISTRY**
Dr. H. F. K. Blaschko, F.R.S., *University of Oxford*

PHYSIOLOGY SERIES ONE

Consultant Editors
A. C. Guyton,
Department of Physiology and Biophysics, University of Mississippi Medical Center and
D. Horrobin,
Department of Medical Physiology, University College of Nairobi

Volume titles and Editors

1 **CARDIOVASCULAR PHYSIOLOGY**
Professor A. C. Guyton and Dr. C. E. Jones, *University of Mississippi Medical Center*

2 **RESPIRATORY PHYSIOLOGY**
Professor J. G. Widdicombe, *St. George's Hospital, London*

3 **NEUROPHYSIOLOGY**
Professor C. C. Hunt, *Washington University School of Medicine, St. Louis*

4 **GASTROINTESTINAL PHYSIOLOGY**
Professor E. D. Jacobson and Dr. L. L. Shanbour, *University of Texas Medical School*

5 **ENDOCRINE PHYSIOLOGY**
Professor S. M. McCann, *University of Texas*

6 **KIDNEY AND URINARY TRACT PHYSIOLOGY**
Professor K. Thurau, *University of Munich*

7 **ENVIRONMENTAL PHYSIOLOGY**
Professor D. Robertshaw, *University of Nairobi*

8 **REPRODUCTIVE PHYSIOLOGY**
Professor R. O. Greep, *Harvard Medical School*

INORGANIC CHEMISTRY SERIES ONE

Consultant Editor
H. J. Emeléus, F.R.S.
Department of Chemistry
University of Cambridge

Volume titles and Editors

1 **MAIN GROUP ELEMENTS—HYDROGEN AND GROUPS I-IV**
Professor M. F. Lappert, *University of Sussex*

2 **MAIN GROUP ELEMENTS—GROUPS V AND VI**
Professor C. C. Addison, F.R.S. and Dr. D. B. Sowerby, *University of Nottingham*

3 **MAIN GROUP ELEMENTS—GROUP VII AND NOBLE GASES**
Professor Viktor Gutmann, *Technical University of Vienna*

4 **ORGANOMETALLIC DERIVATIVES OF THE MAIN GROUP ELEMENTS**
Dr. B. J. Aylett, *Westfield College, University of London*

5 **TRANSITION METALS—PART 1**
Professor D. W. A. Sharp, *University of Glasgow*

6 **TRANSITION METALS—PART 2**
Dr. M. J. Mays, *University of Cambridge*

7 **LANTHANIDES AND ACTINIDES**
Professor K. W. Bagnall, *University of Manchester*

8 **RADIOCHEMISTRY**
Dr. A. G. Maddock, *University of Cambridge*

9 **REACTION MECHANISMS IN INORGANIC CHEMISTRY**
Professor M. L. Tobe, *University College, University of London*

10 **SOLID STATE CHEMISTRY**
Dr. L. E. J. Roberts, *Atomic Energy Research Establishment, Harwell*

INDEX VOLUME

PHYSICAL CHEMISTRY SERIES ONE

Consultant Editor
A. D. Buckingham
Department of Chemistry
University of Cambridge

Volume titles and Editors

1 **THEORETICAL CHEMISTRY**
Professor W. Byers Brown, *University of Manchester*

2 **MOLECULAR STRUCTURE AND PROPERTIES**
Professor G. Allen, *University of Manchester*

3 **SPECTROSCOPY**
Dr. D. A. Ramsay, F.R.S.C., *National Research Council of Canada*

4 **MAGNETIC RESONANCE**
Professor C. A. McDowell F.R.S.C., *University of British Columbia*

5 **MASS SPECTROMETRY**
Professor A. Maccoll, *University College, University of London*

6 **ELECTROCHEMISTRY**
Professor J. O'M Bockris, *University of Pennsylvania*

7 **SURFACE CHEMISTRY AND COLLOIDS**
Professor M. Kerker, *Clarkson College of Technology, New York*

8 **MACROMOLECULAR SCIENCE**
Professor C. E. H. Bawn, F.R.S., *University of Liverpool*

9 **CHEMICAL KINETICS**
Professor J. C. Polanyi, F.R.S., *University of Toronto*

10 **THERMOCHEMISTRY AND THERMO-DYNAMICS**
Dr. H. A. Skinner, *University of Manchester*

11 **CHEMICAL CRYSTALLOGRAPHY**
Professor J. Monteath Robertson, F.R.S., *University of Glasgow*

12 **ANALYTICAL CHEMISTRY—PART 1**
Professor T. S. West, *Imperial College, University of London*

13 **ANALYTICAL CHEMISTRY—PART 2**
Professor T. S. West, *Imperial College, University of London*

INDEX VOLUME

ORGANIC CHEMISTRY SERIES ONE

Consultant Editor
D. H. Hey, F.R.S.,
Department of Chemistry
King's College, University of London

Volume titles and Editors

1 **STRUCTURE DETERMINATION IN ORGANIC CHEMISTRY**
Professor W. D. Ollis, F.R.S., *University of Sheffield*

2 **ALIPHATIC COMPOUNDS**
Professor N. B. Chapman, *Hull University*

3 **AROMATIC COMPOUNDS**
Professor H. Zollinger, *Swiss Federal Institute of Technology*

4 **HETEROCYCLIC COMPOUNDS**
Dr. K. Schofield, *University of Exeter*

5 **ALICYCLIC COMPOUNDS**
Professor W. Parker, *University of Stirling*

6 **AMINO ACIDS, PEPTIDES AND RELATED COMPOUNDS**
Professor D. H. Hey, F.R.S., and Dr. D. I. John, *King's College, University of London*

7 **CARBOHYDRATES**
Professor G. O. Aspinall, *Trent University, Ontario*

8 **STEROIDS**
Dr. W. F. Johns, *G. D. Searle & Co., Chicago*

9 **ALKALOIDS**
Professor K. Wiesner, F.R.S., *University of New Brunswick*

10 **FREE RADICAL REACTIONS**
Professor W. A. Waters, F.R.S., *University of Oxford*

INDEX VOLUME

MTP International Review of Science

Biochemistry
Series One

Volume 11
Plant Biochemistry

Edited by **D. H. Northcote, F.R.S.**
University of Cambridge

Butterworths · London
University Park Press · Baltimore

THE BUTTERWORTH GROUP

ENGLAND
Butterworth & Co (Publishers) Ltd
London: 88 Kingsway, WC2B 6AB

AUSTRALIA
Butterworths Pty Ltd
Sydney: 586 Pacific Highway 2067
Melbourne: 343 Little Collins Street, 3000
Brisbane: 240 Queen Street, 4000

NEW ZEALAND
Butterworths of New Zealand Ltd
Wellington: 26–28 Waring Taylor Street, 1

SOUTH AFRICA
Butterworth & Co (South Africa) (Pty) Ltd
Durban: 152–154 Gale Street

ISBN 0 408 70505 1

UNIVERSITY PARK PRESS

U.S.A. and CANADA
University Park Press
Chamber of Commerce Building
Baltimore, Maryland, 21202

Library of Congress Cataloging in Publication Data
Northcote, Donald Henry.
Plant biochemistry.
(Biochemistry, series one, v. 11) (MTP international review of science)
1. Botanical chemistry. 2. Biological chemistry.
I. Title. II. Series. III. Series: MTP international review of science. [DNLM: 1. Biochemistry.
2. Plants. W1BI633 ser. 1 v. 11 1974/QK861 P713 1974]
QP501.B527 vol. 11 [QK861] 574.1′92′08s [581.1′9′2]
ISBN 0-8391-1075-8 74-6261

MTP MEDICAL AND TECHNICAL PUBLISHING CO LTD
St Leonard's House
St Leonardgate
Lancaster, Lancs
and
BUTTERWORTH & CO (PUBLISHERS) LTD

Typeset and printed in Great Britain by
REDWOOD BURN LIMITED
Trowbridge & Esher
and bound by R. J. Acford Ltd, Chichester, Sussex

Consultant Editors' Note

The MTP International Review of Science is designed to provide a comprehensive, critical and continuing survey of progress in research. Nowhere is such a survey needed as urgently as in those areas of knowledge that deal with the molecular aspects of biology. Both the volume of new information, and the pace at which it accrues, threaten to overwhelm the reader: it is becoming increasingly difficult for a practitioner of one branch of biochemistry to understand even the language used by specialists in another.

The present series of 12 volumes is intended to counteract this situation. It has been the aim of each Editor and the contributors to each volume not only to provide authoritative and up-to-date reviews but carefully to place these reviews into the context of existing knowledge, so that their significance to the overall advances in biochemical understanding can be understood also by advanced students and by non-specialist biochemists. It is particularly hoped that this series will benefit those colleagues to whom the whole range of scientific journals is not readily available. Inevitably, some of the information in these articles will already be out of date by the time these volumes appear: it is for that reason that further or revised volumes will be published as and when this is felt to be appropriate.

In order to give some kind of coherence to this series, we have viewed the description of biological processes in molecular terms as a progression from the properties of macromolecular cell components, through the functional interrelations of those components, to the manner in which cells, tissues and organisms respond biochemically to external changes. Although it is clear that many important topics have been ignored in a collection of articles chosen in this manner, we hope that the authority and distinction of the contributions will compensate for our shortcomings of thematic selection. We certainly welcome criticisms, and solicit suggestions for future reviews, from interested readers.

It is our pleasure to thank all who have collaborated to make this venture possible—the volume editors, the chapter authors, and the publishers.

Leicester — H. L. Kornberg

Oxford — D. C. Phillips

Preface

The topics discussed in this volume are unique to plants but they have applications to all branches of biochemistry.

In those subjects which are concerned with the hormonal control of plant metabolism and growth, attention is focused on the interrelationship of the various parts of a complex multicellular organism. These studies have a direct relevance to work on metabolic control and cellular differentiation in animal and bacterial tissues.

In recent years new techniques have led to fresh concepts for the structure of cell membranes. The function of the chloroplast depends upon movements to and from the organelle of metabolic intermediates and the account of the mechanisms of these translocations is therefore important for any investigation of biological membranes in general.

All aspects of carbohydrate metabolism and polysaccharide synthesis occur in plant tissues. The reviews on these subjects describe the versatility of the enzyme systems of the cells and illustrate how these tissues are very useful for studies of the interdependence and control of the various pathways of sugar metabolism. Complex polysaccharides are a characteristic feature of plant cells and the algae elaborate many novel neutral and acidic polysaccharides as parts of their cell walls. The description of the chemistry and biochemistry of these compounds adds very significant information about the biological role of the polysaccharides within the structure of a living tissue.

Modern ideas of theoretical chemistry are at present being applied to the role of the enzymes in the reactions they bring about. Unique systems for the synthesis of the aromatic ring and nitrogen fixation occur in plant tissues. These take place by a series of very complex biochemical reactions which illustrate many aspects of the mechanism of enzymic processes. The accounts of the investigation of the research in these subjects are relevant to the whole field of enzyme biochemistry and chemistry.

This volume presents reviews of a few specialised subjects which have not been extensively reviewed previously but which nevertheless have a general interest to other workers in biochemistry. I am grateful indeed for the authoritative and interesting contributions which each of the authors has made.

Cambridge D. H. Northcote

Contents

1
Chloroplast and Cell— The movement of certain key substances, etc. across the chloroplast envelope

D. A. WALKER
University of Sheffield

Glossary

2PGA	2-phosphoglycerate
PGA	3-phosphoglycerate
DPGA	1,3-diphosphoglycerate
G3P	glyceraldehyde 3-phosphate
DHAP	dihydroxyacetone phosphate
R5P	ribose 5-phosphate
Ru5P	ribulose 5-phosphate
Xu5P	xylulose 5-phosphate

RDP	ribulose 1,5-diphosphate
FDP	fructose 1,6-diphosphate
F6P	fructose 6-phosphate
G1P	glucose 1-phosphate
G6P	glucose 6-phosphate
6PG	6-phosphogluconate
FDP	fructose 1,6-diphosphate
S7P	sedoheptulose 7-phosphate
SDP	sedoheptulose 1,7-diphosphate
PEP	phosphoenolpyruvate
AMP	adenosine monophosphate
ADP	adenosine diphosphate
ATP	adenoside triphosphate
NADP–NADPH	nicotinamide adenine phosphate dinucleotide phosphate
Pi	orthophosphate
PiPi	inorganic pyrophosphate
OAA	oxaloacetic acid
C3 photosynthesis	Benson–Calvin pathway with PGA as first product
C4 photosynthesis	Hotch–Slack–Kortschack pathway with oxaloacetate as first product

---

1.1 INTRODUCTION

According to Rabinowitch[1] 'the reduction of carbon dioxide by green plants is the largest single chemical process on earth'. The tonnage fixed is probably of the order of 10^{11} tons per annum, 100 times greater than the world's combined output of coal, oil and minerals. Much of this has to move into the chloroplast in one form and out in another. Certainly the bulk of the organic matter from which we are formed has at some stage traversed the chloroplast envelope at least once. In these respects the transport of metabolites between the chloroplast and its immediate environment constitutes a biological process of some considerable importance. Even so, it is not the sheer magnitude of this process which promotes contemporary interest but rather its implications in the area of metabolic control and interaction. In the 1950s, plant biochemists welcomed with something akin to relief the revelations of the Benson–Calvin cycle[2] and the discovery of photosynthetic phosphorylation[3-7]. Since Hill's historic paper in 1937[8], illuminated chloroplasts are seen to be capable of oxygen evolution but apparently incapable of assimilating carbon without some undefined assistance from the cytoplasm[8-10]. Following the work of Arnon, Whatley *et al.*[3-6], chloroplasts seemingly passed into the realms of self-sufficiency and any lingering doubts about their ability to assimilate carbon unaided became even more difficult to sustain in the face of new preparative techniques[11-13] yielding chloroplasts apparently capable of converting CO_2 to carbohydrates as readily as the intact plant[13-15]. In the meantime, however, enzymology had entered the allosteric age and the new expression 'biomembrane' had already acquired connotations of 'control'. What so often intrigues the contemporary biochemist is, therefore, not the

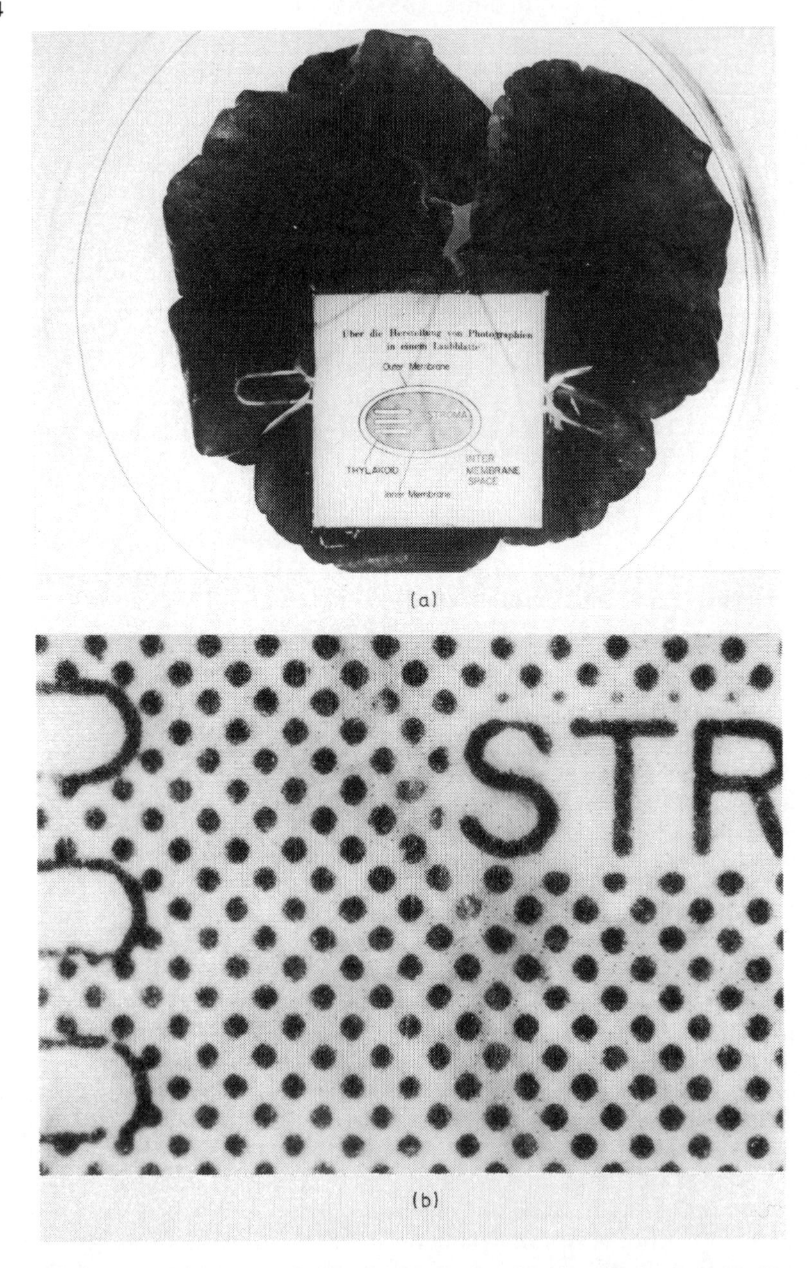

Figure 1.1 (a) Starch print (Section 1.1) produced by illuminating a starch-free *Pelargonium* leaf through a photographic negative. The phase 'On the production of photographs with a leaf' is a facsimile of the title of a chapter in a book by Molisch[19]. The diagram of the chloroplast is from Heldt *et al.*[68]

(b) Detail of (a) to show degree of resolution. Note that starch is not removed from guard cells during darkness so that these remain visible over the whole surface relative independence of chloroplasts and mitochondria but the interaction between these organelles and their immediate cellular environment and their role in the economy of the cell. Accordingly this article attempts to outline the movement (or lack of movement) of certain metabolites and co-enzymes across the chloroplast envelope and the relationship of these movements to carbon metabolism and energy transfer. For this purpose the chloroplast is taken to consist of two compartments (see schematic diagram in Figure 1.1). The first of these (the thylakoid compartment) is enclosed within the series of flattened membrane sacs which comprise the photochemical apparatus and its associated pigments. The second (the stromal compartment) houses the enzymes of the photosynthetic carbon cycle. The whole organelle is surrounded by an envelope comprised of two membranes.

1.2 STARCH PRINTS

For years, the 'starch print'[16] has been one of the classics of practical instruction in elementary botany. In principle, a suitable leaf is made free of starch either by growing it under low light or keeping it in the dark for 48 h or more (some plants will die in the dark before they lose all of their starch). At this stage, if the leaf is killed by brief immersion in boiling water and the chlorophyll extracted in hot aqueous ethanol, the leaf tissue is seen to be white or pale yellow. If it is then washed in water and immersed in a dilute solution of iodine in potassium iodide, it becomes only slightly more yellow or pale orange as it takes up the iodine. On the other hand, if half of the leaf is brightly illuminated for an hour or more prior to killing, then the subsequent starch–iodine reaction[17, 18] almost entirely blackens that half of the leaf (only amylose–iodine in dilute concentration gives a clear blue[17, 18], in higher concentration and combined with the purple of amylopectin–iodine[17, 18]; the overall effect is black). Described in these terms, the starch-print does not appear to pose any great problems. Evidently starch is a food reserve which is consumed by dark respiration and replenished by photosynthesis[16]. For this reason, it reappears only in those parts of the leaf which were illuminated. This attractively simple-minded explanation is, however, inadequate in at least two respects. The first is the failure of starch formation to spread even slightly beyond the illuminated areas. This has been apparent since Molisch[19] published starch prints approaching the same degree of resolution which might be expected of a photographic paper. A more recent example is shown in Figure 1.1 and it will be seen how clearly the details of a photographic negative are reproduced in starch when the negative is placed between an initially starch-free leaf and a light source. The second inadequacy is the finding that leaves will form starch in the dark if they are floated on sugar solutions[20-24]. If these two facts are put together, the simplicity of the first explanation is hard to maintain. Clearly there is no over-riding requirement for light in starch synthesis because the leaf can be made to synthesise starch in the dark just as starch synthesis occurs in certain plant tissues (like potato tubers) which are not normally exposed to light at all while starch accumulation is at its height. The degree of resolution in starch prints is obviously related to the fact that starch in leaves is formed only in plastids[16, 19, 25] and

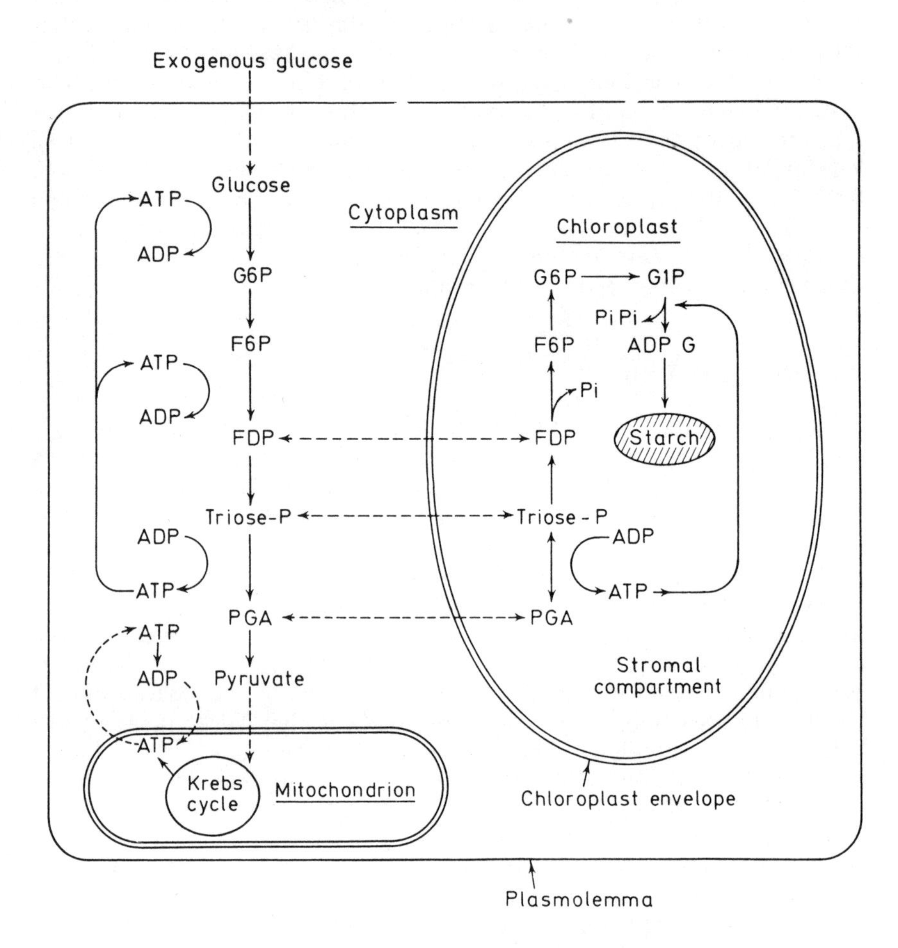

Figure 1.2 Possible co-operation between cytoplasm and chloroplast in the synthesis of starch from exogenous glucose (Section 1.2). Biochemically the shortest sequence is via G1P and ADP–glucose but ATP is required for the penultimate step and the only presently known possibility of ATP formation within the chloroplast in the dark is in the oxidation of triose phosphate to PGA. Other limitations would be imposed by the relative impermeability of the chloroplast envelope to ADP–ATP (Section 1.6.1) and hexose monophosphates (Section 1.5.1.3). FDP translocation (Section 1.5.1.4) would probably be indirect, via triose phosphate

to the vast number of chloroplasts* in a leaf but it is not apparent why photosynthetically produced metabolites fail to substitute for externally added sugars. In order to promote starch synthesis in the dark such exogenous sugars must penetrate the leaf and they or their derivatives must presumably penetrate the chloroplast. However, although the leaf can export sugars[26] (often at a sufficient rate to maintain fairly massive accumulation of starch elsewhere, as in the potato) the average leaf used in starch print experiments seems entirely incapable of using endogenous photosynthetic metabolites for this purpose. If this were not so the high degree of resolution would be lost as starch synthesis took place in areas immediately adjacent to those which were illuminated. Thus the problem posed by the starch print is not the formation of starch in the light but the absence of starch in those parts of the leaf which were shaded by the negative. This is a clear indication of the existence of sophisticated control mechanisms which control the transport of metabolites across the chloroplast envelope and the operation of synthetic processes within the stroma.

What we can also learn from starch prints which is not in any way speculative is that the enzymes required for at least the terminal stages of starch synthesis[29] and the preliminary stages of starch degradation[29] must be present within the chloroplasts of starch-producing species. Added to the information which has been forthcoming from experiments with isolated chloroplasts (see e.g. Arnon[30], Gibbs[31]), this would put beyond reasonable doubt the proposition that the chloroplast is self-sufficient to the extent that it can synthesise starch from CO_2 without assistance from the cytoplasm. To what extent the chloroplast and the cytoplasm co-operate in the synthesis of starch from exogenous sugars is not known but a possible sequence based on established reactions[29] and movements[39] (see also Sections 1.5 and 1.6) is given in Figure 1.2. If the direct movement of ATP/ADP (Section 1.6.1) and hexose phosphates (Section 1.5.1.3) is too slow to meet the requirement of starch synthesis in the dark, then such synthesis from free sugars would almost inevitably rest on influx of triose phosphate and internal synthesis of ATP. A possible contribution of photosynthetically derived ATP to starch synthesis from exogenous sugars in the light[24] could also involve the operation of an ATP/ADP shuttle (Section 1.6.2 and Figure 1.12).

1.3 THE SITE OF SUCROSE SYNTHESIS

In discussing starch synthesis it has been concluded that part of the reaction sequence outlined in Figure 1.2 occurs within the chloroplast and allusion has been made to the belief that sucrose is a major, if not the principal, form in which carbohydrate is moved about the plant[26]. *A priori* it would not be unreasonable to suppose that sucrose, an early end-product of photosynthesis[2] was also synthesised within the chloroplast and that elaborated carbon was exported across the chloroplast in this form. In fact, evidence favouring

* Given a chlorophyll content of *ca.* 0.1% of the fresh weight[27] and supposing that each chloroplast contains 2.5×10^{-12}g chlorophyll[28] a leaf weighing 5g would contain *ca.* 2×10^{9} chloroplasts (i.e. as many chloroplasts as there are people on the earth at this time).

the former supposition is not unequivocal and on the latter point there is evidence to the contrary. Since the development of procedures which allowed the separation of relatively intact and active chloroplasts[11-13] (for a review see Walker and Crofts[15]), many hundreds of chromatograms[7, 13, 30-33, 59, 60, 167] have been made of the products of their photosynthetic assimilation of $^{14}CO_2$. This work was carried out in a number of laboratories under a wide variety of conditions and until 1967 there was agreement (see e.g. Gibbs *et al.*[33]) that sucrose could not be found as an important product. Results which were to shatter this unanimity then came from Gibbs' laboratory where on several occasions, and with an apparent seasonal periodicity, sucrose has been demonstrated as a major constituent[34, 35]. On these occasions, there was no doubt that the product formed was sucrose, that it was present in large quantities, and that the intra-molecular distribution of ^{14}C was consistent with its formation via the normal operation of the Benson–Calvin cycle[2] and subsequent condensation of six carbon units[34, 35]. Moreover, work with chloroplasts isolated by both aqueous[36] and non-aqueous[37] methods has indicated that all the enzymes required for the sequence shown in Figure 1.3

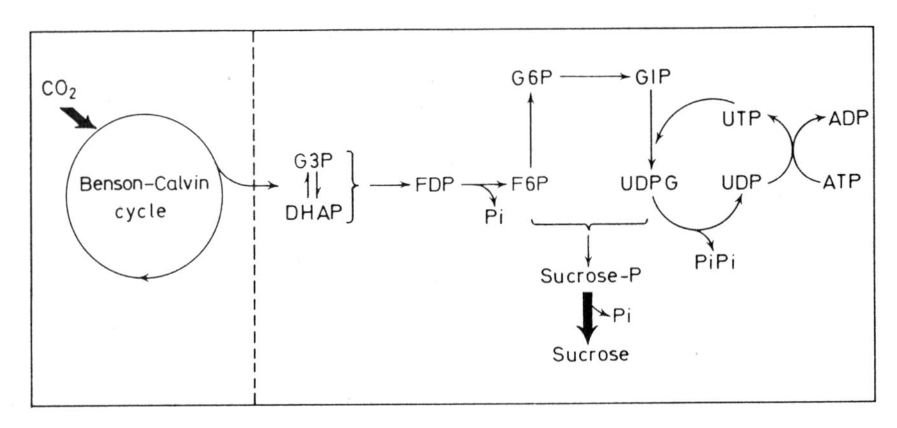

Figure 1.3 Scheme to show photosynthetic production of sucrose from CO_2 (Section 1.3). The site of sucrose synthesis is in doubt so that the reactions which are shown in the right-hand compartment may occur only in the cytoplasm. If sucrose is synthesised within the chloroplast it is unlikely to be exported as such because of the permeability barrier offered by the envelope. (UDP, UTP and UDPG represent uridine diphosphate, uridine triphosphate and uridine diphosphate glucose respectively; for other abbreviations see Table 1.3)

are associated with the chloroplast fraction. There are several ways in which this evidence may be interpreted. One is to accept that sucrose synthesis is a normal event within the chloroplast but that in the vast majority of *in vitro* experiments the synthetic mechanism although present has, for some reason, not functioned[15]. (It may be noted that the exceptional chloroplast preparations which made sucrose[34, 35] were not especially active nor were they prepared in an unusual manner.) Another interpretation is that sucrose synthesis is not a normal event within the chloroplast and that the mechanism is not normally operated and perhaps not even normally present. This latter would be inconsistent with the enzyme evidence but the enzyme evidence itself has never been beyond question. Despite some electron micrographic evidence to the contrary[38], it has always been difficult to accept that non-aqueous solvents do not precipitate any cytoplasmic proteins on to chloroplast surfaces and indeed the non-aqueous technique (see Section 1.4.1) would appear, at face value, to have more validity when applied to the distribution of metabolites[39]. Until recently, however, the agreement between the aqueous and non-aqueous work made this criticism hard to sustain. What has indirectly re-opened the whole question is work by Newcomb and Frederick[40] on the location of catalase within leaf tissues. These workers have produced convincing evidence, based on electron microscopy and histochemical techniques, that this enzyme is neither cytoplasmic nor of the chloroplast but that it is entirely restricted to sub-cellular organelles called micro-bodies (the nomenclature is still evolving, see e.g. Tolbert[41] and Beevers[42]). The significance of this observation in the present context is that intact chloroplasts prepared in sugar media (similar to those employed in Gibbs' laboratory[34, 35]) always exhibit considerable catalase activity unless particularly well washed[43]. If the evidence of Newcomb and Frederick[40] is accepted, it follows that cytoplasmic enzymes and even enzymes from other organelles can become associated with chloroplasts during normal methods of isolation. This does not disprove the notion that isolated chloroplasts may possess a sucrose synthesising mechanism which they do not normally operate but it does inevitably raise fresh doubts. Also there is no present suggestion that sucrose synthesis cannot, and does not, occur within the cytoplasm[39, 44]. Indeed, Heber[39] has concluded that photosynthetically-derived sucrose originates primarily in the cytoplasm (see also Section 1.5.1.5) and Heldt's results[45] suggest that the chloroplast envelope is not freely permeable to sucrose (a conclusion supported by the use of sucrose as an osmoticum[12, 39] in chloroplast preparation). From findings such as these it can be inferred that even if chloroplasts, unaided by cytoplasmic contamination, can synthesise sucrose, they are probably incapable of exporting it at rates which would account for its appearance elsewhere.

In the light of contemporary research[46] phosphoenolpyruvate carboxylation has been cast as an adjunct to ribulose diphosphate carboxylation[47-49] rather than as an alternative to it[50, 51]. There is therefore a return to the view held some years ago[52, 53] that by far the greatest part of the carbon dioxide which enters organic combination in the higher plant must do so via the reactions of the Benson–Calvin cycle[2] and must therefore enter the chloroplast in one form or another (see Sections 1.5.2 and 1.12). Clearly this massive import must (in the long term) be balanced by equally massive export and if sucrose is not readily translocated then elaborated carbon must pass outwards in some other form. Sugar phosphates and related compounds may fill this role (see Section 1.5.2).

1.4 METHODS EMPLOYED TO STUDY THE TRANSLOCATION OF METABOLITES

1.4.1 Non-aqueous techniques

This method[54, 55, 96] has probably reached its peak in the hands of Stocking[97] and Heber *et al.*[39, 56-58]. Essentially it involves feeding $^{14}CO_2$ to an intact leaf which is then dropped into liquid air and fractionated using non-aqueous solvents to prevent the leaking of water-soluble components from the various fractions. As indicated above (Section 1.2), the major uncertainty is the extent to which metabolites located in the cytoplasm or the vacuole may be precipitated (or co-precipitated together with proteins) on to the chloroplasts.

1.4.2 Chromatography

The elucidation of the Benson–Calvin cycle was largely based on feeding $^{14}CO_2$ to *Chlorella* and undertaking radioautography of the products of photosynthesis[2]. Bassham, who made major contributions to this work, has continued to apply these two techniques at Berkeley and has extended their application to isolated chloroplasts[59, 60] (Table 1.1 and Figure 1.4). The overall

Table 1.1 Distribution of labelled metabolites between chloroplast and medium after 3 and 7 min photosynthesis in $^{14}CO_2$

	Supernatant : pellet ratio	
	After 3 *min*	*After* 7 *min*
PGA	4.8	16.6
DHAP	42.5	72.0
G3P	large	large
Pentose monophosphates	8.5	14.7
F6P	0.4	0.37
Glucose monophosphate	0.13	0.5
S7P	0.06	0.2
RDP	0.4	1.2
FDP	35.0	79.2
SDP	2.0	2.5
Glycollate	5.5	77.0

A compound which moved readily from the chloroplast into the medium would be expected to give a high ratio. For a compound which did not move at all the ratio would be zero.

usefulness of this approach is self-evident and there is little doubt that these methods, widely employed elsewhere, have been refined to the highest possible level in the kinetic studies from his laboratory. However, as applied to chloroplasts they are not beyond criticism. Contamination by non-chloroplast enzymes (see Section 1.3) is again a hazard. Chloroplasts which rupture during the experiment may release enzymes and metabolites which would otherwise be retained. Also the sheer magnitude of the work involved in extraction, chromatography, identification, qualification, etc. unavoidably limits the number of experiments and hence the extent to which critical points can be confirmed repeatedly.

1.4.3 Direct measurement of specific compounds

This technique[61, 62], used extensively in work on mitochondria, has been successfully applied to chloroplasts by Heldt[45, 63-69]. It involves the incubation

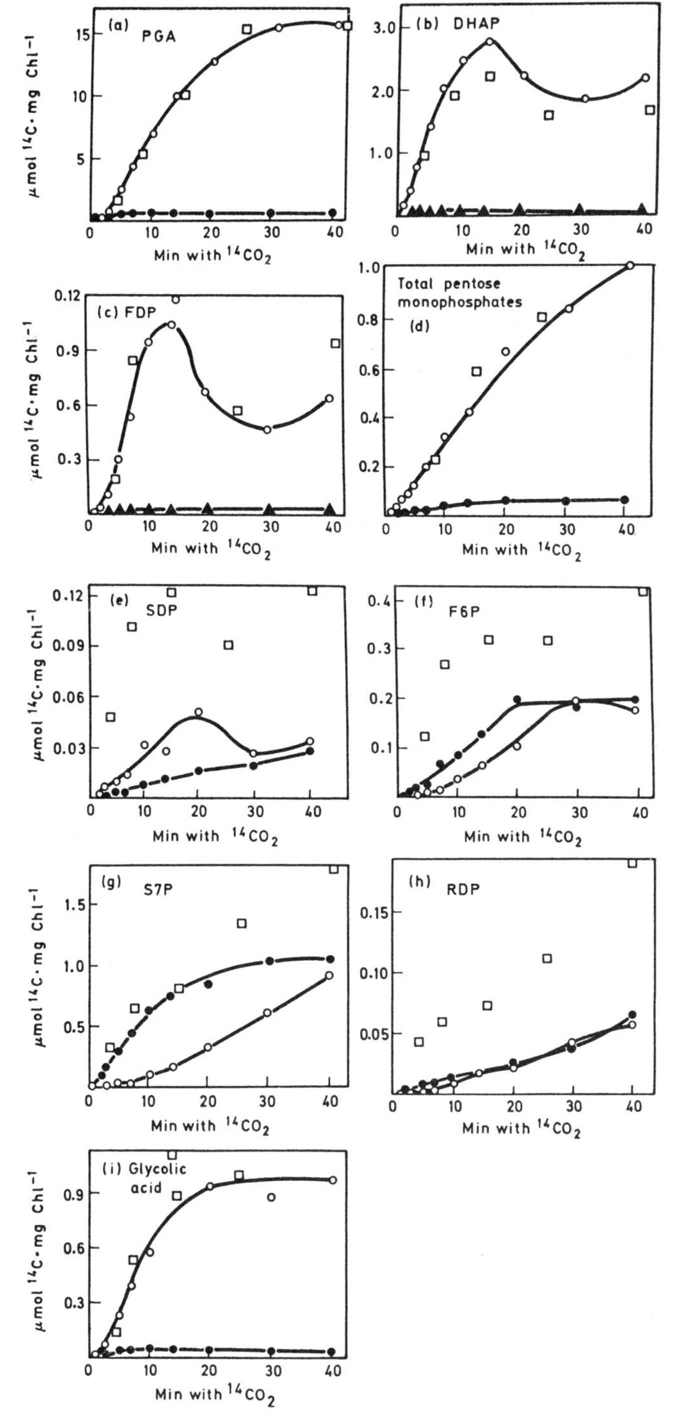

Figure 1.4 Results of chromatographic analysis (see Sections 1.4.2 and 1.5) showing distribution of ^{14}C-labelled compounds between chloroplast pellet and supernatant solution during photosynthesis with isolated chloroplasts in the presence of ^{14}C-labelled bicarbonate. Open circles denote ^{14}C-labelling of compound in supernatant solution, closed circles denote ^{14}C-labelling of compound found in the pellet, and open squares denote ^{14}C-labelling of compound in the samples that were not subjected to centrifugation. The identity of the specific compound is indicated in the figure. (From Bassham *et al.*[60], by courtesy of J. A. Bassham and Elsevier Publ. Co.)

of a particular radioactive compound with intact chloroplasts which are then centrifuged through a layer of silicone oil which removes any of the tracer which has not been taken up. Chloroplasts charged with a tracer in this fashion can also be transferred to new media and the process repeated so that both influx and efflux can be studied. The major uncertainties would appear to involve the problem of distinguishing between complete penetration, partial penetration and adsorption, and also the possibility of membrane damage occasioned by the experimental procedure.

1.4.4 Indirect methods

1.4.4.1 Shortening of induction

A great deal of information may be derived, by implication, from the response of chloroplasts to added metabolites (for reviews see e.g. Gibbs[31]; Walker and Crofts[15]). Normally, isolated chloroplasts do not fix CO_2 or evolve oxygen at maximal rates immediately upon illumination but only after an

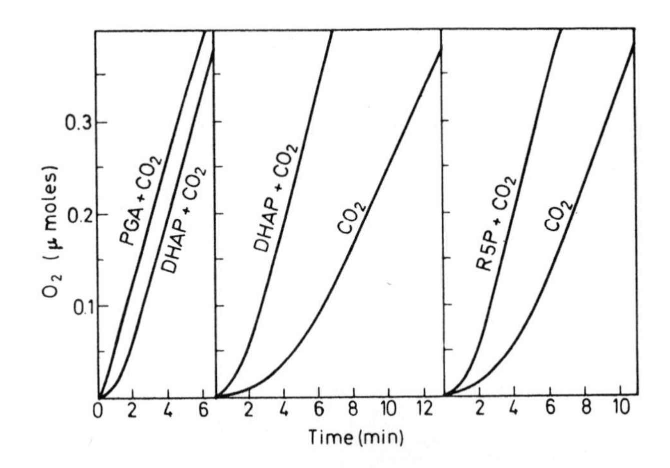

Figure 1.5 Shortening of induction (Section 1.4.4.1) by addition of metabolites (see also Section 1.5). Oxygen evolution by isolated chloroplasts with CO_2 (bicarbonate) as the sole substrate or with other additives as indicated. Each pair of traces recorded simultaneously. (From Walker *et al.*[78], by courtesy of Macmillan.)

induction period of 1–3 min[15, 31, 70, 78]. The lag is believed to represent the time which must elapse before cycle intermediates reach their optimal steady state concentrations[15, 31, 70, 78]. Shortening of the lag (Figure 1.5) by added intermediates can be interpreted as entry of the chloroplast by that intermediate[15, 31, 70, 78].

1.4.4.2 Reversal of orthophosphate inhibition

In the presence of orthophosphate in concentrations greater than 10^{-5} M the induction period is extended and at 10^{-2} M this lag is so prolonged that

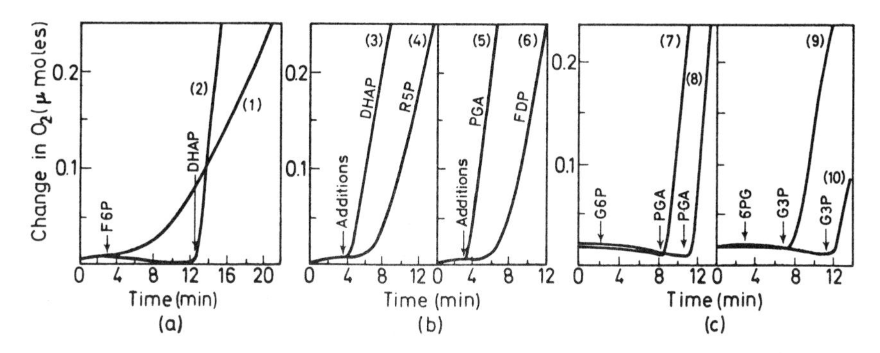

Figure 1.6 Reversal of orthophosphate inhibition (see Sections 1.4.4.2 and 1.5). Each mixture contained sufficient Pi to lengthen the initial lag indefinitely. Metabolites added as indicated. Note rapid response to PGA, DHAP *and* G3P (see Section 1.5.5.1), slow response to F6P (Section 1.5.1.3) and intermediate response to R5P (Section 1.5.1.2) and FDP (Section 1.5.1.4). (From Cockburn *et al.*[72], by courtesy of the Biochemical Society.)

it constitutes complete suppression of photosynthesis[71-73]. Again reversal of this inhibition by an added metabolite (Figures 1.6 and 1.7) may be regarded as evidence of penetration[71-73].

1.4.4.3 Reversal of other inhibitions

Gibbs *et al.* have shown reversal of arsenate inhibition, etc.[74] by cycle intermediates. The inhibition of oxygen evolution by glyceraldehyde[75] is reversed by 3-phosphoglycerate (PGA). Orthophosphate reverses the inhibition brought about by sulphate[76] and by ribose 5-phosphate (R5P)[71] in orthophosphate deficient mixtures (see Sections 1.8.1 and 1.8.2).

1.4.4.4 Reversal of depletion

In order to assimilate CO_2 intact chloroplasts require a supply of this substrate (as CO_2 or bicarbonate) and also exogenous orthophosphate. In deficient reaction mixtures, depletion is reflected by a falling off in rate and net uptake of CO_2 and evolution of oxygen eventually ceases. Photosynthesis may then be restarted by the addition of the deficient component (Figures 1.8, 1.14 and 1.15) and the rapidity of restoration can be taken as a measure of penetration[77-79]. Oxygen evolution in CO_2-deficient chloroplasts can also be restarted by PGA[78] (see also Section 1.5.1.1).

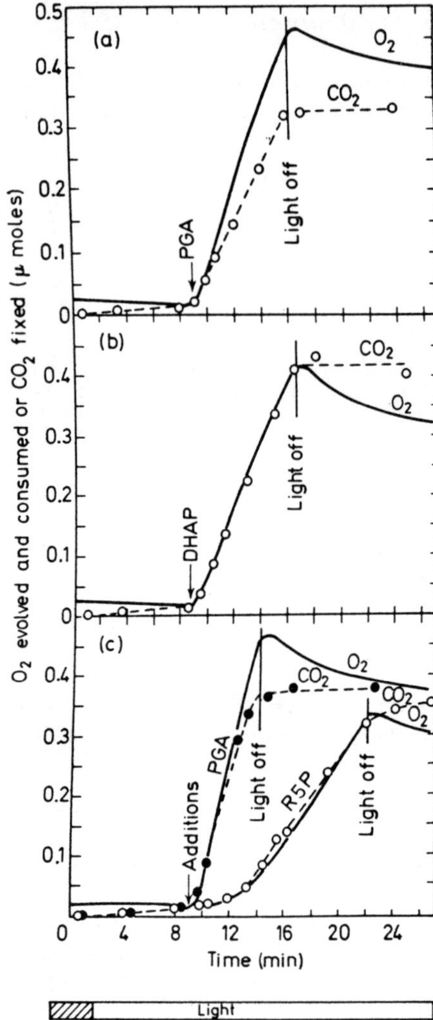

Figure 1.7 Simultaneous measurement of oxygen evolution (——) and CO_2 fixation (– – –) during reversal of Pi inhibition by PGA and sugar phosphates (see Sections 1.4.4.2 and 1.5.1.1). (From Cockburn *et al.*[72] by courtesy of the Biochemical Society.)

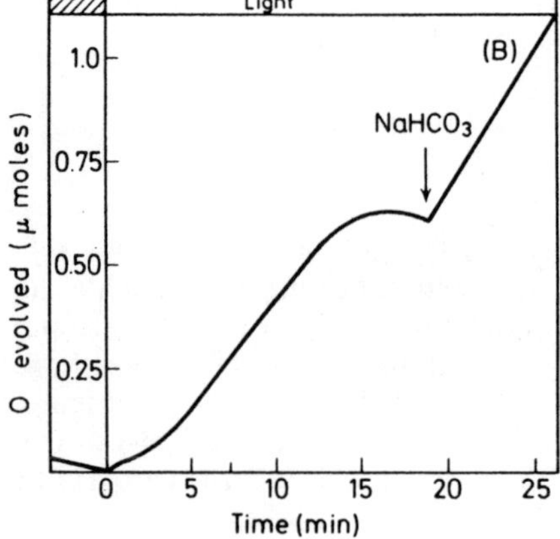

Figure 1.8 Restarting oxygen evolution of isolated chloroplasts by the addition of bicarbonate to a CO_2 deficient reaction mixture (Section 1.5.2). (From Walker and Hill[77], by courtesy of Elsevier Publ. Co.)

1.4.4.5 Catalysis by intact and envelope-free chloroplasts

As in Sections 1.4.4.1–1.4.4.4 this method depends on the presence of an enzyme or catalytic sequence within the chloroplast which is, therefore, separated from exogenous substrate by the envelope (which may or may not act as a diffusion barrier). The catalytic activity to be investigated, however, is one which does not require the presence of the intact envelope to proceed. The Hill reaction comes into this category because it occurs readily in envelope-free[71, 80] or even fragmented chloroplasts[81], whereas an entirely functional carbon reduction cycle (as indicated by the intramolecular spread of radioactivity from CO_2 throughout the products of photosynthesis) does not, since it occurs only in intact cells[82] or intact chloroplasts[83, 84]. Rupture of the chloroplast envelope, therefore, inhibits complete photosynthesis[31] and slows CO_2-fixation[89] and CO_2-dependent oxygen evolution[71] except where these are brought about by partial reactions in augmented systems[91-95]. Conversely, osmotic shock may accelerate the Hill reaction if the envelope is largely or partially impermeable to the exogenous oxidant. Thus intact chloroplasts may be rendered envelope-free in a reaction mixture simply by varying the order of addition of reactants[12, 73] and will then exhibit greatly increased rates of O_2 evolution when provided with NADP (+ ferredoxin)[34, 56, 80, 86, 87] or ferricyanide[71, 80]. The effect of shock is usually, but not always[80], more marked with NADP–ferredoxin (see Section 1.7.1) than with ferricyanide. This indicates either that ferricyanide penetrates slowly whereas NADP scarcely penetrates at all or that ferricyanide can penetrate damaged chloroplasts which (like envelope-free chloroplasts) must presumably always exist as a contaminant of so-called intact chloroplast preparations.

This 'whole *v.* broken' method has been applied not only to the Hill reaction and the Mehler reaction but to photosynthetic phosphorylation[89] (Section 1.6) and to individual enzymes[39]. The principal difficulties in interpretation arise from the presence of numbers (often unknown numbers) of ruptured chloroplasts prior to osmotic shock and, as before, to contamination by cytoplasmic enzymes or enzymes released from damaged chloroplasts. As Heber indicates[39], these difficulties can be minimised by washing (although the washing process itself can lead to envelope rupture). Results become more meaningful if they include some quantitative assessment of the proportion of intact chloroplasts present. Visual estimation[89, 90] is of only limited value because of its subjective nature and the inevitably small size of the sample examined (perhaps no more than 100 chloroplasts whereas in reaction mixtures containing the commonly used concentration of 100 μg chlorophyll ml^{-1} there will be about 40 million chloroplasts ml^{-1}, see footnote on p.7). It should also be noted that the term 'whole chloroplast' was often used in the older literature as the opposite of 'fragmented chloroplast' ('broken chloroplast' or 'grana') and did not necessarily imply the presence of an intact envelope[99]. Several attempts have been made to introduce more explicit nomenclature, see, e.g. Spencer and Unt[98] and Walker[12], and a particularly useful contribution by Hall[99]. (In this paper the terms 'whole chloroplast' and 'intact chloroplast' are synonomous and are applied to chloroplasts which retain an entire double envelope and fix CO_2 and support CO_2-dependent O_2

evolution at high rates. In these and other respects they would be designated Type A in Hall's terminology[99].)

In addition to the difficulties outlined above, all of the indirect methods (Section 1.4.4) are subject to criticism on the basis of interpretation. For example, a slow response (Figure 1.6a) might indicate slow penetration but equally it could imply quick penetration followed by slow metabolism or even slow external conversion to a freely permeable metabolite (see Section 1.8.2).

1.4.5 Summation

All of the methods used are open to criticism. The difficulties experienced in design and execution are substantial, the interpretation of results seldom unequivocal. Nevertheless, when several widely different methods are employed independently in a number of laboratories and they all point clearly to the same conclusion, then that conclusion is as authoritative as can be expected at this time. The evidence relating to the movement of a variety of key compounds is considered below and is summarised in Table 1.3.

1.5 THE TRANSPORT OF METABOLITES

1.5.1 Sugar phosphates and related compounds

1.5.1.1 3-Phosphoglycerate and the triose phosphates

Whether or not PGA is the sole product of RDP carboxylation is still not beyond doubt (for alternative possibilities see e.g. Gibbs[100]) but there is no question that PGA and the two triose phosphates (G3P and DHAP) constitute the first major products of C3 photosynthesis[2]. All three of these metabolites probably move across the envelope freely in both directions. Thus Heber (see Section 1.4.1) found labelled PGA and DHAP in the cytoplasm of the leaf within minutes of the onset of photosynthesis[44,57,88] and similarly fast movements of PGA have been reported for *Chlorella*[59,102]. Bassham *et al.* (see Section 1.4.2) have also shown that PGA, DHAP and G3P pass freely from isolated spinach chloroplasts into the suspending medium[59,60] (Table 1.1 and Figures 1.4a and 1.4b). Heldt and Rapley[64] have proposed a specific translocator for PGA, DHAP and Pi and have concluded that the entry of PGA and Pi is *ca.* 500 times as fast as that of FDP (see Section 1.8.4). Gibbs *et al.*[31,33,74,102] and Walker *et al.*[11,70,103,104] have included PGA and the triose phosphates amongst those which affect induction phenomena (Section 1.4.4.1) in isolated chloroplasts (see Figure 1.5).

In two respects PGA deserves special mention. It may be regarded as the natural Hill oxidant, being capable of initiating oxygen evolution in intact chloroplasts almost as readily as ferricyanide in envelope-free chloroplasts[77,78,105]. In these circumstances CO_2 fixation lags behind[72,75] but when PGA is used to reverse the orthophosphate inhibition of photosynthesis, CO_2

fixation and oxygen evolution start simultaneously (Figures 1.7a and 1.7c) as they do following the addition of the triose phosphates (Figure 1.7b) in the same situation[72]. Neither the mechanism of the inhibition nor its reversal is known with certainty (though the notion of accelerated export of intermediates in the presence of high concentration of orthophosphate[15] has been supported by Heldt and Rapley[65]) but this simultaneous initiation of oxygen evolution *and CO_2 fixation* by PGA is consistent with the concept of a multi-enzyme system[106] or some other fully integrated regulatory system (see also Section 1.8.4). In this regard it may also be noted that while PGA will initiate a limited oxygen evolution in the absence of CO_2, the two triose phosphates (as might be expected) initiate O_2 evolution only in the presence of high orthophosphate if CO_2 is also present[78].

More recently, Heber and Santarius[80] have proposed that DHAP is exported (see also Ref. 87) but not G3P. This conclusion was based on results obtained during an investigation of a shuttle mechanism (Figure 1.12) for the export of ATP[107] (Section 1.6.2) which involves external oxidation of G3P (see also Krause[85]). In Heber's experiments this system did not work in the absence of added triose phosphate isomerase and the simplest explanation appeared to be that G3P was formed externally following export of DHAP. The reversal of orthophosphate inhibition[71-73] (Section 1.4.4.2) works as well, and almost as quickly, with G3P as it does with DHAP (cf. lines 2 and 9, Figure 1.6) but rapid external interconversion catalysed by isomerase released from damaged chloroplasts cannot be completely ruled out even though this evidently did not occur in Heber's experiments. If both sets of results are accepted at their face value it could be inferred that G3P moves in but not out, or that the factors controlling the movement of the triose phosphates are even more complex than presently supposed (cf. Heldt *et al.*[65-68]). On the other hand, DHAP is recognised to be a major product of short-term photosynthesis[59,60] by isolated chloroplasts (its preponderance over G3P perhaps reflecting the equilibrium position of triose phosphate isomerase which favours DHAP by a factor of 10) and the failure of the shuttle (Figure 1.12) in the absence of the isomerase could merely reflect a dearth of exported G3P rather than any innate inability of G3P to move out through the envelope. Chromatography (Section 1.4.2) showed that virtually no G3P was retained in the chloroplasts but that (after 3 min) the concentration of G3P in the medium was only about 4% of the DHAP concentration[60] (Table 1.1). Because of its higher concentration within the chloroplast, more DHAP than G3P will be translocated in most circumstances.

1.5.1.2 Pentose monophosphates

Chromatography (Section 1.4.2) indicates release of ribose 5-phosphate (R5P)[59,60] and this compound also shortens induction[15,31,70,78,103,104,109] (Section 1.4.4.1) and reverses orthophosphate inhibition (Section 1.4.4.2) after a short lag[71-73]. As with PGA, the kinetics of reversal are the same whether CO_2 or O_2 is measured[72]. Ribulose 5-phosphate and xylulose 5-phosphate also reverse orthophosphate inhibition[108]. R5P reverses inhibition by iodo-acetate, etc.[74] (Section 1.4.4.3).

Table 1.2 Theoretical relationship between rate of carboxylation, endodiffusion of CO_2, affinity of RDP carboxylase for CO_2 and intercellular concentration of CO_2

Rate of carboxylation µmol mg chlorophyll^{-1} h^{-1}	[CO_2] *at the carboxylation site needed to maintain this rate* p.p.m.	*Difference between this concentration and atmospheric* p.p.m.	*Intercellular* CO_2 *concentration* p.p.m.	*Rate of endodiffusion* cm^3 cm^{-2} h^{-1}
zero	zero	300	zero	0.15†
50	50	250	50	0.125
100*	100	200	100	0.1
150	150	150	150	0.75
300	300‡	zero	300	zero
600	excess	negative	excess	negative

* The value of 100 µmol mg chlorophyll^{-1} is taken to be that achieved by the average plant under favourable conditions in its natural environment[120]. Assuming a chlorophyll content of 0.05 mg chlorophyll cm^{-2} this is approximately 22 mg (CO_2) 100 cm^{-2} h^{-1} or 1 cm^3 cm^{-2} h^{-1}

† Similarly the value of 0.150 cm^3 cm^{-2} h^{-1} for endodiffusion is approximately equal to 0.147 cm^3 cm^{-2} h^{-1} given by Heatn[130] for the calculated rate of assimilation at 20 °C in high light, with a mean stomatal width of 10 µm and a wind speed of 1 m s^{-1}. The concentrations of CO_2 required to maintain the average carboxylation rate falls within the range of concentrations measured in C3 plants[191].

‡ This assumes a V_{max} of 600 µmol mg chlorophyll^{-1} h^{-1} and a K_m (CO_2) of 300 p.p.m. Rates of assimilation in excess of 100 µmol mg chlorophyll^{-1} h^{-1} could only be achieved in this model by increasing the external CO_2 concentration, windspeed, etc. or by invoking the CO_2 pump. Alternative models giving higher rates could be based on higher values of the V_{max}, higher [RDP carboxyllase] mg chlorophyl^{-1}, or lower values of the K_m.

1.5.1.3 Hexose and heptose monophosphates

Fructose 6-phosphate (F6P) and glucose 6-phosphate (G6P) appear fairly quickly in the cytoplasm of leaves illuminated in the presence of $^{14}CO_2$[44, 110] (indicating export from the chloroplast) but, as with FDP (Section 1.5.1.4(b)), there is ambiguity because of the possibility of external synthesis from exported triose phosphate. Chromatography of isolated chloroplasts[59, 60] indicates a low permeability to F6P and G6P (Table 1.1, Figure 1.4(f)) but, conversely, F6P (Figure 1.6, line 1) brings about a moderately fast reversal of orthophosphate inhibition (Section 1.4.4.2) under conditions in which G6P (Figure 1.6, line 8) produces no detectable response[72]. It seems doubtful that there would be sufficient external catalytic activity to bring about the formation of FDP from F6P at sufficient rates to explain this latter effect in terms of transport as FDP or triose phosphate (see Section 1.5.1.4b).

Sedoheptulose 7-phosphate (S7P) does not appear rapidly in the cytoplasm[44, 110] or in the medium[59, 60] suggesting that it is slow to leave the chloroplast (Figure 1.4(g) and Table 1.1). Similarly, 6-phosphogluconate (which is known to inhibit RDP carboxylase[176]) apparently fails to cross the envelope because it does not inhibit CO_2 fixation by intact chloroplasts nor does it reverse Pi inhibition (Section 1.4.4.2) or interfere with the subsequent reversal of Pi inhibition by triose phosphate[72] (Figure 1.6, line 10) or facilitate the release of PGA, etc.[65].

1.5.1.4 Sugar diphosphates

(a) *Ribulose 1,5-diphosphate (RDP)*—There is general agreement (Figure 1.4(h) and Table 1.1) that RDP does not move through the envelope. It does not appear in appreciable quantities in the cytoplasm[44, 110, 111] (Section 1.4.1) or in the medium[59, 60] (Section 1.4.2). It neither shortens the lag[73] (Section 1.4.4.1), nor reverses orthophosphate inhibition[72] (Section 1.4.4.1) and only slightly affects inhibition by arsenate etc.[74] (Section 1.4.4.3). Intact chloroplasts supplied with RDP fix less CO_2 in the dark than similar chloroplasts which have been osmotically shocked in the reaction mixture[73, 87]. Dark deactivation of RDP carboxylation together with the failure of RDP to move out of the chloroplast could ensure that enough of this metabolite is retained to restart photosynthetic carboxylation in the next light period[70].

(b) *Fructose 1,6-diphosphate (FDP) and sedoheptulose 1,7-diphosphate (SDP)*—Both are formed in relatively large quantities in illuminated chloroplasts *in situ* but SDP does not pass readily into the cytoplasm[44, 110] nor from isolated chloroplasts into the medium[60] (Figure 1.4(e), Table 1.1). Apparent movement of FDP is considerable (Figure 1.4(c) Table 1.1) but is questioned in view of the possibility of external condensation of freely permeable triose phosphates[59, 60, 87, 111] (Section 1.5.1.1). Phosphate inhibition is quite quickly reversed by FDP[72] (Figure 1.6, line 6) and induction shortened[104] but again external lysis followed by endo diffusion of DHAP, G3P, or both, cannot be discounted, and (in the absence of more definitive evidence) it may be supposed that the envelope is as impermeable to FDP as it is to RDP and SDP. Direct measurements[65] support this view.

(c) *1,3-Diphosphoglycerate* (*DPGA*)—Intact chloroplasts fail to increase the phosphorylation of added ADP when supplied with external phosphoglycerate kinase and it is concluded[80] that an abbreviated shuttle (cf. Section 1.6.2) transporting 'high-energy phosphate' to the exterior (as DPGA) can not work because the envelope is impermeable to this acid.

1.5.1.5 Free sugars

Sucrose has already been considered in Section 1.2. The fact that other sugars (such as glucose and fructose) and sugar alcohols (such as sorbitol and mannitol) have also been successfully used as osmotics in the preparation of isolated chloroplasts[12] itself indicates that these compounds do not freely enter the stroma. Heldt and Sauer[45] have shown that sucrose can penetrate the outer but not the inner envelope (which they regard as the site of location of the specific translocators[45, 65]) and this membrane may be similarly impermeable to other sugars. On the other hand, chloroplasts given ribose or fructose have a slightly, but significantly, shorter induction period (Section 1.4.4.1) than those given xylose or glucose respectively[103]. These results could be explained by slow uptake of ribose and fructose followed by phosphorylation and further metabolism in the Benson–Calvin cycle.

DL-Glyceraldehyde is a potent and specific inhibitor of photosynthetic carbon assimilation in intact chloroplasts (and in a reconstituted chloroplast system) indicating that it must readily enter the stroma[91].

1.5.2 CO_2–bicarbonate

Dissolved CO_2 undergoes hydration in a reaction catalysed by carbonic anhydrase and by various inorganic ions such as orthophosphate[112].

$$CO_2 + H_2O \rightleftharpoons H_2CO_3 \rightleftharpoons H^+ + HCO_3^- \qquad (1.1)$$

As the pH is raised, the distribution of molecular species changes and above pH 9 an appreciable and increasing proportion of the total CO_2 is present as the carbonate ion. At physiological pH values however, the CO_2 is present in the forms indicated in the above equation with the proportion of bicarbonate ion (HCO_3^-) increasing from *ca.* 2% at pH 5 to 95% at pH 8[112].

Because of the ready interconversion of these species it is not easy to say whether green plants utilise free CO_2 or bicarbonate ion in photosynthesis but a great many observations (such as the fact that CO_2 saturation in *Chlorella* relates to dissolved CO_2 rather than bicarbonate ion[112]) imply that it is CO_2 rather than bicarbonate which readily penetrates plant membranes. Similarly, a weakly-buffered bicarbonate medium containing aquatic plants[113, 114] or isolated chloroplasts[115] becomes more alkaline on illumination and the kinetics and magnitude of this pH shift are consistent with the preferential uptake of CO_2 from the medium. There is also now good evidence that CO_2 is the species consumed in the carboxylation of ribulose diphosphate[116, 117]. If it is, therefore, assumed (a) that CO_2 is probably the penetrant species; (b) that, at least in C3 plants, there is unlikely to be any appreciable cytoplasmic prefixation of CO_2[48, 49, 118]; and (c) that the primary carboxylation mechanism is located in the stromal compartment of the chloroplast[119], it follows that CO_2 must penetrate the envelope at least as fast as it is taken up by the actual process of photosynthesis. Rabinowitch[120] puts the rate of photosynthesis by the average plant under favourable conditions in its natural environment at *ca.* 100 μmol mg chlorophyll^{-1} h^{-1}. (Assuming a chlorophyll concentration of 0.05 mg cm^{-2} this is equivalent to a rate of 22 mg (CO_2) 100 cm^2 h^{-1} or *ca.* 0.1 cm^3 cm^{-2} h^{-1}. This is a useful yardstick[15] which has been employed to determine the significance of fixation rates achieved by isolated chloroplasts[13-15, 34] and one which may be similarly applied to the values in Table 1.3 (see also Table 1.2). Some of the highest rates of photosynthesis are achieved by C4 plants[121] (see Section 1.12) where there is doubt about the site of the initial carboxylation and CO_2 may be transported through the envelope as malate[118]. It is clear, however, that the average value of 100 can be exceeded 3–5-fold by plants of impeccable C3 ancestry[121] and values as high as 235 have even been reported for spinach chloroplasts (see Ref. 14, Figure 1 and Ref. 34, p. 113). If all of these rates are sustained by the penetration and utilisation of CO_2, it is difficult to see what role is played in the plant by carbonic anhydrase unless it functions as a permease, or in some other more subtle fashion[122-126]. Photosynthetic CO_2 fixation can proceed 20 times faster than CO_2 hydration[126] (but see Zelitch[125]) from which it can be inferred that hydration is unnecessary or that it must be catalysed. Isolated chloroplasts respond rapidly to the addition of bicarbonate[77, 78] (see e.g. Figure 1.8) but at present it is not clear whether the response would be even faster with free CO_2. In the experiments[14] referred to above, bicarbonate was used as a source of CO_2 but the ionic composition of the reaction mixture together with carbonic anhydrase released from damaged chloroplasts etc. (see Sections 1.3 and 1.4) would catalyse the dehydration of bicarbonate ions.

Werdan and Heldt[69] have used direct measurement (Section 1.4.3) and calculations of the size of the stromal compartment, etc. to measure the accumulation of radioactive bicarbonate within the intact chloroplast. In one experiment they found that the internal radioactive bicarbonate concentration increased from 0 to 2 mM within 10 s of being placed in a solution of 0.5 mM bicarbonate. In another experiment the internal bicarbonate concentration increased from 5.5 mM to 8.0 mM on illumination. The maintenance of additional bicarbonate within the stromal compartment was attributed to a pH difference (increased in the light) according to the relationship

$$\log \frac{[HCO_3^-]_{\text{int}}}{[HCO_3^-]_{\text{ext}}} = \text{pH (int)} - \text{pH (ext)} \qquad (1.2)$$

Werdan and Heldt[69] believe that their results are consistent with the mechanism (equation (1.3) in which CO_2 is the penetrating species

Outside	Envelope	Inside
$HCO_3^- + H^+ \rightleftharpoons H_2O + CO_2$ - -	- - -	→ $CO_2 + H_2O \rightleftharpoons HCO_3^- + H^+$

(1.3)

Table 1.3 Summary of the permeability of the chloroplast envelope to metabolites, co-enzymes etc.

	Section	*Maximal feasible rate*					Authority	Counter evidence
		100	10–100	1.0–10	0.1–1.0	0–0.1		
CO_2–bicarbonate	1.5.2	—	—	—	—	—	14, 69, 77, 78, 120, 121, 130	
Sugar phosphates etc.								
2-Phosphoglycerate (2 PGA)	1.5.1			—	—	—	11, 108	65
3-Phosphoglycerate (PGA)	1.5.1.1	—	—	—	—	—	44, 45, 57, 59, 60, 64, 71–74, 77, 78, 88, 103–5	
1,3-Diphosphoglycerate (DPGA)	1.5.1.4					—	80	
Glyceraldehyde 3-phosphate (G3P)	1.5.1.1	—	—	—	—	—	59, 60, 72, 74, 78	87, 80
Dihydroxyacetone phosphate (DHAP)	1.5.1.1	—	—	—	—	—	13, 45, 59, 60, 64, 65, 72, 74, 78, 102–104, 109	
Ribose 5-phosphate (R5P)	1.5.1.2		—	—	—	—	59, 60, 71–74, 78, 102–104	
Ribulose 5-phosphate (Ru5P)	1.5.1.2		—	—	—	—	59, 60, 108	
Xylulose 5-phosphate (Xu5P)	1.5.1.2		—	—	—	—	59, 60, 108	
Ribulose 1,5-diphosphate (RDP)	1.5.1.4					—	44, 59, 60, 72, 74, 87, 110, 111	
Fructose 6-phosphate (F6P)	1.5.1.3				—	—	59, 60, 64, 74, 102, 103, 110	
Glucose 6-phosphate (G6P)	1.5.1.3				—	—	59, 60, 64, 65, 67, 68, 72, 74, 102, 103, 110	
Glucose 1-phosphate (G1P)	1.5.1.3					—	103	
6-Phosphogluconate (6PG)	1.5.1.3					—	65, 67, 68, 72, 103	
Fructose 1,6-diphosphate (FDP)	1.5.1.4					—	11, 59, 60, 65, 67, 68, 72, 74, 87, 100, 103, 111	
Sedoheptulose 7-phosphate (S7P)	1.5.1.3					—	44, 59, 60, 110, 111	
Sedoheptulose 1,7-diphosphate (SDP)	1.5.1.4					—	44, 59, 60, 110	
Phosphoenolpyruvate (PEP)						—	65, 67, 68, 103, 115, 150	

Free sugars				
Glyceraldehyde	1.5.1.5	————————	75	
Ribose	1.5.1.5	———	103	
Xylose	1.5.1.5	—	103	
Fructose	1.5.1.5	———	103	
Glucose	1.5.1.5	—	103	
Sucrose	1.3	—	64	
Carboxylic and amino acids				
Malate	1.5.3.2	——————————	45, 64, 65, 115, 150	
Oxaloacetate (OAA)	1.5.3.2	——————————	45, 65, 115, 150	
α-Oxoglutarate	1.5.3.2	————————	39, 65, 87	
Aspartate	1.5.3.3	————————	39, 65, 87	
Glutamate	1.5.3.3		103	
Glycerate	1.5.3.1	- - - - - - - - - -	31, 41, 138	
Glycollate	1.5.3.1	————————	31, 41, 59, 60, 138, 148	
Glyoxylate	1.5.3.1	- - - - - - - - ——	31, 41, 115, 138	
Glycine	1.5.3.1	- - - - - - - - - -	31, 41, 138	
Co-enzymes				
Adenosine diphosphate (ADP)	1.6.1.1	- - - —	63, 65, 67, 68, 89, 91, 92	105, 164
Adenosine triphosphate (ATP)	1.6.1.2	- - - ——	63, 65, 67, 68, 91, 92, 171	164, 169
Nicotinamide adenine phosphate dinucleotide phosphate (NADP–NADPH)	1.7.1	—	56, 71, 86, 87	
Orthophosphate (Pi)	1.8.1	————————	45, 65, 67, 68, 71, 79	38
Inorganic pyrophosphate (PiPi)	1.8.2	—	12, 13, 45, 65, 71, 79, 170	

The speed of direct movement is indicated approximately by a solid line to the maximum values. There is usually some doubt and this represents a subjective judgement which may not concur with the reference listed. The column 'counter evidence' indicates views or results which are entirely contrary to this judgement. A dotted line indicates where it is more difficult to arrive at a meaningful judgement. Other qualifying comments are made in the text. Differences in experimental conditions are ignored and it is assumed that transport can occur equally well in either direction. According to Heldt and Sauer it is the inner membrane of the chloroplast envelope which is the site of specific metabolic transport. The above values (expressed in μmol mg chlorophyll^{-1} h^{-1}) relate to penetration of this membrane and may be compared with a rate of photosynthesis achieved by the average plant in its natural environment of 100. Indirect transport of high energy phosphate (Section 1.6.2) and reducing equivalents (Section 1.7.2) may well occur at faster rates than those listed for ATP and NADP–NADPH.

and that the formation of bicarbonate in the stroma is facilitated by the presence of a highly-active carbonic anhydrase. This, together with the alkalisation of the stroma brought about by the light driven proton movement, would constitute the 'CO_2 pump' which has been postulated as a mechanism for maintaining RDP carboxylation at an appropriate level[15]. Because the RDP carboxylase uses CO_2 rather than bicarbonate[116, 117] an accumulation of bicarbonate would not achieve this end in itself, but Werdan and Heldt[198] have proposed that acidification at the carboxylase surface (due to the formation of 2 molecules of PGA from one molecule of RDP, CO_2 and H_2O) would lead to a local increase in CO_2 concentration which would also be catalysed by carbonic anhydrase. It is also conceivable that if bicarbonate does not act as a homotropic substrate activator of RDP carboxylase[127] it might still function as a non-substrate allosteric modulator.

The basic problem at the heart of these considerations is the need to provide enough CO_2 at the enzyme surface to allow a rate of fixation of 300 μmol mg chlorophyll^{-1} h^{-1} or more[121] and at the same time an influx of CO_2 from the external atmosphere at a comparable rate in order to maintain such a concentration. The greater the gradient from source to sink the faster the influx of CO_2 but with a fixed external concentration of 300 p.p.m. the simultaneous achievement of fast influx and high internal concentration seems incompatible in the absence of some sort of CO_2 pump. It should be noted in this respect that the recent re-evaluation of the K_m for RDP carboxylase from 22 mM[128] *bicarbonate* to 0.45 mM CO_2[116] does nothing, in itself, to ease this problem[70]. However, if in view of Jensen's recent findings[129] the *bicarbonate* value is itself decreased to 0.4 mM (approximately equivalent to air levels of CO_2) then the gap is considerably narrowed if not entirely closed. For example the rate of influx of atmospheric CO_2 into a leaf from moving air has been calculated by several workers to be *ca.* 0.150 cm^3 cm^{-2} h^{-1} assuming a concentration of CO_2 of zero or near zero at the chloroplast surface[130]. Granting the acknowledged absurdity of fast rates of carboxylation in the presence of zero CO_2 a value of 0.150 cm^3 cm^{-2} h^{-1} would still appear to be of the right order of magnitude. It would mean that when the CO_2 concentration at the chloroplast surface was one third of that in the atmosphere then the rate of CO_2 entry would fall to *ca.* 0.100 cm^3 cm^{-2} h^{-1}. Nevertheless this would be sufficient (assuming a half maximal velocity of 300 μmol CO_2 mg chlorophyll^{-1} h^{-1} for RDP carboxylase in an average leaf and direct proportionallity between rate of carboxylation and stromal CO_2 concentration) to permit CO_2-assimilation to proceed at the average rate of 100 μmol mg chlorophyll^{-1} without any requirement for a pump to maintain the CO_2 concentration within the chloroplast at a higher concentration than at its surface (Table 1.2). In these circumstances the CO_2 at the carboxylation site would come into balance with an intercellular CO_2 concentration of *ca.* 100 p.p.m. This would be consistent with the observed inter-cellular concentration of CO_2 in bright light in a number of C3 species[131] and the fact that the external CO_2 is rate limiting in these circumstances, and more especially in still air.

The values given in this table are based on a V_{max} for RDP carboxylase of 600 μmol mg chlorophyll^{-1} h^{-1} which is a slightly generous estimate based on a rather smaller value reported by Jensen in experiments with isolated spinach chloroplasts[129]. The chlorophyll content of the hypothetical leaf is put at 0.05 mg cm^{-2} which is again within the recorded range[132, 133] and allows the values expressed as μmol mg $chlorophyll^{-1}$ h^{-1} to be converted directly (at a first approximation) to cm^3 cm^{-2} h^{-1} (one of several physiological units[130]). Only the values underlined represent the steady state. For example, the intercellular concentration of CO_2 (which because of respiration) would be in excess of atmospheric in the dark, would fall in the light until the rate of carboxylation matched the rate of entry of CO_2. The rate of endo-diffusion is not corrected for respiratory CO_2. The value of 0.15 cm^3 cm^{-2} h^{-1} (for endo-diffusion) may be compared with calculated assimilation values (at 20 °C in high light intensity) of *ca.* 0.67 and 0.147 cm^3 cm^{-2} h^{-1} for mean stomatal apertures of 10 μm and 'still air' and wind speed of 1 m s^{-1} respectively[130].

It has been known for some years that phosphoenolpyruvate carboxylase works at half maximal rate in the presence of *ca.* 0.2 mM bicarbonate[31, 53, 134]. If RDP carboxylase also works as well at this concentration as Jensen's recent values suggest[129] there will be little to choose between these enzymes at pH values near 7.5 with respect to their affinity for CO_2[70] (see Section 1.11). On this basis the relatively low CO_2 compensation points observed in C4 plants[135] would be most readily explained by the presence of a relatively high concentration of PEP carboxylase in the mesophyll. Low CO_2 compensation would then be related to a higher concentration of catalyst and a shorter diffusion path rather than superior catalysis.

1.5.3 Carboxylic and amino acids

1.5.3.1 Glycollate and glyoxylate

'Photorespiration' is defined by Zelitch[136] as 'the respiration (especially the CO_2 evolution) that differs biochemically from normal dark respiration and is specifically associated with substrates produced during photosynthesis'. More simply it is light stimulated CO_2 release and O_2 uptake [41]. Photorespiration[15, 137] is a characteristic of C3 plants (such as tobacco) which evolve CO_2 when brightly illuminated in CO_2-free air and tend to have high CO_2 compensation points (*ca.* 50 p.p.m.), i.e. they are unable to diminish the CO_2 in an enclosed space to a low level (near zero) in the same way as C4 plants (Section 1.12) such as maize[135]. Factors which favour photorespiration (e.g. high light, high O_2, high temperatures, low CO_2) also favour glycollate formation[138]. Glycollate is a product of CO_2 fixation by isolated chloroplasts[11, 13, 32, 60, 139-141, 148] and though its derivation[14] is uncertain its immediate precursor may be α,β-dihydroxyethylthiamine (the 2-carbon transketolase addition complex) split from F6P[142] or Xu5P[143] or a corresponding 2-carbon unit from RDP[145] or FDP[144] (which would yield phosphoglycollate rather than the free acid[14]). Photorespiration is attributed to the oxidation of glycollate[138] but glycollate oxidase is believed to be located in microbodies[42] or peroxisomes[41]. Further consideration of such proposals is completely beyond the scope of this article but it may be inferred that if these suppositions are correct then glycollate must pass across the chloroplast envelope (either as the free acid or as phosphoglycollate) prior to oxidation in the microbody. Figure 1.9, which is derived from Gibbs[31], incorporates several features of glycollate metabolism based on the work of Tolbert, Zelitch and others and is seen to require exodiffusion of glycollate and endodiffusion of glycerate. Glyoxylate is also supposed to re-enter the chloroplast (see e.g. Butt and Peel[146]) to be

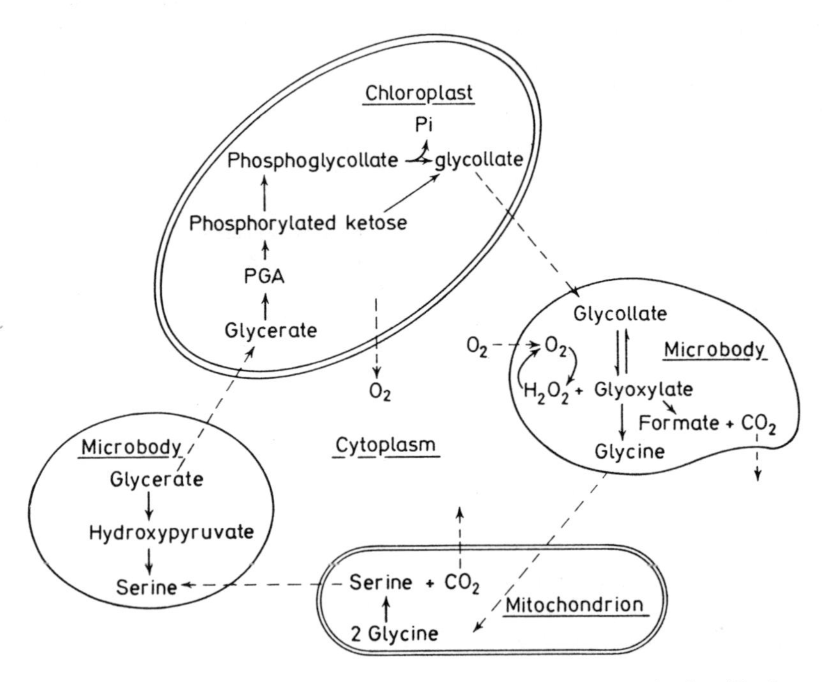

Figure 1.9 Possible movement of intermediates during photorespiration (Section 1.5.3.1). (After Gibbs[31], by courtesy of the author and Springer-Verlag.)

reduced, by NADPH, in a reaction catalysed by a glyoxylate reductase[147] (the corresponding NADH enzyme is associated with the peroxisome[41]). Direct evidence of glycollate diffusion is limited but consistent with free movement[60, 148]. On the other hand, Heber and Kraus[115] consider that 'a cyclic shuttle system involving glyoxylate reductase would be too slow to permit significant hydrogen transfer'.

1.5.3.2 Malate and oxaloacetate (OAA)

The dicarboxylate translocation[45, 65] which also facilitates transport of succinate, α-oxoglutarate, fumarate, aspartate and glutamate allows malate and oxaloacetate to exchange at rates similar to those recorded for phosphoglycerate. These findings, based on direct measurement (Section 1.4.3) are supported by experiments[150] in which the observed rates of OAA-dependent oxygen evolution demanded rates of penetration by OAA of up to 300 μmol mg chlorophyll^{-1} h^{-1} (see also Section 1.7.2). Kirk and Leech[157] found that the enzymes necessary for oxaloacetate synthesis are missing from intact chloroplasts and concluded that OAA transport from the cytoplasm is necessary for aspartate synthesis. They also demonstrated stimulation of amino acid synthesis in the presence of an external OAA generating system.

1.5.3.3 Amino acids

Conversion of exogenous aspartate and α-oxoglutarate to glutamate and oxaloacetate by intact chloroplasts is accelerated from *ca.* 10 to 40 μmol mg chlorophyll^{-1} h^{-1} following osmotic shock, indicating that the intact envelope limits transport of the slowest of these reactants to the lower rate[87].

Other evidence (see e.g. Refs. 58, 151, 152) based on the distribution of labelled amino acids between cytoplasm and chloroplasts suggests rapid transport (especially of glycine and serine) but again metabolic conversion on one side of the envelope and resynthesis on the other cannot be excluded[39] (cf. Figure 1.13). Difficulties of interpretation are also reflected in the conclusions of Roberts *et al.*[152] that while glycine and serine move freely from chloroplasts to cytoplasm the same is not true of sugar phosphates. In view of considerable evidence (Section 1.5.1) that triose phosphates *can* move readily from the chloroplast, it could be equally well concluded that sugar phosphates do not always *accumulate* in the cytoplasm. Indeed, the metabolic route from triose phosphate to sucrose is short and direct and there is no reason why accumulation of sucrose (formed from exported triose phosphate) should necessarily lead to concomitant accumulation of an appreciable quantity of sugar phosphates. The practical difficulties associated with non-aqueous extraction of this nature (see Section 1.4.1) are also exemplified by the finding of Ogun and Stocking[151] that 15% of total starch was associated with the non-plastid fraction (see Section 1.1).

Recently[153], Nobel and Cheung (see also Refs. 154, 155) have proposed two carriers (translocators) on the basis of light independent shrinkage in chloroplasts caused by osmotic extraction of water. This is taken to be low for solutes which enter freely and high for solutes to which the membrane is impermeable but it should be noted that in some circumstances (light induced) shrinkage is equated with penetration of acids[146] and that the whole question of volume changes in chloroplasts is a matter of some complexity[156]. It is proposed[153] that one carrier transports glycine, L-alanine, L-leucine, L-isoleucine and L-valine and the other L-serine, L-threonine and L-methionine.

1.6 THE TRANSPORT OF ADP AND ATP

1.6.1 Direct transfer

Prior to the discovery of photosynthetic phosphorylation[3-7] the plant biochemist was obliged to consider the possibility that ATP utilised in photosynthesis might be generated in the mitochondrion, albeit from a photosynthetically reduced co-enzyme or newly-formed product of photosynthesis[158]. When it became clear that isolated chloroplasts could support very rapid rates of cyclic photophosphorylation[159-162] the converse line of thought was favoured and it was suggested that ATP formed within the chloroplast might be used in reactions other than CO_2 assimilation[24, 30]. In the sense that all metabolites are ultimately derived from photosynthesis, all ATP is light-generated but the important possibility of direct transfer of adenylates across the chloroplasts called for investigation. In this respect only a reasonably fast exchange of ATP with ADP (or AMP) would be of physiological significance. Rapid unilateral movement of ATP or ADP would deplete the concentration of these compounds within given cellular compartments with equal rapidity. In short, direct export of ATP is of major importance only if it can be established as part of a mechanism of energy transduction which would allow the chloroplast to contribute to the economy of the cell over and above its traditional contribution of the end-products of photosynthesis.

1.6.1.1 ADP

From an early stage the use of the term 'intact chloroplast' as applied to a discrete chlorophyll-containing organelle (in contrast to a similar but fragmented body[12, 99]) has caused confusion. Used in this sense 'intact chloroplasts' could evidently phosphorylate exogenous ADP at rapid rates, implying an equally rapid movement of ADP and ATP to and from the phosphorylating sites. Nevertheless, osmotic shock brought about some acceleration of ATP formation even in these preparations[163] which could sustain only very low rates of CO_2 fixation. The possible significance of this acceleration became more obvious when the introduction of new methods led to the isolation of chloroplasts with intact envelopes capable of much higher rates of CO_2 fixation[11]. It was then demonstrated that osmotic rupture of the envelope inhibited CO_2 fixation and greatly accelerated ATP formation[89]. Under the conditions used in the phosphorylation experiments CO_2 fixation was insignificant and it was suggested that the difference in rates of phosphorylation might be attributable to the exclusion of an endogenous reactant (such as ADP) by the intact envelope (intact envelopes were largely absent from the earlier preparations[12] judging by their poor rates of CO_2 fixation). In the best preparation (shown by light and electron microscopy to contain only *ca.* 10% chloroplasts without envelopes) the rate of cyclic photophosphorylation was only 102 μmol of Pi esterified mg chlorophyll^{-1} h^{-1} but this could be increased to 864 by osmotic shock so that it was possible to conclude that 'most if not all of the phosphorylation may have been mediated by the membrane (envelope)-free chloroplasts'[89]. This conclusion was subsequently supported by Heber and Santarius[80] who measured pseudocyclic phosphorylation of exogenous ADP by spinach chloroplasts in the absence of co-factors such as pyocyanine (which was used in the above work). In their experiments chloroplasts which had been osmotically shocked gave rates of *ca.* 20 μmol mg chlorophyll^{-1} h^{-1}, whereas with chloroplasts which were *ca.* 70–90% intact the rates ranged from 0 to 4 μmol mg chlorophyll^{-1} h^{-1}.

A seemingly contradictory view was implicit in the work of West and Wiskich[90] who reported 'photosynthetic control' (i.e. acceleration of electron transport by ADP) in what they described as Class I chloroplasts, i.e.

chloroplasts with intact envelopes (cf. Spencer and Unt[98] and Hall[99]). Here the implication is clear that if ADP or ATP can rapidly alter the rate of oxygen evolution by controlling the rate of electron transport they must penetrate to the site of transport with equal rapidity. However, if envelope integrity had been an essential feature in their experiments it ought not to be possible to show photosynthetic control in envelope-free chloroplasts. In fact excellent photosynthetic control has since been demonstrated in 100% envelope-free chloroplasts undergoing the Mehler reaction[43] and Hill reaction[165] (Figure 1.10) and this must obviously add to the difficulties of interpretation when

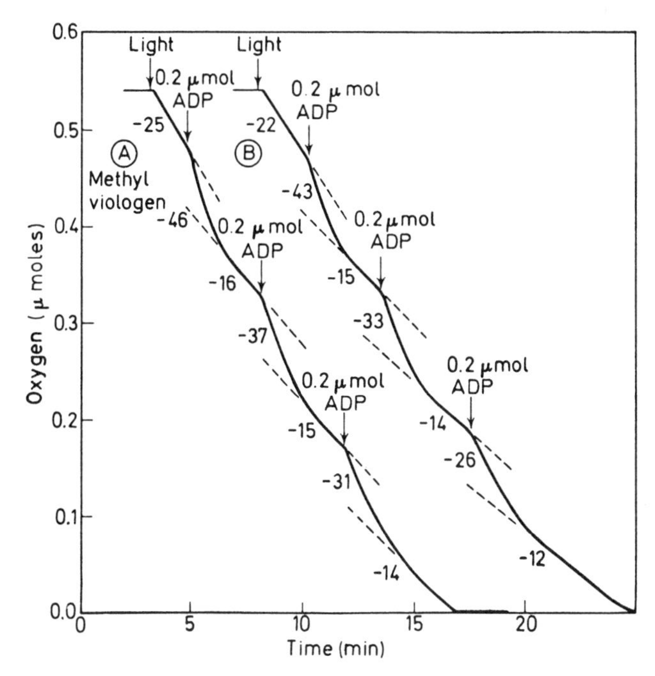

Figure 1.10 'Photosynthetic control' in envelope chloroplasts (Section 1.6.1.1) undergoing the Mehler reaction. (From Whitehouse *et al.*[43], by courtesy of the Society for Experimental Biology.)

mixed populations of whole and envelope-free chloroplasts are used, particularly if no attempt is made to quantify their respective proportions. Preparations containing 90% or more intact chloroplasts, capable of rates of CO_2 fixation well in excess of 100 μmol mg chlorophyll^{-1} h^{-1} have now been obtained in several laboratories[34] but these are still the exception rather than the rule. As the proportions approach 50% intact and 50% envelope-free, then the necessity for control experiments designed to show the contribution of ruptured chloroplasts becomes more pressing. Whether or not West and Wiskich's 'photosynthetic control'[90] was brought about by envelope-free chloroplasts in their preparations can only be unequivocally established by further experiment but it clearly exists as a possibility.

Fast inward movement of ADP is also implied by the work of Stocking *et al.*[105, 164] who showed stimulation of PGA-dependent oxygen evolution when ADP and Pi were added to intact chloroplasts immediately prior to illumination. No corresponding stimulation was observed when ADP was added in the light. If it can be established that this stimulation was caused by rapid influx of ADP in the dark it will be of considerable interest but it would not, of course, provide a mechanism for the continuous export of ATP in the light. (Attention must also be drawn to the fact that Pi, in particular, may affect the rate of entry of PGA into chloroplasts[45, 65] and that at least some of the apparent effects of ADP + Pi on O_2 evolution might be attributable to changes in the rate of entry of PGA rather than to fast entry of ADP. For example, if the addition of PGA to mixtures containing high [Pi] was delayed (Cockburn *et al.*[72], Figure 5) the subsequent rate was faster though no exogenous ADP was present (cf. Stocking *et al.*[164], Figure 4). Similarly Werdan and Heldt[67] (Figure 5) have shown that PGA uptake is stimulated by pre-illumination and that the stimulation was gradually built up as the period of pre-illumination was extended.)

Direct measurement by Heldt[63] puts ADP translocation at *ca.* 0.2 μmol mg chlorophyll^{-1} h^{-1} which value would appear to set an upper limit on the continuous operation of his 'ATP translocator' (see Section 1.6.1.2).

1.6.1.2 ATP

If anything, the evidence relating to the direct movement of ATP is even more contradictory than that for ADP. While direct measurements by Heldt *et al.*[63, 68] indicate a slow movement (max 5 μmol mg chlorophyll^{-1} h^{-1}) these workers do not believe that this could be of importance in direct export of ATP in the light and indeed conclude 'that direct transport of ATP from the stroma into the cytoplasm does not appear to exist to any considerable extent'[68]. Conversely results of Stocking *et al.*[164] indicate a relatively fast movement, at least in the dark. Also Jensen and Bassham[169] have detected a rapid accumulation of ^{32}P-labelled ATP in the medium in which intact chloroplasts were illuminated (implying export of ATP) and an increase in the concentration of RDP when ATP was supplied to chloroplasts in the dark (implying penetration of ATP). Again, however, alternative explanations could be suggested. For example, the export of ribose 5-phosphate from the chloroplast is not in question (Section 1.5.1.2) and external formation of ribulose diphosphate would follow in the presence of added ATP if an appreciable concentration of ribulose 5-phosphate kinase escaped from damaged chloroplasts. It is also extremely easy to show an effect of added ATP on O_2 evolution but, in our own experience, much more difficult to produce one which cannot be copied by free Pi. Thus ATP and ADP and Pi all restore O_2 evolution which has ceased in Pi deficient reaction mixtures[71] but external hydrolysis followed by uptake of Pi seems a more credible explanation than rapid direct entry in view of the other contrary evidence. Slow direct entry could conceivably account in part for the report by Schuman *et al.*[166, 167] that ATP shortens induction (Section 1.4.4.1) because their rates (*ca.* 2–12 μmol O_2 mg chlorophyll^{-1} h^{-1}) are only a little faster at maximum than the fastest recorded entry of ATP based on direct measurement. Once more, however, it must be pointed out that chloroplasts suspended in media containing inorganic pyrophosphate (as were theirs[166, 167]), but deficient in Pi will, on occasion, show a positive response to the addition of *small* quantities of Pi if the external pyrophosphatase activity is inadequate to produce optimal Pi by hydrolysis. It is general experience that ATP (and other co-enzymes) added in dark or light do not significantly affect the normal course of carbon assimilation by isolated chloroplasts (see e.g. Jensen and Bassham[168]).

In this laboratory our results have been consistent with those of Heldt *et al.*[45, 63-69] and in a number of experimental situations we have found no effect of added ATP beyond that which might be expected from small quantities of orthophosphate released by ATPase activity. Possibly the best example (Figure 1.11) is the failure of ATP to reverse inhibition of CO_2-

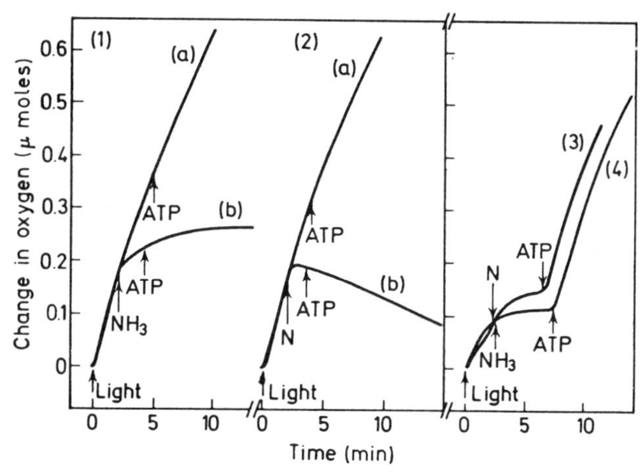

Figure 1.11 The chloroplast envelope as a barrier to rapid entry of ATP (Section 1.6.1.2). Curves (1a) and (1b) show inhibition of PGA dependent oxygen evolution by ammonium chloride (added to (b) and similarly (2a) and (2b) show inhibition by nigericin (added to (b). ATP then failed to reverse this inhibition. Curves 3 and 4 show comparable inhibitions in a reconstituted system containing envelope-free chloroplasts. In the absence of the envelope, ATP reverses the inhibition. (From Stokes and Walker[92], by courtesy of Wiley Interscience.)

dependent or PGA-dependent oxygen evolution by uncouplers. Thus nigericin and ammonium chloride accelerate electron transport to NADP in envelope-free chloroplasts but inhibit oxygen evolution supported by CO_2 or PGA[92] in intact chloroplasts. If exogenous ATP could freely penetrate the envelope, then its addition should not only reverse this inhibition but even bring about an acceleration because of the increased rate of uncoupled electron transport. In fact, no restoration of rate was observed in these experiments or when inhibition of ATP formation has been brought about by phloridzin[92]. However, in a reconstituted chloroplast system[91-93] (in which envelope-free chloroplasts fortified with NADP and chloroplast extract are capable of PGA-dependent oxygen evolution) the uncouplers were equally inhibitory but ATP restored oxygen evolution to rates faster than those initially observed[91,92] (Figures 1.11 (3) and (4)). Similarly, the phloridzin inhibition was reversed by the addition of ATP *plus* an uncoupler[92]. It is conceivable, of course, that nigericin, ammonium chloride and phloridzin inhibit the uptake of PGA by intact chloroplasts either directly or by interfering with an ATP-activated pump but the simplest explanation of the above results is that the intact envelope offers a barrier to the ready entry of ATP.

Similarly, intact chloroplasts are permeable to R5P (Section 1.5.1.2) but will fix $^{14}CO_2$ at fast rates only when supplied with R5P and ATP in the dark (see e.g. Johnson and Bruff[197]) if they are osmotically shocked.

In summary it may be stated that present evidence does not warrant the conclusion that there is rapid direct movement of ADP and ATP across the chloroplast envelope in the light and that if the chloroplast is capable of exporting excess ATP or 'reducing power' it is more likely to do it indirectly (Section 1.6.2).

1.6.2 Indirect transfer of ADP and ATP

Any metabolite which is exported from the chloroplast and can subsequently enter the normal pathways of catabolism constitutes an indirect transport of ATP but this would not, in itself, enable cyclic or pseudocyclic photophosphorylation to contribute to the economy of the cell beyond their possible role in carbon assimilation. Several workers have, therefore, speculated independently about the possibility of 'shuttle' mechanisms[15,39,80]. Evidence in favour of such proposals was first produced by Stocking and Larsen in 1969[107]; and has received subsequent support[65,80,85,115,150]. The most likely shuttle (Figure 1.12) involves the export of DHAP to the cytoplasm where it is

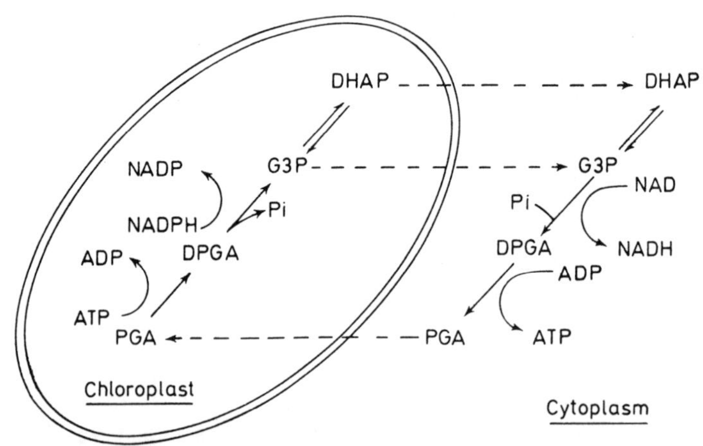

Figure 1.12 Proposed export of high energy phosphate and reducing equivalents via the triose phosphate shuttle (Section 1.6.2). The reduction of PGA to triose phosphate within the chloroplast is driven by light-generated ATP and NADPH. Triose phosphate then passes to the cytoplasm where it is oxidised, yielding ATP, NADH and PGA which can re-enter the chloroplast to recycle. (From Walker[196], by courtesy of Macmillan.)

oxidised (via G3P and DPGA) to PGA via the normal glycolytic sequence so that it also gives rise externally to reduced NAD and ATP. The PGA then re-enters the chloroplast and is reduced back to triose phosphate at the expense of photosynthetically generated NADPH and ATP. The net effect is an export of ATP and reducing equivalents. If direct transfer of ATP and ADP is as slow as has been suggested (Section 1.6.1), a shuttle of this type could account for the observed increase of cytoplasmic ATP in the light and its decrease in the dark[149, 174, 175]. It could also explain several observations which implicate the utilisation of photosynthetically-derived ATP in cytoplasmic events[171-174].

1.7 THE TRANSPORT OF NADP AND NADPH

1.7.1 Lack of direct transfer of NADP

Experiments in several laboratories have shown that intact chloroplasts will not reduce NADP or evolve O_2 with NADP as the oxidant. Conversely, osmotically shocked (envelope-free) chloroplasts (Section 1.4.4.5) will do both[56, 71, 86, 87].

1.7.2 Indirect transfer of reducing equivalents

As outlined in Section 1.6.2, a triose phosphate shuttle has been invoked as a means of transferring high energy phosphate between chloroplast and cytoplasm. This shuttle, involving the phosphate translocator (Section 1.9.3), would bring about concomitant transfer of reducing equivalents. Another shuttle, moving reducing equivalents only, and based on the dicarboxylate

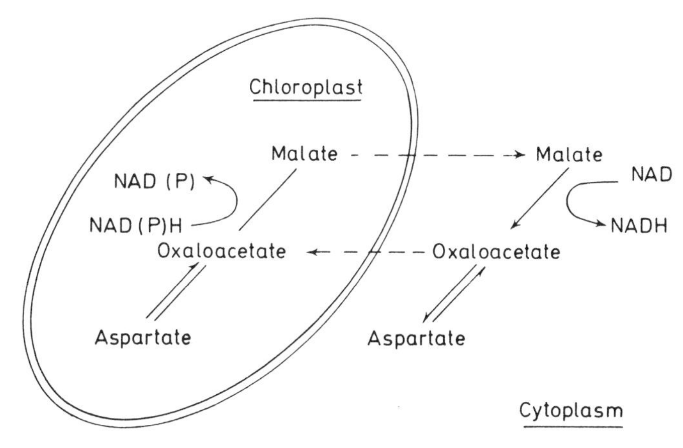

Figure 1.13 Proposed export of reducing equivalents via the dicarboxylate shuttle (Section 1.7.2). Oxaloacetate is reduced to malate within the chloroplast (either directly by light-generated NADPH or indirectly by NADH derived from NADPH). Malate is exported and reoxidised in the cytoplasm yielding NADH and OAA which recycles. OAA formed in the cytoplasm may constitute the carbon skeleton for aspartate synthesis within the chloroplast.

translocator (Section 1.9.2.) has also been proposed[39, 115, 150]. As illustrated in Figure 1.13, cytoplasmic OAA would enter the chloroplast where it would be reduced to malate. This would then return to the cytoplasm to complete the cycle. As mentioned in Section 1.5.3.2, oxaloacetate readily acts as a Hill oxidant with intact chloroplasts, implying rapid entry and equally rapid reduction[150]. Reduction of NAD has been observed in illuminated mixtures containing intact chloroplasts, OAA and malic dehydrogenase[115, 150]. If PGA is also present, this system is capable of reversal, i.e. it will oxidise external NADH added in relative excess[115].

If the enzymic machinery of the chloroplast is utilised in the dark to operate an oxidative pentose phosphate pathway as suggested by Bassham *et al.*[175, 176], then one or other of these shuttles, if they exist *in vivo*, could acquire importance in the mitochondrial re-oxidation of NADPH generated within the chloroplast by the catabolism of glucose 6-phosphate.

The proposed dicarboxylate shuttle also lends new interest to two earlier observations. The first[177] was that in the presence of the appropriate aminotransferase, labelled oxaloacetate gives rise to labelled aspartate even more readily when aspartate itself is the amino donor than when glutamate is the donor. In this way, aspartate can reflect changes in OAA (irrespective of net amino acid synthesis) which the reactive nature and lack of stability of OAA would otherwise make impossible. The second[178] was that a change in the malate:aspartate ratio is a consistent feature of the labelling pattern of green leaves in passing from dark to light. The ratio, which is high in the light and low in the dark, was taken to be an indication of corresponding fluctuations in the reduction status of nicotinamide nucleotide co-enzymes. Evidently it might also reflect the operation of the dicarboxylate shuttle (Figure 1.13).

1.8 THE TRANSPORT OF ORTHOPHOSPHATE AND PYROPHOSPHATE

1.8.1 Orthophosphate

Despite some initial uncertainty[88] it now seems clear that Pi enters the chloroplast at a rate at least one-third as fast as CO_2–bicarbonate[65, 67, 68, 71, 79]. Carbon assimilation leading to carbohydrate is not a Pi consuming process[2] but even though isolated chloroplasts can synthesise starch[30], the Pi releasing reactions in this sequence do not appear to operate with sufficient rapidity to offset an increasing Pi deficiency during short-term photosynthesis. Certainly if chloroplasts are prepared and assayed in the absence of Pi (or some source of Pi such as PiPi), carbon assimilation and its associated oxygen evolution both cease within minutes of the commencement of illumination[79]. Photosynthesis can then be restarted without appreciable delay by the addition of Pi[79]. The kinetics and magnitude of the response to Pi in these circumstances[79] are comparable to the response to added CO_2–bicarbonate in CO_2–bicarbonate deficient systems[77, 78]. If a sufficiently small quantity of Pi is added when photosynthesis has ceased, the amount of oxygen then evolved is roughly equivalent to three molecules of oxygen for each molecule of added Pi[79]. This is consistent with equation (1.4) and results obtained using $^{14}CO_2$ and ^{32}Pi

which showed that dihydroxyacetone phosphate is the major product of short-term photosynthesis by isolated chloroplasts[179].

$$3CO_2 + Pi + 3H_2O \rightarrow 1 \text{ triose phosphate} + 3O_2 \qquad (1.4)$$

It also agrees with evidence that triose phosphates move freely across the chloroplast envelope (Section 1.5.1.1). Obviously if this is a normal and continuing process, one molecule of Pi must be imported for each molecule of triose phosphate exported. Direct observations point to the same conclusion and, as previously noted (Section 1.5.1.1), Heldt *et al.*[65,68] have provided evidence for the operation of a specific Pi translocator, which also transports DHAP.

The optimal concentration of Pi in the medium for the initiation and maintenance of photosynthesis by isolated chloroplasts is *ca.* 10^{-5} M[71] (but see also Section 1.8.3). Above this concentration, Pi at first extends the lag (Section 1.4.4.1) and then also depresses the maximal rate until at *ca.* 5–20 mM (Section 1.4.4.2) inhibition may be complete during short term (5–30 min) measurement. At any time during this period oxygen evolution and CO_2 fixation can be re-initiated by the addition of PGA, triose phosphate etc.[72] (Section 1.4.4.2). The nature of the Pi inhibition and its reversal remains to be established. It is conceivable (cf. Refs. 15 and 65) that high external Pi brings about compulsory exchange export of cycle intermediates so that the steady-state concentration of these intermediates required to sustain full photosynthesis is never achieved. Pi is also a known competitive inhibitor of RDP carboxylase[128,180] and must (as an end product) affect the steady state equilibrium position of the freely reversible triose phosphate dehydrogenase reaction (equation (1.5)) which has only a slightly negative free energy (0.25 kcal) as written[181].

$$DPGA + NADPH_2 \rightleftharpoons G3P + NADP + Pi \qquad (1.5)$$

Any complete explanation of the reversal of Pi inhibition (Section 1.4.4.2) will have to account for the special case of PGA which, under some conditions, restarts O_2 evolution and CO_2 fixation simultaneously and immediately[72] (Figure 1.7).

The requirement for Pi in PGA-dependent O_2 evolution (in the absence of CO_2) is less than that required for CO_2-dependent oxygen evolution[71], presumably because of recycling of Pi released in reaction (1.2).

Other evidence for Pi uptake is provided by the Pi reversal of inhibitions brought about by R5P[71] and SO_4^{2-}[76]. Both of these inhibitions occur only in Pi deficient systems. Thus the addition of R5P to a mixture containing PGA and just sufficient Pi to support rapid oxygen evolution will bring about complete inhibition[71]. This has been attributed[71] to the siphoning off, via ATP and R5P kinase, of Pi (which would otherwise be recycled in the conversion of PGA to G3P) thus suppressing NADP regeneration and O_2 evolution. In view of contemporary conjecture, a feasible alternative is that R5P might inhibit competitively the access of Pi to the phosphate translocator (Section 1.9). The sulphate inhibition is also believed to be a competition between Pi and SO_4^{2-} (which results in the preferential formation of ADP-S when SO_4^{2-} is in relative excess)[76]. Both types of inhibition are rapidly and totally reversed by the addition of small quantities of Pi and if the conclusions regarding the mechanism of the inhibitions are correct, then the rate of entry must be related to the rate of O_2 evolution or CO_2 fixation then observed. As indicated above, the stoichiometry of reaction (1.4) would require uptake of one molecule of Pi for every 3 molecules of CO_2 fixed or oxygen evolved. Formation of products with a higher C: Pi ratio (such as starch with an infinite C: Pi ratio) would be expected to alter the overall stoichiometry between CO_2, O_2 and Pi only in the long term. Moreover, if triose phosphates and PGA are the principal carbon exports (Section 1.5.1.1) from the chloroplast and if there is no rapid direct movement of ADP–ATP (Section 1.6.1), PiPi (Section 1.8.2) or free sugars (Section 1.5.1.5), it seems inescapable that one molecule of orthophosphate must enter the chloroplast for each molecule of triose phosphate released.

1.8.2 Inorganic pyrophosphate (PiPi)

The study of the effect of this molecule on photosynthesis by isolated chloroplast has yielded results[71, 79, 182-184] which have been extraordinarily difficult to understand but at this stage it may be stated with some certainty that PiPi does not normally enter the chloroplast at appreciable rates (cf. Ref. 13). This is in agreement with the failure of PiPi to react with the Pi translocator[65,68].

The problems associated with PiPi first became apparent in 1967 when results obtained in this laboratory[79] showed that PiPi relieved Pi deficiency almost as readily as Pi itself but with a stoichiometry of 1 PiPi to $6O_2$ (compared with 1 Pi to $3O_2$). When added at half concentration, the kinetics of the response to PiPi were almost the same as the response to Pi except for an initial lag of *ca.* 15 s[79] (Figure 1.14). In themselves, these results were evidently

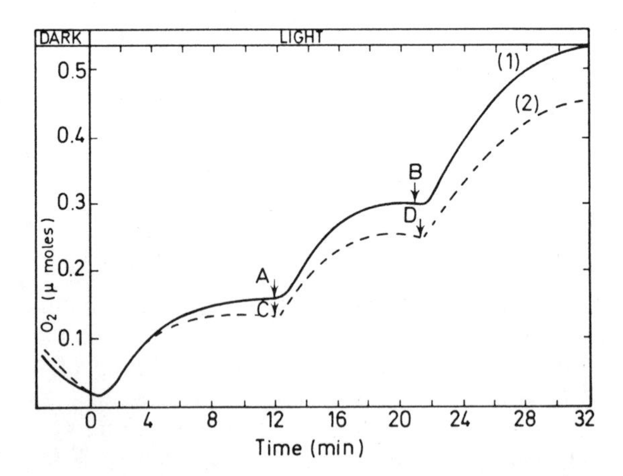

Figure 1.14 Response of Pi-deficient chloroplasts to Pi and PiPi (Sections 1.8.2 and 1.8.3). Curve (1), 0.025 μmol PiPi added at A and 0.05 added at B. Curve 2, 0.05 μmol Pi added at C and 0.10 added at D. Traces recorded consecutively. (From Cockburn *et al.*[79], by courtesy of Elsevier Publ. Co.)

consistent with a rapid entry of PiPi followed by equally rapid hydrolysis but this interpretation was difficult to equate with the fact that Pi was inhibitory at higher concentrations whereas PiPi was not. The matter was complicated further by the finding that SO_4^{2-} inhibition of photosynthetic carbon assimilation was reversed by Pi but not by PiPi[76]. One possible explanation was that PiPi did not enter and that it was only hydrolysed by an external PiPiase when added in low concentrations. Accordingly, Ludwig and Walker re-examined the response to PiPi using washed chloroplasts and found

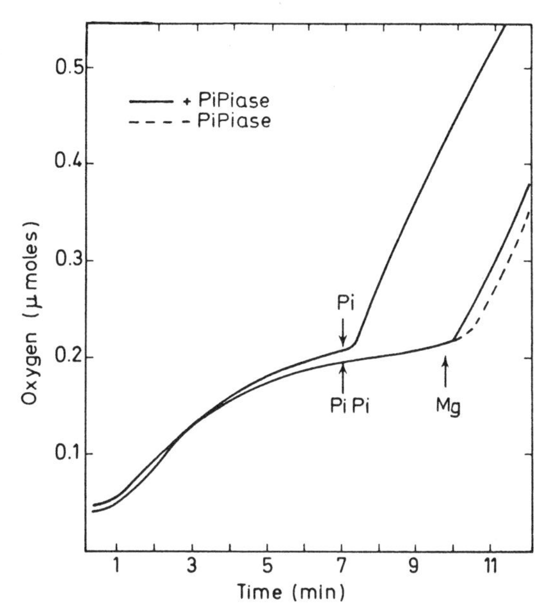

Figure 1.15 Response of Pi-deficient chloroplasts to Pi and PiPi in the presence and absence of Mg (Section 1.8.3). Note lack of significant response to PiPi until further addition of Mg whereas response to Pi was independent of Mg. Lower curve also contained added PiPiase, broken line indicates difference observed if this was omitted. (Previously unpublished results of Lilley *et al.*[170])

that the response to PiPi was then delayed and (on one occasion) completely abolished. The rapid response could be restored by the addition of ruptured chloroplasts. Because of the difficulty of abolishing the response to PiPi at will (normal preparations contain at least 10% envelope-free chloroplasts and better preparations are achieved only by rare chance) these observations were never published. Recently, however, an alternative approach was used[170] in which external PiPiase activity was diminished by preparing and assaying chloroplasts in Mg-free medium. The response to PiPi was then abolished as before but could be restored by the subsequent addition of magnesium (Figure 1.15) and hastened by the presence of commercial PiPiase[170]. Similarly, the SO_4^{2-} inhibition could be reversed bv PiPi if the rate of external hydrolysis was raised to an adequate level. All of these results strongly imply that PiPi is unable to enter the intact chloroplast but that it is normally hydrolysed (in the presence of Mg^{2+}) by PiPiase from damaged chloroplasts. The failure of PiPi to inhibit photosynthesis (as Pi does) when added in excess would then be explained by its known inhibition of PiPiase[185]. In such experiments there was no commensurate addition of Mg so that any modest increase in Mg-PiPi (believed to be the true substrate[185]) would be more than offset by inhibition of hydrolysis by excess PiPi. The interpretation (cf. Ref. 12) would also account for the fact that while PiPi differs from Pi in failing to inhibit CO_2-fixation by intact illuminated chloroplasts it readily inhibits RDP carboxylation in ruptured chloroplasts[71]. Clearly, once the envelope barrier had gone PiPi would have access to the carboxylation site where it would either inhibit directly or as Pi after hydrolysis. In other circumstances PiPi would act either as an inhibitor or as an accelerator depending upon its concentration and that of the Mg and the accessible PiPiase in the reaction mixture (see also Section 1.8.3).

Whether or not PiPiase is a stromal enzyme or one loosely associated with the thylakoids is hard to determine. Intact chloroplasts are not readily washed free of the enzyme which could indicate that the PiPiase activity normally observed is associated with envelope-free chloroplasts rather than freely soluble protein which has escaped from such chloroplasts.

1.8.3 Interaction between orthophosphate and pyrophosphate

The role of Pi and PiPi in the translocation of molecules across the chloroplast envelope may be further complicated by several types of interaction. Pyrophosphatase is inhibited by excess PiPi and possibly by its end product. The Pi inhibition of photosynthesis is overcome by high concentrations of PiPi and as suggested[71] it is difficult to visualise the nature of the protection afforded by high PiPi if it does not limit entry of Pi by interfering with phosphate translocation.

This observation bears on the proposal by Bassham *et al.*[183, 184] that FDPase regulates the transport of metabolites across the chloroplast envelope in a mechanism mediated by Mg and PiPi and one in which the FDPase does not produce its primary effect 'by means of its function in converting Fru $1,6\text{–}P_2$ to Fru 6–P'[183]. The addition of FDPase and Mg^{2+} (to increase the $[Mg^{2+}]$ from 1 to 6 mM) in a reaction mixture containing 5 mM PiPi 'increased greatly the appearance of metabolites in the suspending medium'[183]. In contrast, 5 M PiPi in the presence of low concentrations of Mg^{2+} (1 mM) and with no added FDPase tended to retain metabolites within the chloroplast. It is of particular interest that in these experiments (and their predecessors in which a spinach juice fraction was used in place of FDPase[182]) FDPase + low PiPi inhibited photosynthetic CO_2 fixation whereas FDPase + higher PiPi restored or even increased it. In addition, the quantity of PiPi needed to restore the rate increased as the quantity of added enzyme was increased. Moreover at 1 mM PiPi, FDPase and (1.5 mM)$MgCl_2$ both stimulated when added alone and inhibited by 96% when added together[183]. From what has been said in preceding sections, it is clear that this behaviour could be repeated with PiPiase and in this respect it would be interesting to know whether the FDPase fraction used was entirely free of PiPiase activity. If it were not, then all of the observed effects could be explained in terms of known effects of Pi and PiPi on photosynthesis and the proposed role of Pi in the export of metabolites[15, 65]. Thus 5 mM PiPi plus 1 mM Mg^{2+} added to chloroplasts (in the absence of added PiPiase) would slow the Pi-induced export of metabolites (by interfering with Pi uptake) and yet maintain the Pi concentration at near optimal levels by replacing that consumed in photosynthesis by slow hydrolysis catalysed by endogenous PiPiase (from or in ruptured chloroplasts). The rate of hydrolysis would be limited by the low Mg and the presence of an inhibitory excess of PiPi not complexed with Mg. In the presence of higher Mg (6 mM) and added PiPiase (FDPase) the rate of hydrolysis would increase and the Pi would rise to an inhibitory level causing more metabolites to appear in the medium. If, however, the PiPi concentration was progressively raised still further, the inhibition would be reversed (see Cockburn *et al.*[71]).

Interaction between Pi and PiPi must also be borne in mind in considering the report by Jensen and Bassham on the effect of adding various intermediates and co-factors to isolated chloroplasts[168]. For example a wide tolerance to Pi is reported[168] but the experiments were carried out in the presence of 5 mM PiPi which is known to broaden the sharp sensitivity to Pi seen in its absence[71]. Similarly, PGA and DHAP were found inhibitory[168] in what were relatively Pi-deficient mixtures, whereas these compounds will stimulate in the presence of adequate Pi[78]. In the same way R5P will stimulate at high [Pi] and inhibit at low [Pi][71] just as high [Pi] will inhibit in the absence of sugar phosphate or stimulate in its presence[71]. *In short, no conclusion concerning an effect produced by varying the concentration of Pi, PiPi or sugar phosphate is completely meaningful unless considered in the context of the prevailing concentration of the other two reactants* (see also Section 1.8.4).

1.8.4 Phosphate–sugar phosphate regulation

One fact which cannot fail to impress anyone who has worked with isolated chloroplasts is their sensitivity (under appropriate conditions) to sugar phosphates (including sugar acid phosphates such as PGA) and to orthophosphate. This is seen in an extreme form in the Pi inhibition of photosynthesis and its reversal by sugar phosphates (Section 1.4.4.2) and in the complex interactions discussed in the preceding sections (especially Section 1.8.3). Some of these findings, although they undoubtedly provide invaluable experimental tools may appear to be concerned with situations which are far removed from the chloroplast *in vivo*. However, the Pi inhibition and its reversal is really only an exaggeration of induction phenomena which occur in whole plants[186] and intact chloroplasts alike[31, 70]. There are good grounds for believing that induction (the attainment of maximal photosynthesis only after an initial lag) can be explained in terms of the Osterhout–Haas hypothesis which postulates an autocatalytic build up of vital intermediates[70, 186]. Induction in chloroplasts[31, 70] can be shortened by catalytic quantities of added intermediates (sugar phosphates)[78, 104] and lengthened, in their absence, by small quantities ($>10^{-5}$M) of Pi[71]. In other words, the time of attainment of maximal rate is governed (largely, if not entirely) by the phosphate:sugar phosphate (Pi:SP) ratio. *In vitro*, once induction is passed the rate of photosynthesis becomes increasingly insensitive to otherwise super-optimal Pi because of an increasing concentration in the medium of metabolites such as PGA which can reverse Pi inhibition (Section 1.4.4.2). For this reason, induction in isolated chloroplasts is not normally repeated following a brief dark interval,[32, 70, 77, 195] whereas in whole organisms the extent of induction is usually related to the length of the preceding dark period[186]. To what extent this is, in turn, related to the concentration of sugar phosphates in the cytoplasm can only be guessed but it is clear that the metabolism of these compounds in the cytoplasm will produce a situation materially different from that in the suspending medium and that the concentration of Pi will not necessarily become less important than that of the sugar phosphates.

Considerations of this sort point to the Pi:SP ratio as a major factor in photosynthetic control particularly if it exerts its effect through a specific translocator. Thus a high external [Pi] would favour substantial export of triose phosphate and commensurate import of Pi. A low external [Pi] would favour internal build up of photosynthetic intermediates, short induction, starch formation within the chloroplast, etc.

1.9 SPECIFIC TRANSLOCATORS

One of the most useful concepts to arise in this field in recent years is that of the specific translocator. This was introduced to chloroplast metabolism by Heldt[63] and has been mentioned throughout this article. To date Heldt and his colleagues[63, 65, 67, 68] have defined three translocators (see also Nobel and Cheung[153] and Section 1.5.3.3).

1.9.1 The ATP translocator

This has a maximum rate of 5 μmol mg chlorophyll^{-1} h^{-1} at 20°C. It is highly specific for ATP, translocating ADP at *ca.* 12% of the ATP rate and is not believed to participate in the phosphorylation of cytoplasmic ADP.

1.9.2 The dicarboxylate translocator

This transports malate, oxaloacetate, aspartate and glutamate at rates of the order of 100 μmol mg chlorophyll^{-1} h^{-1} and may play an important role in the exchange of reducing equivalents between the chloroplast and the cytoplasm.

1.9.3 The phosphate translocator

Transports Pi, PGA, DHAP at 100 μmol mg chlorophyll^{-1} h^{-1} or more but not PiPi or hexose monophosphate. The transport of PGA is inhibited by Pi

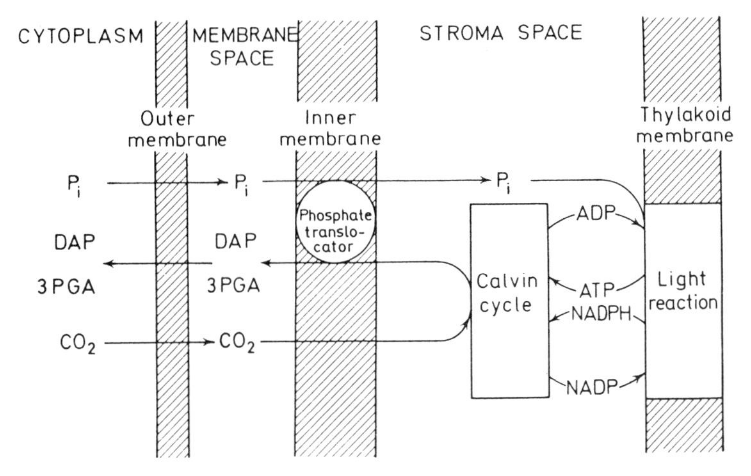

Figure 1.16 The role of the phosphate translocator in photosynthesis (Section 1.9.3). (From Heldt *et al.*[68], by courtesy of H. Heldt and Dr. W. Junk N. V. Publisher.)

and DHAP and that of Pi by PGA and DHAP. Release of Pi is facilitated by PGA, DHAP, G3P and arsenate and exchange of external Pi for internal PGA and sugar phosphates (and vice versa) may be the basis of Pi inhibition (and its reversal). The rate of PGA uptake is accelerated by light and a low external pH which is consistent with stimulation by a light dependent proton gradient across the thylakoid membrane (Figure 1.16).

1.10 THE TRANSPORT OF PROTONS

Jagendorf and Hind[187] showed that when a suspension of envelope-free chloroplasts is illuminated it rapidly becomes more alkaline. This is believed to be caused by release of protons into the thylakoid compartment during light driven electron transport[188-190]. In the intact chloroplast it is the stroma surrounding the thylakoids which will *tend* to become more alkaline in response to this proton movement and it is the stroma which will be immediately affected by the movement of co-ions and counter-ions. This could have profound effects on reactions within the stroma (see e.g. Section 1.11) and on the movement of metabolites, etc. into and out of this compartment. A link has been postulated between the proton pump and uptake of PGA via the phosphate translocator[68]. It has also been proposed that the increase in stromal pH would favour the accumulation of a reserve of bicarbonate[69].

Intact chloroplasts do not exhibit the pronounced light–dark pH shifts exhibited by envelope-free chloroplasts but instead, when illuminated in the presence of PGA or bicarbonate, exhibit a steady rise in pH with a stoichiometry of *ca.* 1 μequiv H^+ μmol O_2^{-1} for CO_2 and 0.5 μequiv H^+ μmol of O_2^{-1} for PGA[148, 150].

1.11 THE TRANSPORT OF MAGNESIUM

Although this article will not attempt to cover the movement of metal ions in general an exception is made for magnesium because of its new-found importance in the control of photosynthetic carbon fixation. It has been known for some time that there is an efflux of Mg ions from illuminated envelope-free chloroplasts,[191, 192] presumably moving as counter-ions in response to proton uptake (Section 1.10). More recently, Lin and Nobel[193] have described a light-driven uptake of Mg^{2+} into the stroma from the cytoplasm and have calculated that the Mg^2 content of this compartment can, as a consequence of receiving Mg^{2+} from both cytoplasm and thylakoids, increase from *ca.* 0 to 10 mM with respect to this ion. Such increases in Mg^{2+} could affect several

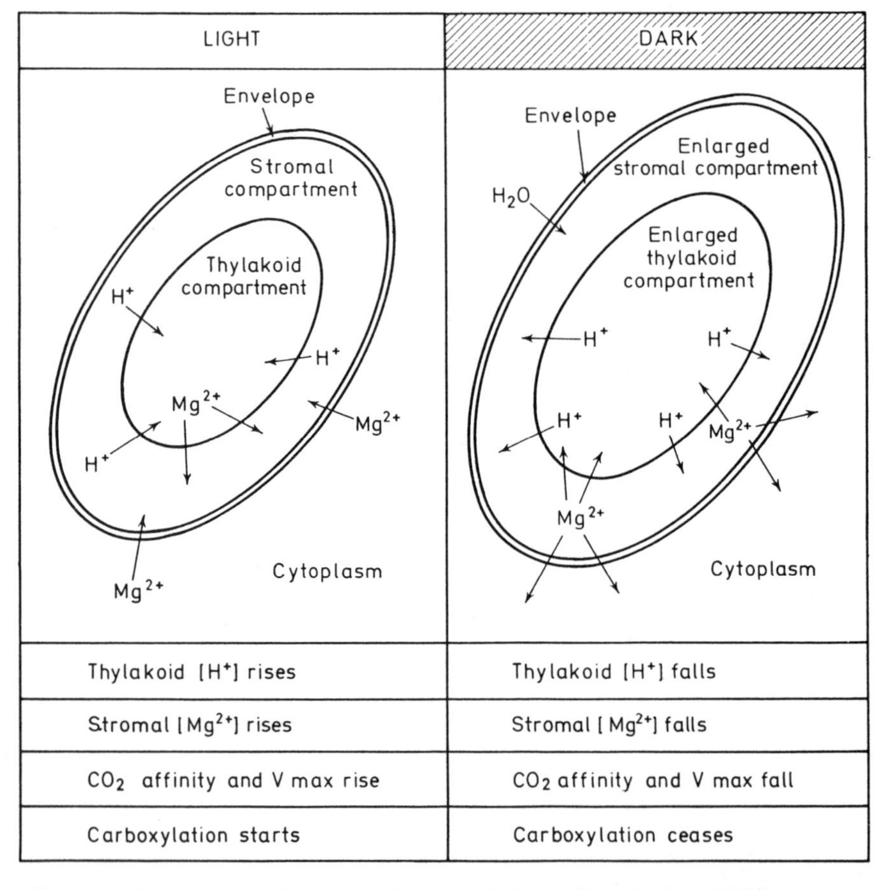

Figure 1.17 Hypothetical sequence of events in light–Mg^{2+} activation of RDP carboxylase (Section 1.11). The changes are initiated by light-driven electron transport which establishes a proton gradient across the thylakoid membrane. Mg^{2+} ions move to counteract the consequent charge separation and these movements together with volume changes increase the concentration of magnesium in the stromal compartment. As a result, the affinity of RDP carboxylase for CO_2 rises and CO_2 fixation is 'switched on'.

reactions in the Benson–Calvin cycle and in particular it has been shown that the affinity of ribulose diphosphate carboxylase for CO_2 is greatly increased at higher concentrations of Mg^{2+} [93,94,127,129,194]. Ribulose diphosphate carboxylase is known to 'switch off' in the dark and to 'switch on' in the light[59,60] and the observed changes in Mg concentration could provide the basis of this light activation[129,169,193]. In a reconstituted chloroplast system (envelope-free chloroplasts supplemented with stromal proteins and co-enzymes) it has been demonstrated that CO_2-dependent oxygen evolution can be 'switched on' either by increasing the Mg^{2+} concentration from 1 to 5 mM[70,94] or by increasing the CO_2–bicarbonate concentration tenfold[93]. This indicates that Mg activation of the reconstituted system works primarily by altering the K_m and V_{max} of the carboxylase and constitutes an experimental simulation of the sequence outlined in Figure 1.16[70,93,94].

1.12 C4 PHOTOSYNTHESIS

A number of plants, of which maize (*Zea mays*), sugar cane (*Saccharum officinarum*) and the 'grain'-bearing amaranth (*Amaranthus edulis*) are perhaps the three most commercially important examples initially incorporate radioactivity into malate and aspartate, rather than phosphoglycerate and related sugar phosphates, when first exposed to $^{14}CO_2$ in the light. This behaviour is now best known as C4 photosynthesis[46] though it has also been referred to as the dicarboxylic acid, β-carboxylation or Hatch–Slack–Kortschak pathway of photosynthesis[15,46-51]. What actually happens in C4 photosynthesis is still a matter for argument and conjecture but it is now clearly recognised as an adjunct to C3 (Benson–Calvin) photosynthesis, rather than a substitute for it[48,49]. As yet there is no known route by which a 4-carbon acid such as oxaloacetate, aspartate or malate can be converted to phosphoenolpyruvate without decarboxylation (transcarboxylation, in C4 plants, is no longer entertained as a likely possibility). For these and other reasons C4 photosynthesis has been assigned an auxiliary role and at present its most plausible function is seen as a system of carbon dioxide trapping and transport which could confer an ecological advantage[47]. Thus the rapid appearance of radioactivity in malate and aspartate is thought to occur because phosphoenol pyruvate is carboxylated in an outer compartment (the mesophyll) to which atmospheric CO_2 has first access. Malate and/or aspartate (derived from oxaloacetate by reduction or transamination) is then transferred to an inner compartment (the bundle sheath) where it is decarboxylated and the liberated CO_2 re-fixed by ribulose diphosphate carboxylase. The actual sites of initial fixation, decarboxylation and re-fixation are still in question. These sites may be in the chloroplasts or in the cytoplasm. Similarly, carboxylation of ribulose diphosphate may occur in the bundle sheath chloroplasts or in both bundle sheath and mesophyll chloroplasts. Until these problems are resolved the question of transport of metabolites in C4 photosynthesis must also remain a matter for conjecture. As it stands, however, the results obtained with C3 plants (preceding sections) pose no great problems and it would be surprising if acids such as malate, OAA and aspartate do not move as freely in C4 plants as the current hypothesis requires.

1.13 SUMMARY AND CONCLUSIONS

The study of the movement of compounds across the chloroplast envelope is still in its infancy and lack of evidence and contradictory evidence make it difficult to draw many conclusions with any degree of certainty. Even so it seems beyond dispute that the envelope exhibits selective permeability to a high degree and with proper regard for the qualifications made in the text the overall position may be summarised as follows:

1. The major imports are CO_2 (as dissolved or hydrated CO_2 rather than bicarbonate) and phosphate (as orthophosphate).
2. The major exports are DHAP and PGA.
3. The envelope is largely impermeable to free sugars and sugar diphosphates, only moderately permeable to heptose and hexose monophosphates but somewhat more permeable to pentose monophosphates.
4. Amino and carboxylic acids probably move in and out of the chloroplast freely and such exchange may be a normal feature of cellular amino acid synthesis.
5. The envelope is largely impermeable to NADP, ADP, ATP and inorganic pyrophosphate but export of 'reducing power' may be achieved by shuttles involving PGA, DHAP, malate and oxaloacetate.
6. Import and export may be channelled through specific translocators which moderate exchange across the envelope and competition by metabolites at these sites may influence the rate of photosynthesis and its contribution to cellular metabolism. In this respect the balance between endogenous and exogenous orthophosphate and sugar phosphates may be the largest single controlling factor.
7. Light-generated proton uptake into the thylakoid compartment may be expected to influence the movement of other ions into and out of the stroma and in so doing have far-reaching effects on the movement of metabolites across the envelope.

Acknowledgements

I am grateful to Robert Hill for his continuing encouragement and criticism. I have drawn extensively on two excellent articles by Martin Gibbs[31] and Ulrich Heber[39] and I have had the advantage of many conversations with these authors and with Hans Heldt. The work from my own laboratory was principally supported by the Science Research Council.

References

1. Rabinowitch, E. I. (1945). *Photosynthesis and Related Processes*, **1**, 9 (New York: Interscience)
2. Bassham, J. A. and Calvin, M. (1957). *The Path of Carbon in Photosynthesis* (Englewood Cliffs, N. J.: Prentice Hall)
3. Allen, M. B., Arnon, D. I., Capindale, J. B., Whatley, F. R. and Durham, L. J. (1955). *J. Amer. Chem. Soc.*, **77**, 4149
4. Arnon, D. I., Allen, M. B. and Whatley, F. R. (1954). *Nature* (*London*), **174**, 394

5. Arnon, D. I. (1955). *Science*, **122,** 9
6. Arnon, D. I. (1967). *Physiol. Rev.*, **47,** 317
7. Arnon, D. I. (1960). *Light and Life, Cell-Free Photosynthesis and the Energy Conversion Process*, 489 (Baltimore: Johns Hopkins Press, 1961)
8. Hill, R. (1937). *Nature (London)*, **139,** 881
9. Rabinowitch, E. I. (1945). Ref. 1, p. 355
10. Lumry, R., Spikes, J. D. and Eyring, H. (1954). *Ann. Rev. Plant Physiol.*, **5,** 271
11. Walker, D. A. (1964). *Biochem. J.*, **92,** 22
12. Walker, D. A. (1971). *Methods in Enzymology*, **23,** 211 (A. San Pieto, editor) (London and New York: Academic Press)
13. Jensen, R. G. and Bassham, J. A. (1966). *Proc. Nat. Acad. Sci. USA*, **56,** 1095
14. Plaut, Z. and Gibbs, M. (1970). *Plant Physiol.*, **45,** 470
15. Walker, D. A. and Crofts, A. R. (1970). *Ann. Rev. Biochem.*, **39,** 389
16. Sachs, J. (1887). *Lectures on the Physiology of Plants.* (Translated by H. M. Ward), 309 *et seq.* (Oxford: Clarendon Press)
17. Meyer, K. H. and Gibbons, G. C. (1951). *Advan. Enzymol.*, **12,** 341
18. Whelan, W. J. (1955). *Modern Methods of Plant Analysis*, **2,** 145 (K. Paech and M. V. Tracey, editors) (Berlin: Springer-Verlag)
19. Molisch, H. (1922). *Populare Biologische Vortrage*, 243 (Jena: Verlag von Gustav Fischer)
20. Boehm, J. (1883). *Bot. Ztg.*, **41,** 33, 49
21. Meyer, A. (1886). *Bot. Ztg.*, **44,** 81
22. Parkin, J. (1899). *Roy. Soc. Lond. Phil. Trans. B.*, **191,** 35
23. Phillis, E. and Mason, T. G. (1937). *Ann. Bot. Lond. (N.S.)*, **1,** 231
24. Maclachlan, G. A. and Porter, H. K. (1959). *Proc. Roy. Soc. B.*, **150,** 460
25. Rabinowitch, E. I. (1945). Ref. 1, p. 42
26. Thomas, M., Ranson, S. L. and Richardson, J. A. (1958). *Plant Physiology*, 205 (London: Churchill)
27. Rabinowitch, E. I. (1945). Ref. 1, p. 409
28. Rabinowitch, E. I. (1945). Ref. 1, p. 411
29. Gibbs, M. (1966). *Plant Physiology*, Volume 4B, 3 (F. C. Steward, editor) (New York and London: Academic Press)
30. Arnon, D. I. (1958). *Brookhaven Symposia in Biology Number 11 Chloroplasts and Photosynthesis*, 181 (Upton, N.Y.: Brookhaven Nat. Lab. 1958)
31. Gibbs, M. (1971). *Structure and Function of Chloroplasts*, 169 (M. Gibbs, editor) (Berlin, Heidelberg, New York: Springer-Verlag)
32. Walker, D. A. (1965). *Proc. NATO Ad. Study Inst. 'Biochemistry of Chloroplasts', Photosynthetic Activity of Isolated Pea Chloroplasts*, **2,** 53 (New York: Academic Press, 1967).
33. Gibbs, M., Bamberger, E. S., Ellyard, P. W. and Everson, R. G. (1965). *Assimilation of Carbon Dioxide by Chloroplast Preparations.* Ref. 32, vol. 2, p. 3.
34. Gibbs, M., Latzko, E., Everson, R. G. and Cockburn, W. (1966). *Proc. Intern. Minerals Chem. Symp. Chicago.* Harvesting the Sun, Carbon Mobilisation by the green plant, 111 (New York, London: Academic Press, 1967)
35. Everson, R. G., Cockburn, W. and Gibbs, M. (1967). *Plant Physiol.*, **42,** 840
36. Haq, S. and Hassid, W. Z. (1965). *Plant. Physiol.*, **40,** 591
37. Bird, I. F., Porter, H. K. and Stocking, C. R. (1965). *Biochim. Biophys. Acta.*, **100,** 366
38. Stocking, C. R., Shumway, L. K., Weier, T. E. and Greenwood, D. (1968). *J. Cell Biol.* **36,** 270
39. Heber, U. (1970). *Internat. Symp. Transport and distribution of Matter in Cells of Higher Plants, Flow of Metabolites and Compartmentation Phenomena in Chloroplasts*, 151 (Berlin: Akademie-Verlag)
40. Newcomb, E. H. and Frederick, S. E. (1970). *Distribution and Structure of Plant Microbodies (Peroxisomes)*, Ref. 46, p. 442
41. Tolbert, N. E. (1970). *Leaf Peroxisomes and Photorespiration*, Ref. 46, p. 458
42. Beevers, H. (1970). *Comparative Biochemistry of Microbodies (Glyoxysomes, Peroxisomes)*, Ref. 46, p. 483
43. Whitehouse, D. G., Ludwig, L. J. and Walker, D. A. (1971). *J. Exp. Bot.*, **23,** 772
44. Heber, U. and Willenbrink, J. (1964). *Biochim. Biophys. Acta*, **82,** 313
45. Heldt, H. W. and Sauer, F. (1971). *Biochim. Biophys. Acta*, **234,** 83

46. Proceedings of a conference held at Australian National University, Canberra (1970). *Photosynthesis and Photorespiration.* (New York, London, Sydney, Toronto: Wiley-Interscience, 1971)
47. Hatch, M. D. (1970). *Mechanism and Function of the C4 Pathway of Photosynthesis* as Ref. 46, p. 139
48. Walker, D. A. (1970). *CO_2 Fixation: Assessment.* Ref. 46, p. 294
49. Slack, C. R. (1970). *The C4 Pathway: Assessment.* Ref. 46, p. 297
50. Hatch, M. D. and Slack, C. R. (1967). *Biochem. J.*, **102,** 417
51. Hatch, M. D. and Slack, C. R. (1970). *Annu. Rev. Plant Physiol.*, **21,** 141
52. Bassham, J. A. and Kirk, M. (1960). *Biochim. Biophys. Acta*, **43,** 447
53. Walker, D. A. (1962). *Biol. Rev.*, **37,** 215
54. Thalacker, R. and Behrens, M. (1959). *Z. Naturforsch.*, **14b,** 443
55. Stocking, C. R. (1959). *Plant Physiol.*, **34,** 56
56. Heber, U. and Santarius, K. A. (1965). *Biochim. Biophys. Acta*, **109,** 309
57. Urbach, W., Hudson, M. A., Ullrich, W., Santarius, K. A. and Heber, U. (1965). *Z. Naturforsch.*, **20b,** 890
58. Aach, H. G. and Heber, U. (1967). *Z. Pflanzenphysiol.*, **57,** 317
59. Bassham, J. A. and Jensen, R. G. (1967). *Photosynthesis of Carbon Compounds.* Ref. 34, p. 79
60. Bassham, J. A., Kirk, M. and Jensen, R. G. (1968). *Biochim. Biophys. Acta*, **153,** 211
61. Werkheiser, W. C. and Bartley, W. (1957). *Biochem. J.*, **66,** 79
62. Klingenberg, M. and Pfaff, E. (1967). *Methods in Enzymol.*, **10,** 680
63. Heldt, H. W. (1969). *FEBS Lett.*, **5,** 11
64. Heldt, H. W. and Rapley, L. (1970). *FEBS Lett.*, **7,** 139
65. Heldt, H. W. and Rapley, L. (1970). *FEBS Lett.*, **10,** 143
66. Strotmann, H. and Heldt, H. W. (1968). *Phosphate containing Metabolites Participating in Photosynthetic Reactions of Chlorella pyrenoidosa.* Ref. 73, Vol. 3, p. 1131
67. Werdan, K. and Heldt, H. W. (1971). *Proc. Second Internat. Congress, Stresa. Progress in Photosynthesis, The Phosphate Translocator of Spinach Chloroplasts*, **2,** 1337 (The Hague: Dr. W. Junk) N. V.
68. Heldt, H. W., Sauer, F. and Rapley, L. (1971). *Differentiation of the Permeability Properties of the Two Membranes of The Chloroplast Envelope.* Ref. 67, p. 1345
69. Werdan, K. and Heldt, H. W. (1972). *Proceedings of the Conference on Mechanisms in Bioenergetics. Pugnochiuso, Italy. Bicarbonate Uptake into the Chloroplast Stroma* (Academic Press: New York)
70. Walker, D. A. (1973). *New Phytol.*, **72,** 209
71. Cockburn, W., Baldry, C. W. and Walker, D. A. (1967). *Biochim. Biophys. Acta*, **143,** 614
72. Cockburn, W., Walker, D. A. and Baldry, C. W. (1968). *Biochem. J.*, **107,** 89
73. Walker, D. A. (1969). *Proc. First Internat. Congress. Freudenstadt, Progress in Photosynthesis. Permeability of the Chloroplast Envelope.* Vol. 1, 250 (Tubingen, 1969: Internal. Union of Biol. Sci.)
74. Schacter, B., Eley, J. H. and Gibbs, M. (1971). *Plant Physiol.*, **48,** 707
75. Stokes, D. M. and Walker, D. A. (1972). *Biochem. J.*, **128,** 1147
76. Baldry, C. W., Cockburn, W. and Walker, D. A. (1968). *Biochim. Biophys. Acta*, **153,** 476
77. Walker, D. A. and Hill, R. (1967). *Biochim. Biophys. Acta*, **131,** 330
78. Walker, D. A., Cockburn, W. and Baldry, C. W. (1967). *Nature (London)*, **216,** 597
79. Cockburn, W., Baldry, C. W. and Walker, D. A. (1967). *Biochim. Biophys. Acta*, **131,** 594
80. Heber, U. and Santarius, K. A. (1970). *Z. Naturforsch.*, **25b**, 718
81. Rabinowitch, E. I. (1956). Ref. 1, Vol. 2, Part 2, p. 1561 *et seq.*
82. Gibbs, M. and Kandler, O. (1957). *Proc. Nat. Acad. Sci. (USA)* **43,** 446
83. Gibbs, M. and Cynkin, M. A. (1958). *Nature (London)*, **182,** 1241
84. Havir, E. A. and Gibbs, M. (1963). *J. Biol. Chem.*, **238,** 3183
85. Krause, G. H. (1971). *Z. Pflanzenphysiol.*, **65,** 13
86. Mathieu, Y. (1967). *Photosynthetica*, **1,** 57
87. Heber, U., Hallier, U. and Hudson, M. A. (1967). *Z. Naturforsch.*, **22b,** 1200
88. Heber, U., Santarius, K. A., Urbach, W. and Ullrich, W. (1964). *Z. Naturforsch.*, **19b,** 576

89. Walker, D. A. (1965). *Plant Physiol.*, **40,** 1157
90. West, K. R. and Wiskich, J. T. (1968). *Biochem. J.*, **109,** 527
91. Stokes, D. M. and Walker, D. A. (1971). *Plant Physiol.*, **48,** 163
92. Stokes, D. M. and Walker, D. A. (1971). *Relative Impermeability of the Intact Chloroplast Envelope to ATP.* Ref. 46, 226
93. Stokes, D. M., Walker, D. A. and McCormick, A. V. (1971). *Nature (London)*, **233,** 346
94. Walker, D. A. (1971). *The Affinity of Ribulose Diphosphate Carboxylase for CO_2–Bicarbonate.* Ref. 67, Vol. 3, p. 1773
95. Stokes, D. M., Walker, D. A. and McCormick, A. V. (1971). *Photosynthetic Oxygen Evolution in a Reconstituted Chloroplast System.* Ref. 67, Vol. III, p. 1779
96. Behrens, M. (1932). *Z. Physiol. Chem.*, **209,** 59
97. Stocking, C. R. (1971). *Methods in Enzymol.*, Vol. 23, 221 (A. San Pietro, editor) (London and New York: Academic Press)
98. Spencer, D. L. and Unt, H. (1965). *Aust. J. Biol. Sci.*, **18,** 197
99. Hall, D. O. (1972). *Nature New Biol.*, **235,** 125
100. Gibbs, M. (1963). *Nat. Acad. Sci. Pub.*, **1145,** 663
101. Pedersen, T. A., Kirk, M. and Bassham, J. A. (1966). *Physiol. Plantarum*, **19,** 219
102. Bamberger, E. S. and Gibbs, M. (1965). *Plant Physiol.*, **40,** 919
103. Bucke, C., Walker, D. A. and Baldry, C. W. (1966). *Biochem. J.*, **101,** 636
104. Baldry, C. W., Walker, D. A. and Bucke, C. (1966). *Biochem. J.*, **101,** 641
105. Robinson, J. M. and Stocking, C. R. (1958). *Plant Physiol.*, **43,** 1597
106. Bassham, J. A. (1963). *Advan. Enzymol.*, **25,** 39
107. Stocking, C. R. and Larson, S. (1969). *Biochim. Biophys. Res. Commun.*, **37,** 278
108. Walker, D. A. unpublished results
109. Cockburn, W., Baldry, C. W. and Walker, D. A. (1967). *Biochim. Biophys. Acta*, **143,** 603
110. Heber, U., Santarius, K. A., Hudson, M. A. and Hallier, U. (1967). *Z. Naturforsch.*, **22b,** 1189
111. Heber, U. (1967). *Biochemistry of Chloroplasts*, Vol. 2, 71. (T. W. Goodwin, editor) (London and New York: Academic Press)
112. Rabinowitch, E. I. (1945). Ref. 1, p. 176
113. Blinks, L. R. and Skow, R. K. (1938). *Proc. Nat. Acad. Sci. USA*, **24,** 413
114. Neuman, J. and Levine, R. P. (1971). *Plant Physiol.*, **47,** 700
115. Heber, U. and Krause, G. H. (1971). *Hydrogen and Proton Transfer Across the Chloroplast Envelope.* Ref. 67, p. 1023
116. Cooper, T. G., Filmer, D., Wishnick, M. and Lane, M. D. (1969). *J. Biol. Chem.*, **244,** 1081
117. Filmer, D. L. and Cooper, T. G. (1970). *J. Theoret. Biol.*, **29,** 131
118. Smith, F. A., Beevers, H. *et al.* (1970). *The C-Two Three Through Four Pathway.* Ref. 46, p. 549
119. Losada, M., Trebst, A. V. and Arnon, D. I. (1960). *J. Biol. Chem.*, **235,** 832
120. Rabinowitch, E. I. (1956). Ref. 1, Vol. 2, part 1, p. 997
121. Zelitch, I. (1971). *Photosynthesis Photorespiration and Plant Productivity*, 99 (New York and London: Academic Press)
122. Graham, D., Atkins, C. A., Reed, M. L., Patterson, B. D. and Smillie, R. M. (1970). *Carbonic Anhydrase, Photosynthesis, and Light-induced pH Changes.* Ref. 46, p. 267
123. Everson, R. G. (1970). *Carbonic Anhydrose in Photosynthesis.* Ref. 46, p. 275
124. Everson, R. G. and Graham, D. (1970). *Effects of an Inhibitor of Carbonic Anhydrase on Light Induced pH Changes in Pea Chloroplasts.* Ref. 46, p. 281
125. Zelitch, I. (1971). Ref. 121, p. 241
126. Rabinowitch, E. I. (1945). Ref. 1, p. 199
127. Sugiyama, T., Nakayama, N. and Akazawa, T. (1968). *Arch. Biochem. Biophys.*, **126,** 737
128. Paulsen, J. M. and Lane, M. D. (1966). *Biochemistry*, **5,** 2350
129. Jensen, R. G. (1971). *Biochim. Biophys. Acta*, **234,** 371
130. Heath, O. V. S. (1969). *The Physiological Aspects of Photosynthesis*, 63 (London: Heinemann)
131. Heath, O. V. S. (1969). Ref. 130, p. 140
132. Heath, O. V. S. (1969). Ref. 130, p. 198 *et seq.*
133. Willstatter, R. and Stoll, A. (1918). *Untersuchungen über die Assimilation der Kohlensaure* (Berlin: Springer)

134. Walker, D. A. and Brown, J. M. A. (1957). *Biochem. J.*, **67,** 79
135. Moss, D. N. (1971). *Carbon Dioxide Compensation in Plants with C4 Characteristics.* Ref. 46, p. 120
136. Zelitch, I. (1971). Ref. 121, p. 130
137. Beevers, H. (1970). *Photorespiration: Assessment.* Ref. 46, p. 541
138. Zelitch, I. (1971). Ref. 121, p. 173 *et seq.*
139. Gibbs, M. (1969). *Ann. N.Y. Acad. Sci.*, **168,** 356
140. Ellyard, P. W. and Gibbs, M. (1969). *Plant Physiol.*, **44,** 1115
141. Bradbeer, J. W. and Anderson, C. M. A. (1965). *Glycollate formation in Chloroplast Preparations.* Ref. 32, p. 175
142. Bradbeer, J. W. and Racker, E. (1961). *Fed. Proc.* (*Fed. Amer. Soc. Exp. Biol.*), **20,** 88
143. Holzer, H. and Schroter, W. (1961). *Biochim. Biophys. Acta*, **65,** 271
144. Richardson, K. E. and Tolbert, N. E. (1961). *J. Biol. Chem.*, **236,** 1285
145. Bassham, J. A. and Kirk, M. (1962). *Biochem. Biophys. Res. Commun.*, **9,** 376
146. Butt, V. S. and Peel, M. (1963). *Biochem. J.*, **88,** *31p.*
147. Tolbert, N. E., Yamazaki, R. K. and Oeser, A. (1970). *J. Biol. Chem.*, **245,** 5129
148. Kearney, P. C. and Tolbert, N. E. (1962). *Arch. Biochem. Biophys.*, **98,** 164
149. Keys, A. J. and Whittingham, C. P. (1968). *Nucleotide Metabolism in Chloroplast and Non-Chloroplast Components of Tobacco Leaves.* Ref. 73, p. 352
150. Heber, U. and Krause, G. H. (1970). *Transfer of Carbon, Phosphate Energy and Reducing Equivalents across the Chloroplast Envelope.* Ref. 46, p. 218
151. Ongun, A. and Stocking, C. R. (1965). *Plant Physiol.*, **40,** 825
152. Roberts, G. R., Keys, A. J. and Whittingham, C. P. (1970). *J. Exp. Bot.*, **21,** 683
153. Nobel P. S. and Cheung Y. S. (1972). *Nature New Biol.*, **237,** 207
154. Nobel, P. S. and Wang, C. -t. (1970). *Biochim. Biophys. Acta*, **211,** 79
155. Wang, C. -t. and Nobel, P. S. (1971). *Biochim. Biophys. Acta*, **241,** 200
156. Packer, L. and Crofts, A. R. (1967). *Current Topics in Bioenergetics*, **1,** 24
157. Kirk, P. R. and Leech, R. N. (1972). *Plant Physiol.*, **50,** 228
158. Vishniac, W. and Ochoa, S. (1952). *J. Biol. Chem.*, **198,** 501
159. Jagendorf, A. T. and Avron, M. (1958). *Fed. Proc.* (*Fed. Amer. Soc. Exp. Biol.*), **17,** 248
160. Jagendorf, A. T. and Avron, M. (1958). *J. Biol. Chem.*, **231,** 277
161. Allen, M. B., Whatley, F. R. and Arnon, D. I. (1958). *Biochim. Biophys. Acta*, **27,** 16
162. Hill, R. and Walker, D. A. (1959). *Plant Physiol.*, **34,** 240
163. Whatley, F. R., Allen, M. B., Rosenburg, L. L., Capindale, J. B. and Arnon, D. I. (1956). *Biochim. Biophys. Acta*, **20,** 462
164. Stocking, R. C., Robinson, I. M. and Weier, T. E. (1968). *Interrelationships between the Chloroplast and its Cellular Environment.* Ref. 73, p. 258
165. Reeves, S. G., Hall, D. O. and West, J. (1971). *Correlation of the Stoichiometry of Photophosphorylation with the Integrity of Isolated Spinach Chloroplasts.* Ref. 67, p. 1357
166. Schurmann, P., Buchanan, B. B., and Arnon, D. I. (1971). *Biochim. Biophys. Acta*, **267,** 111
167. Schurmann, P., Buchanan, B. B. and Arnon, D. I. (1971). *Role of Cyclic Photophosphorylation in Photosynthetic Carbon Dioxide Assimilation.* Ref. 67, p. 1283
168. Jensen, R. G. and Bassham, J. A. (1968). *Biochim. Biophys. Acta*, **153,** 219
169. Jensen, R. G. and Bassham, J. A. (1968). *Biochim. Biophys. Acta*, **153,** 227
170. Lilley, R. McC., Schwenn, J. D. and Walker, D. A. (1972). Unpublished results
171. Tanner, W., Loos, E. and Kandler, O. (1966). *Currents in Photosynthesis*, 243 (J. B. Thomas and J. C. Goedheer, editors) (Rotterdam: A. D. Donker Publ.)
172. Kandler, O., Dachsel, L. and Tanner, W. (1965). *Plant Physiol.*, **40,** 1151
173. Jeschke, W. D. (1967). *Planta*, **73,** 161
174. Keys, A. J. (1968). *Biochem. J.*, **108,** 1
175. Bassham, J. A. (1971). *Science*, **172,** 526
176. Chu, K. D. and Bassham, J. A. (1972). *Plant Physiol.*, **50,** 224
177. Hiller, R. G. and Walker, D. A. (1961). *Biochem. J.*, **78,** 56
178. Graham, D. and Walker, D. A. (1962). *Biochem. J.*, **82,** 554
179. Baldry, C. W., Bucke, C. and Walker, D. A. (1966). *Nature* (*London*), **210,** 793
180. Weissbach, A., Horecker, B. L. and Hurwitz, J. (1956). *J. Biol. Chem.*, **218,** 795
181. Bassham, J. A. and Krause, G. H. (1969). *Biochim. Biophys. Acta*, **189,** 207

182. Moore, R. E., Springer-Lederer, H., Ottenheym, H. C. J. and Bassham, J. A. (1969). *Biochim. Biophys. Acta*, **180,** 368
183. Bassham, J. A., El-Badry, A. M., Kirk, M. R., Ottenheym, H. C. J. and Springer-Lederer, H. (1970). *Biochim. Biophys. Acta*, **223,** 261
184. Springer-Lederer, H., El-Badry, A. M., Ottenheym, H. C. J. and Bassham, J. A. (1969). *Biochim. Biophys. Acta*, **189,** 464
185. El-Badry, A. M. and Bassham, J. A. (1970). *Biochim. Biophys. Acta*, **197,** 308
186. Rabinowitch, E. I. (1956). Ref. 2, Vol. 2, part 2, p. 2323 *et seq.*
187. Jagendorf, A. T. and Hind, G. (1963). *Photosynthetic Mechanism of Green Plants*, **1145,** 599 (A. T. Jagendorf and B. Kok, editors) (Washington, D.C.: Nat. Acad. Sci. Nat. Res. Council Publ.)
188. Mitchell, P. (1961). *Nature (London)*, **191,** 144
189. Mitchell, P. (1966). *Biol. Rev.*, **41,** 455
190. Witt, H. T., Rumberg, B. and Junge, W. (1968). *Colloquium der Gesellschaft für Biologische Chemie*, 262 (Berlin: Springer-Verlag)
191. Dilley, R. A. and Vernon, L. P. (1965). *Arch. Biochem. Biophys.*, **111,** 365
192. Nobel, P. S. (1967). *Biochim. Biophys. Acta*, **131,** 127
193. Lin, D. C. and Nobel, P. S. (1971). *Arch. Biochem. Biophys.*, **145,** 622
194. Bassham, J. A., Sharp, P. and Morris, I. (1968). *Biochim. Biophys. Acta*, **153,** 898
195. Walker, D. A., Kosciukiewicz, K. and Case, C. (1973). *New Phytol.* in the press
196. Walker, D. A. (1970). *Nature (London)*, **226,** 1204
197. Johnson, E. J. and Bruff, B. S. (1967). *Plant Physiol.*, **42,** 1321
198. Werdan, K. and Heldt, H. W. (1973). *Biochim. Biophys. Acta*, in the press

2
Chemistry and Biochemistry of Algal Cell-wall Polysaccharides

A. HAUG
University of Trondheim, Norway

2.1 INTRODUCTION

Human civilisation is based on the cultivation of plants belonging to the division Spermatophyta. For human culture and economy, this group of plants is by far the most important. When production of organic matter on this planet is considered, however, the higher plants and algae are most probably of about equal importance.

The Spermatophyta is a relatively homogenous group of plants specialised in terrestrial life, which have required a high degree of differentiation into specialised organs like root, stem, leaves, etc. The algae form an extremely heterogeneous group. In most cases the algae have remained in an aquatic environment which requires a lesser degree of differentiation, but not necessarily a lesser degree of specialisation. The algae are divided into a number of divisions, in many cases with only a remote relationship to each other. No universally accepted system of classification of algae exists. In the present review, the classification is based mainly on that of Silva[1] and Christensen[2]. Modern studies have suggested that Cyanophyta may be more conveniently regarded as a group of bacteria[3], distinguished from other photosynthetic bacteria by their pigment system and by performing aerobic photosynthesis. They will, therefore, not be considered here.

A rigid cell wall is characteristic of plants and bacteria, and is often regarded as one of the major distinctions between the plant and the animal kingdom. The plant cell wall consists of fibrous elements embedded in an amorphous matrix. In multicellular organisms the space between the cells is filled with an intercellular substance which may be identical to the matrix substance in the cell wall proper.

It has been customary to separate the algal polysaccharides into cell-wall components and mucilages[4,5]. This distinction is mainly based on a difference in solubility and the assumption that this difference is related to a difference in function. At least in some cases, this may be misleading. The polysaccharides of brown algae may be considered as an example. A sulphated fucan, fuciodan, may be extracted with water from brown algae, or isolated from exudates[5] and is accordingly described as a mucilage[4]. A chemically related compound, containing in addition xylose and glucuronic acid residues, is regarded as a cell-wall constituent[6], being originally isolated from a weed residue after extensive extraction. Recent work has indicated that both these polysaccharides may occur as components of the same complex molecule, containing, in addition, protein and alginate[7]. The localisation of the latter compound has been studied by several methods and it was found to be present both in the cell wall and the intercellular substance[8-10].

No attempts will be made in this review to distinguish between cell-wall components and mucilages, or cell walls and intercellular substances, in order to avoid introducing a classification of polysaccharides which may not be based on a real difference in function or localisation. It will be attempted, however, to distinguish between the fibrillar and the matrix components.

Several valuable reviews about plant cell walls have been published recently[11-15]. These reviews are concerned mainly with higher plants and much emphasis is put upon problems concerned with the biogenesis of the walls. Little is known about the biogenesis of the cell walls of algae. The main work has been concerned with the elucidation of the structure of the great variety of polysaccharides present in algae, and still, in some of the algal divisions which is most important from an ecological point of view, the structure of the polysaccharides is largely unknown. In the present review, the polysaccharides of the main algal divisions will be treated separately. In the case of two groups of algal polysaccharides (Rhodophyta galactans and Phaeophyta alginates) significant progress has been made recently in the study of physical properties of biological interest. This aspect of algal cell wall polysaccharides, and studies primarily concerned with biosynthesis, will be considered in separate sections.

2.2 ISOLATION OF POLYSACCHARIDES AND THE PROBLEM OF HOMOGENEITY

The matrix and fibrillar components of the cell walls may be separated by bringing the matrix components in solution by some extraction procedure. Usually the matrix material is extracted with hot water or alkali[16,17]. In the case of algae, the matrix components are in most cases negatively-charged polysaccharides, the solubility of which depends upon the cations bound to the polyanions and the ionic strength of the extraction medium. The extraction may, thus, often conveniently be regarded as a two-stage process, (a) an exchange of cations which may be regarded as a change from an insoluble to a soluble salt of the polyanion, and (b) the extraction of this soluble polysaccharide. This is well exemplified by the extraction of alginate[18] (see later). It is by this means often possible to avoid the use of alkali in the extraction procedure which, particularly in connection with polyuronides[19] and sulphated polysaccharides[20], should be used with caution.

The fibrillar material remaining insoluble after extraction does, in many cases, give a well defined x-ray diffraction pattern and reveal the presence of only one type of monosaccharide and one type of linkage on chemical investigation. Thus, chemically homogeneous fibrils composed of cellulose, β-1,3-linked xylan or β-1,4-linked mannan have been prepared from algal cell walls[17]. In other cases, however, either more than one type of monomer[17] or one type of linkage[21] was present in the remaining fibrillar material. In most of these cases the homogeneity is doubtful; it is often not clear whether the different monomers or linkages occur in the same molecule or whether the fibrillar material is a mixture of homopolymers. It is safe to assume, however, that the formation of insoluble fibrils requires molecules of high regularity, and that the polysaccharides forming the fibrils are either homopolymers or block copolymers with long homopolymeric sequences.

Compared to the fibrillar components, the matrix polysaccharides are often chemically very complex, and different types of matrix materials usually occur in the same plants. The fact that these polysaccharides are most often polyanions may be taken advantage of in the separation procedure; the different effects of salts on the solubility of neutral, carboxylated and sulphated polysaccharides[22, 23] make it possible to choose conditions where these types of polysaccharides may be separated by fractional precipitation.

No universally accepted criteria of homogeneity for polysaccharides exist. Separation on columns with anion exchangers have been used, and separation into distinct fractions has been reported, sometimes, however, without any detectable chemical difference between the fractions[5]. Complete elution of highly sulphated material from the columns is often difficult to achieve. In the experience of the author, electrophoresis at several pH values is a convenient and reliable method for examination of the homogeneity of charged polysaccharides[24]. Sometimes the use of small amounts of cations with special affinity to one of the types of the negatively charged groups may lead to separation of polysaccharides which otherwise have identical mobilities[25].

It should be kept in mind, however, that chemically homogeneous fractions of matrix polysaccharides, in the sense that all molecules have the same chemical structure, should not be expected. The usual way of preparing these polysaccharides is to use whole plants, which in the case of multicellular organisms include different types of tissues. Few investigations of the composition and structure of polysaccharides in different types of algal tissue have been carried out, but at least in the case of alginate very marked differences have been reported[26]. The use of whole plants, often many plants in different stages of development, possibly, in some algal groups, including both sporophytes and gametophytes, might in itself be expected to lead to heterogenous polysaccharide preparations.

Even in the absence of any biological heterogeneity, polymer molecules which are synthesised in a non-template process might be expected to vary in chemical structure. This can most easily be discussed by considering the synthesis of a heteropolysaccharide consisting of two monomers, A and B[27, 28]. The sequence of the two monomers in the polymer chain will depend upon the specificity of the polymerase system. This specificity may in the most simple situation be expressed as the probability of adding a monomer A or a monomer B to a growing chain ending with an A (the sum of the two probabilities is 1), and correspondingly for the addition to a chain ending with B. Two limiting situations may easily be recognised; (a) when the chain ends with an A, the probability of adding an A is zero and that of adding a B is one (and vice versa when the chain ends with a B) and (b) when the chain ends with an A, the probability of adding a B is zero and that of adding an

A is one (and again vice versa when the chain ends with a B). The first set of conditions would lead to a strictly alternating copolymer (ABAB. . . .) while the second set would give two homopolymers (AAA. . . and BBB. . .). All other types of specificities of the polymerase would lead to sequences which must be described by statistical methods, and chain molecules of a limited size would show compositional polydispersity, i.e. chains with different monomer composition will occur. The degree of compositional polydispersity will depend upon the degree of polymerisation and the type of sequence.

Compositional polydispersity is of particular importance in connection with the breakdown of the polymer chains which may take place during the isolation procedure. When the specificity of the polymerase leads to the formation of copolymers containing long homopolymeric blocks, the compositional distribution changes from being unimodal to become bimodal (in the Gibbon's sense[29]) at a certain degree of degradation[30]. This means that a polysaccharide, being homogeneous in the sense that it is synthesised by one single polymerase system, may, after a certain degradation, appear as fractions which may be separated by ordinary fractionation methods. In the case of alginate, which is a block copolymer of two types of uronic acid residues, this development of a compositional heterogeneity by degradation has been studied in some detail[25,30]. Alginate is a relatively stable polysaccharide and the degradation taking place in an ordinary isolation procedure will not lead to compositional heterogeneity. This may, however, not always be the case, and work on the fucose-containing polysaccharides of brown algae[7] has indicated the presence of a labile complex which, when extracted at very gentle conditions, has a unimodal composition distribution and by a mild degradation splits into components forming separate peaks on electrophoretic examination. The usual isolation procedures will lead to the extraction of these components and the original complex will not be detected.

2.3 CHLOROPHYTA (GREEN ALGAE)

2.3.1 General

The division Chlorophyta is a very diverse group, containing unicellular, sometimes mobile organisms and multicellular organisms with different cellular organisations, e.g. colonial, thalloid, siphonaceous. Marine, freshwater and terrestrial forms occur and also highly specialised forms living symbiotically with fungi in the form of lichens, or with animals like sponges. The Chlorophyta is divided into several orders; we shall here follow Christensen[2], dividing Chlorophyta into 10 orders.

2.3.2 Fibrillar components of the wall

The Chlorophyta fall into several distinct groups with regard to the composition of the fibrillar components of their cell walls[17].

Valonia (Siphonocladales), *Cladophora* and *Chaetomorpha* species (Cladophorales) have cell walls consisting of well defined microfibrils arranged parallel to the wall surface, orientated in two directions usually about perpendicular to each other, giving a strong x-ray diffraction pattern of cellulose I and giving only glucose after hydrolysis when prepared in the standard way as α-cellulose (in amounts up to 30–40% dry matter)[31]. The high crystallinity of their cellulose fibrils have made these algae, particularly *Valonia ventricosa*, favourite model organisms, and studies on *Valonia* cellulose have formed important parts in some of the theories of cellulose microfibril structure[11, 15, 32, 33]. Detailed structural investigations based on x-ray examinations of *Chaetomorpha melagonium* cellulose[34] and on infrared and Raman spectroscopy of *Valonia* cellulose[35] have recently been published. The unit cell of algal cellulose differs from that of ramie cellulose, and the differences in the diagrams suggest that more than a difference in the number of chains in the unit cell occurs[34]. The degree of polymerisation of *Valonia* cellulose has been investigated by Marx-Figini[36]. By fractionation she found this cellulose to consist of two fractions, one small polydisperse fraction with a relatively low degree of polymerisation and the bulk of the material which was approximately monodisperse, with a degree of polymerisation of *ca.* 19 000. Similar results were obtained with cellulose from higher plants[37], with a monodisperse fraction with a degree of polymerisation of approximately 14 000. No effect of colchinin in the culture medium on the degree of polymerisation of the *Valonia* cellulose was observed[38], and this was interpreted as indicating that microtubules were not directly involved in the deposition of the cellulose molecules in the wall or involved as templates in the biosynthesis.

Microfibrillar fractions[31, 39] giving cellulose I diagrams[17] have also been isolated from other green algae (*Ulva*, *Enteromorpha* (Ulotrichales), *Chlorella* (Chlorococcales)). The amount of microfibrils and the degree of crystallinity were low, and the fibrillar fraction gave by hydrolysis to sugars other than glucose (mainly xylose). In this group of plants, the situation is much the same as in Florideophycea (Rhodophyta) and Phaeophyta. The rather confusing situation is illustrated by two recent studies on *Chlamydomonas* (Volvocales) using electron microscopy. Barnett and Preston[40] observed by freeze-etching techniques orientated microfibrils which they assumed to be cellulose, and also particles of the type suspected to be involved in the biosynthesis of the cellulose microfibrils[11]. Horne *et al.*[41] used electron microscopy and analysed the micrographs by an optical diffractometer. They concluded that their results gave no support to the assumption of cellulose fibrils, and found analogies to the structure of some bacterial cell walls.

A third group of the Chlorophyta contain cell walls with a more or less well defined microfibrillar structure, apparently devoid of cellulose[17]. These plants were earlier classified in the order Siphonales (which also included *Valonia*), but are now grouped in two orders, Caulerpales and Dasycladales. Anatomically they are characterised by the lack of transverse walls between the cells. A β-1-,3-linked xylan was isolated and described chemically by Mackie and Percival[42] from *Caulerpa filiformis* and by Miwa and his co-workers[43] from a number of Japanese seaweeds of the order Caulerpales. x-Ray diagrams and electron-microscopy studies of the xylan microfibrils were carried out by Frei and Preston[44], and revealed clear x-ray diagrams and well-defined microfibrils. End-group determinations had suggested a surprisingly low degree of polymerisation for a fibrillar material (DP_n =

40–60)[42,43]. Determinations by physical methods of nitrated xylans from *Penicillus dumetosus* (Caulerpales) showed that the end-group determinations were misleading and osmometry suggested a number-average degree of polymerisation of 1000 as a minimum[45]. The nitration procedure led to a considerable degradation, but light scattering and gel permeation chromatography indicated that a significant number of xylan molecules with a degree of polymerisation above 10 000 existed[46]. A detailed study of the conformation of the crystalline β-1,3-linked xylan from *Penicillus dumetosus* by x-ray diffraction and infrared spectroscopy[47] led to the conclusion that the polysaccharide molecules are intertwined to form a three-strand helix, with six residues per turn. The three chains are supposed to be bound together by interchain hydrogen bonds between the hydroxyl groups attached to C-2 in the xylose residues, arranged in a cyclic triode, as suggested in Figure 2.1.

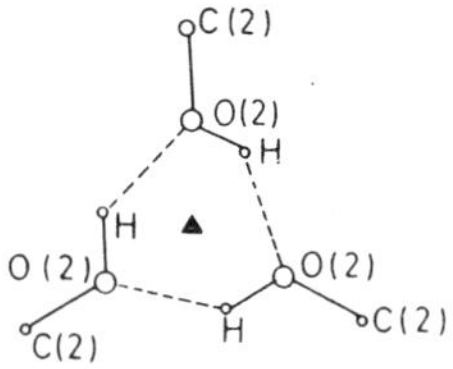

Figure 2.1 The interchain hydrogen bonds stabilising the triple helix arrangement of the xylans in Chlorophyta. (From Atkins *et al.*[47], by courtesy of the Royal Society.)

A β-1,4-mannan was described from species of the genus *Codium* (Caulerpales) and some species of the order Dasycladales by Miwa and his group[43] and the chemical structure confirmed by Love and Percival[48], using mannan from *Codium fragile*. Frei and Preston[49] investigated two species of *Codium* and several members of Dasycladales (species from the genera *Acetabularia*, *Batophora*, *Dasycladus*, *Neomeris*, *Cymopolia*) and found x-ray diagrams closely similar to those observed for ivory nut mannan. Electron microscopy did not reveal a typical microfibrillar structure, only short rodlets, in two layers, orientated longitudinally and transversely relative to the siphon axis. As was the case with the xylan from the Caulerpales, the chemical end-group determinations[43] had indicated a low mol. wt. ($DP_n \approx 16$), and again physical determinations gave a different result. Nitration of mannan from *Codium fragile* and osmometry, light scattering and gel permeation chromatography[50] showed that 90% of the material had degrees of polymerisation between 100 and 2500, with a peak logarithmic distribution at *ca.* 600. Whether nitration led to degradation was in this case doubtful.

2.3.3 Matrix polysaccharides

Most, possibly all, Chlorophyta contain water-soluble polysaccharides containing charged groups. Two different groups of polysaccharides of this type have emerged from the studies of the last 10 years. The first group may best be exemplified by the water-soluble polysaccharides of *Cladophora rupestris*. Hot water extraction removed an amount of polysaccharide corresponding to *ca.* 10% of the dried algae. Preparations from which starch was removed contained typically from 8–20% protein, 20% half-ester sulphate and D-galactose, L-arabinose and D-xylose in a ratio of 3:3.5:1 after hydrolysis. Attempts to remove the protein without causing excessive degradation of the polysaccharide proved unsuccessful[51] and gel electrophoresis indicated that the protein and the sulphated polysaccharide moved together[52]. Fractionation on anion exchange columns indicated that molecules with varying degrees of protein and ester sulphate occurred, but that the ratio of the three monosaccharides remained constant[53]. Studies employing periodate oxidation, desulphation and methylation have revealed the structure of this polysaccharide in considerable detail[54,55]. The polysaccharide appeared to be highly branched and a major structural feature of the inner part of the molecule consists of 1,4-linked arabinose units with some 1,3-linked galactose units. Xylose is probably part of the same macromolecule. Some of the half-ester sulphate is bound at C-6 in galactose units having a free hydroxyl group at C-3, as shown by the formation of 3,6-anhydrogalactose by alkali treatment. Sulphate is also bound to C-3 in arabinose units.

Polysaccharides of much the same composition have been isolated from two *Chaetomorpha* species[53], and in a recent survey[56] 10 members of the Cladophorales were investigated and found to contain water-soluble polysaccharides giving D-galactose, L-arabinose and D-xylose on hydrolysis. Sulphated polysaccharides of a related structure have also been isolated from species of the genus *Caulerpa*[57] and *Codium fragile*[58]. In the latter case, fractionation experiments (DEAE cellulose) clearly demonstrated heterogeneity and fractions containing only galactose, arabinose and sulphate were obtained. The polysaccharide preparations from both *Caulerpa* and *Codium* contained considerable amounts of protein (*ca.* 20%) as did the *Cladophora* polysaccharide. In some cases, small amounts of 3,6-anhydro-sugars have been reported[58].

The second group of charged water-soluble polysaccharides from Chlorophyta may be exemplified by the polysaccharide from *Ulva lactuca* (Ulotrichales). Water extraction gave *ca.* 25% (of dry weed) of an acid polysaccharide[59], consisting of 32% L-rhamnose, 10% D-xylose, 8% D-glucose, 24% D-glucuronic acid and 19% sulphate half-ester. Isolation of di- and oligosaccharides confirmed that the different monomers were bound together in the same molecule. The most easily isolated and characteristic disaccharide of this group of polysaccharides is *O*-β-D-glucuronosyl 1,4-L-rhamnose. A major part of the sulphate is probably bound to the rhamnose units. Methylation of the desulphated and carboxyl-reduced polysaccharide[60] indicated a highly-branched polymer, but with no backbone consisting of one particular monomer as the inner core of the molecule contained the same sugar units as the whole molecule. A polysaccharide of a similar composition has been isolated from another member of Ulothrichales, *Enteromorpha compressa* and from *Acrosiphonia arcta* (Cladophorales)[5]. The latter polysaccharide contains less rhamnose than the other two, but appears otherwise closely related to the *Ulva* polysaccharide, and distinctly different from the water soluble polysaccharide of other Cladophorales. It is in this connection interesting that *Acrosiphonia* lack the well developed, highly crystalline microfibrils of *Cladophora* and *Chaetomorpha*[17].

The polysaccharides described above are all extracted from multicellular organisms with a thalloid or siphonaceous organisation. Olaitan and Northcote[61] examined the polysaccharides from the unicellular *Chlorella pyrenoidosa*

(Chlorococcales) grown in culture. They isolated two fractions containing complex heteropolysaccharides, of which one was shown to be homogeneous by a thorough electrophoretic examination. This fraction contained D-galactose (7 parts), L-rhamnose (15 parts), L-arabinose (3 parts), D-xylose (3 parts), D-mannose (2 parts) and D-glucose (1 part). The other fraction contained the same monomers, and in addition an unidentified component. The presence of uronic acids or half-ester sulphate groups was not reported. In a recent article, White and Barber[62] described a polysaccharide from *Chlorella pyrenoidosa*, isolated in an amount of 2.3% of the dry weight. This polysaccharide contained the same monomers (except glucose) as described by Olaitan and Northcote, and in addition D-glucuronic acid in an amount of *ca.* 8%. Rhamnose was a dominating component (47% of the polymer), and a glucuronosyl–rhamnose disaccharide was isolated. This polysaccharide may thus have some features in common with the *Ulva* type, but appears considerably more complex, as the galactose was shown to be a mixture of D and L isomers. By enzymatic means it was shown that the ratio between the D and L form was *ca.* 7:3. This rather unusual feature of D and L galactose present in the same polysaccharide has, thus, been observed for both green and red algae (see later).

2.4 CHRYSOPHYTA (INCLUDING HAPTOPHYTA)

This group comprises mainly unicellular flagellates, both marine and freshwater forms. The cells are often covered by scales embedded in a gelatinous matrix. The scales may be calcareous as in the coccolithophorids, silicified, e.g. in some freshwater Chrysophyta (*Mallomonas*, *Synura*), or unmineralised. It is mainly representatives of the latter type which have formed the basis of studies of the polysaccharides of this group. The study of the chemical nature of the scales is of particular importance as ultra structural studies by Manton and her associates have provided considerable insight in the formation of the scales, which takes place in the cisterna of the Golgi bodies[63, 64], from where they are extruded in a vesicular membrane flow mechanism.

The scales of *Chrysochromulina chiton* (Haptophyta, Prymnesiales) were shown to have a fibrillar structure resistant to the attack of a number of enzymes (proteases, pectinase, lysozyme), to 40% NaOH, but which was destroyed by 6 M HCl[65]. No unambiguous identificationof hydrolysis products could be carried out due to small amounts of purified scales, but ribose and galactose were indicated as the main products. It should be noticed that a complete hydrolysis of cellulose fibres should not be expected to take place in the conditions used in this study. A distinct x-ray diffraction pattern was obtained which did not correspond to cellulose or any other known polysaccharide.

Fibrous components giving colour reactions corresponding to cellulose have been reported from *Apedinella spinifera* (Chromulinales)[66]. The most detailed studies of the scales of Chrysophyta have been carried out on *Pleurochrysis scherffelii* (Haptophyta). The scales from this organism have been described as consisting of three components[67, 68]; (a) a fibrillar cellulose-like network with fibre cross-sections of 12–25 × 25–40 Å; (b) an amorphous matrix probably consisting of acid polysaccharides; and (c) a proteinaceous component. The matrix material could be removed by treatment of the water-washed scale fraction with 10% NaOH and the remaining fibrillar material gave x-ray diagrams with spacings corresponding to cellulose II[69]. The water-washed scales before alkali-treatment gave diagrams of the cellulose I type but with considerably broader lines than from cotton cellulose. Gas–liquid chromatography of the hydrolysis products showed glucose to be the main monosaccharide present together with traces of galactose and pentoses, and the presence of cellobiose was also indicated, The authors therefore conclude that the fibrillar component of *Pleurochrysis* scales are cellulose, and it is particularly interesting that this fraction contains the main part of the protein in the scales, amounting to 30% of the alkali-treated scales. The protein, which is rich in acidic amino acids, is not removed from the scales by treatment with 8 M urea or 5 M guanidin hydrochloride. The authors conclude that the peptide moieties are covalently bound to the cellulose in a way which does not interfere with the crystal order of the cellulose, and probably occur in the coat of the fibrillar elements.

The flagellate *Ochromonas malhamensis* (Ochromanadales) is partly surrounded by a cellulose-containing tunica[70] which attaches the organism to the substrate. In a study of the formation of this tunica[71], the cellulose fibrils were found to be composed of very thin (10–20 Å) elementary fibrils, loosely fasciated. By studying the shape of the ends of the fibrils, the authors concluded that the glucan chains ended at some distance from each other and that the polysaccharide chains probably grew separately, and were joined in a subsequent step. The results were also interpreted as indicating that the cellulose of *Ochromonas* tunicae most probably are synthesised extracellularly and not in the Golgi apparatus, as shown for the scales of *Pleurochrysis* and other scale-bearing Chrysophyta.

2.5 BACILLARIOPHYTA (DIATOMS)

Bacillariophyta comprises unicellular or colonial algae of marine, freshwater or terrestrial habitat. The cell wall is divided into two distinct halves and contains silica and polysaccharides; the latter is often described as 'pectin'[72, 73]. In a study of the formation of the silica shell, electron microscopy has revealed several details about the organisation of the organic components and the silica in the walls of *Cylindrotheca fusiformis*[74], *Navicula pelliculosa*[75] and *Phaeodactylum tricornutum*[76]. Important differences between the species were observed, but in all cases the silica appears to be tightly enclosed by organic material. In some cases a mucilaginous layer surrounded the cell wall. An organic fibrillar material was not described, but in another species with a particularly low content of silica, *Subsiliceae fragilarioides*, a coarse (200–700 Å) fibrillar structure embedded in an amorphous matrix was observed[77]. The colour reactions of the fibres indicated the presence of acidic, possibly sulphated polysaccharides.

The chemical composition of the organic 'skin' from the cell walls of *Navicula pelliculosa* was investigated by Volcani and his co-workers and found to contain both polysaccharide, protein and lipid[78]. Using cultures synchronised by silica starvation[79] they found[80], by studying the ^{14}C incorporation, that material added to the newly-formed wall during silica deposition mainly contained ^{14}C in amino acids, while after the silica-deposition had ceased, more ^{14}C was found as fucose and xylose in polysaccharides. Secondary material added to old walls showed ^{14}C mainly in the form of mannose and glucuronic acid residues. The results thus indicate the existence of more than one polysaccharide in the organic part of the *Navicula* cell wall.

The diatom *Phaedactylum tricornutum* occurs both as oval or fusiform cells[81]. Both contain silica, but only the former is in the form of an organised silica shell. The oval cells also contain a water-soluble polysaccharide giving rise to xylose, mannose, fucose and galactose by hydrolysis. The same organism has been investigated by Ford and Percival[82] who treated the diatom sample with hot water, chlorite and cold alkali and, from the residue, extracted with hot 4% alkali, a polysaccharide described as a sulphated glucuronomannan. Partial hydrolysis, methylation and periodate oxidation indicated that the polysaccharide consisted of a backbone of mannose units with occasional sulphate half-ester groups, and side chains containing both mannose and glucuronic acid residues.

Some diatoms form colonies where the cells are kept together by extracellular polysaccharides. The slime capsule of *Navicula pelliculosa* was reported to consist of polyglucuronic acid[83], but the method of preparation involved extraction with 20% sodium hydroxide. The mucilage tubes of *Amphipleura rutilans* gave on hydrolysis xylose, mannose and traces of rhamnose[84], and the mucilaginous stalks of *Gomphonema olivaceum* consisted mainly of D-galactose, D-xylose and sulphate half-ester groups[85]. In some culture experiments, soluble extracellular polysaccharides have been isolated from the culture medium; from *Chaetoceros affinis* cultures a sulphated polysaccharide giving fucose, rhamnose and galactose on hydrolysis[86], and from *Nitzschia frustulum* cultures a polysaccharide giving rhamnose, mannose, minor amounts of galactose and probably methylated xylose derivatives[87] and glucuronic acid.

A unique and surprising feature of some diatoms (*Thallassiosira fluviatilis* and *Cyclotella cryptica*) is the existence of extracellular threads of highly crystalline chitan[88,89].

2.6 PYRROPHYTA (DINOFLAGELLATES)

This group comprises photosynthetic and colourless unicellular flagellates. The Pyrrophyta has a widespread occurrence, but is most important in the marine environment where organisms of this group often play a major part in the production of organic matter, and are known to form sometimes dense and conspicuous blooms.

The cells are surrounded by a complex structure called the theca which consists of a single outer membrane surrounding the cell and, beneath the membrane, a layer of flattened vesicles, usually, but not always, containing wall plates[90,91]. The theca often has a complex morphology which has formed the basis of the taxonomy of the group.

The cell wall plates are usually described as consisting of cellulose[72], but a clearly defined fibrillar structure is often not observed. Treatment with acetic acid and hypochlorite or dilute potassium hydroxide has been reported to reveal a fibrillar structure of the theca[92,93].

In several species of *Pyrocystis*, which normally occur as non-motile, cyst-like cells, the cell walls were found to have an outer, non-cellulosic layer, beneath which a structure of crossed parallel fibres was observed by electron microscopy of freeze-etched preparations and thin sections[94]. The fibres were 40–50 Å thick and 120 Å wide, and appeared to consist of smaller fibrils with a width of 30 Å. Staining reactions and x-ray diagrams indicated that the fibrils consisted of cellulose. Between the layer of orientated fibrils and the plasma membrane a layer of smaller non-oriented fibrils were observed, and the authors suggest this to be the area of fibril synthesis.

Cell wall preparations of *Peridinium westii*, washed with water and organic solvents contained 95% carbohydrate and 3% protein[21]. Glucose was the major monosaccharide present in the hydrolysate in addition to traces of mannose, fucose and rhamnose. Partial hydrolysis gave cello-biose, -triose and -tetraose and laminari-biose, -triose and -tetraose, revealing the presence of both β-1,4- and β-1,3-linkages. x-Ray diagrams were different from those of cellulose and laminaran and the preparation did not dissolve in Schweitzer reagents or in cadoxen. It is not possible from the results to decide whether the two types of linkages are present in separate macromolecules or occur in the same molecule; in the latter case, however, a blockwise distribution is indicated.

2.7 PHAEOPHYTA (BROWN ALGAE)

2.7.1 General

The division Phaeophyta comprises almost exclusively multicellular, marine organisms, with a filamentous or thalloid organisation. Benthic forms predominate, and some of them are of considerable commercial importance. With few exceptions the chemical investigations have been carried out on species belonging to the orders Fucales and Laminariales.

2.7.2 Fibrillar components of the wall

Both chemical[95] and x-ray evidence[17] indicates the presence of cellulose in Phaeophyta in relatively small amounts[97] (1–10% of dry weight). The presence of another component in Phaeophyta cell walls giving an x-ray diagram was demonstrated and this component was identified tentatively as polyguluronic acid[96]. Later work has shown that these x-ray diagrams were caused by the L-guluronic acid blocks in alginate[98]. In spite of a certain degree of crystallinity, alginate should be regarded as a matrix component. In *Chorda* sp. (Laminariales), the cortical cells show a spiral striation and the molecular chains of alginate appear to lie in identically the same helical arrangement as do those of cellulose[96]. In other species this is not so, but both types of chains seem to be orientated parallel to the cell surface.

2.7.3 Matrix polysaccharides

2.7.3.1 *Alginate*

The most well-known polysaccharide of brown algae is alginate, a polyuronide of considerable commercial importance. Alginic acid consists of D-mannuronic and L-guluronic acid in varying proportions[18, 26, 99], in ordinary vegetative tissue varying from 3:1 to 1:3. In the intercellular substance of receptacles of *Fucus vesiculosus* and *Ascophyllum nodosum* (Fucales), alginate with 90% or more mannuronic acid is present[26].

Alginate occurs in the plant as a mixed salt, with calcium, magnesium and sodium as the main cations[18]. As will be discussed in some detail below, calcium alginate is insoluble and forms a gel or a precipitate. The first step in the extraction procedure is the transformation of this insoluble, mixed salt into soluble sodium alginate (Figure 2.2). This transformation may be regarded as an ion exchange reaction, and may be carried out either by using acid treatment followed by alkali or directly by treatment with sodium chloride solution or by using calcium complexing compounds such as EDTA. This transformation is then followed by extraction of the soluble sodium alginate.

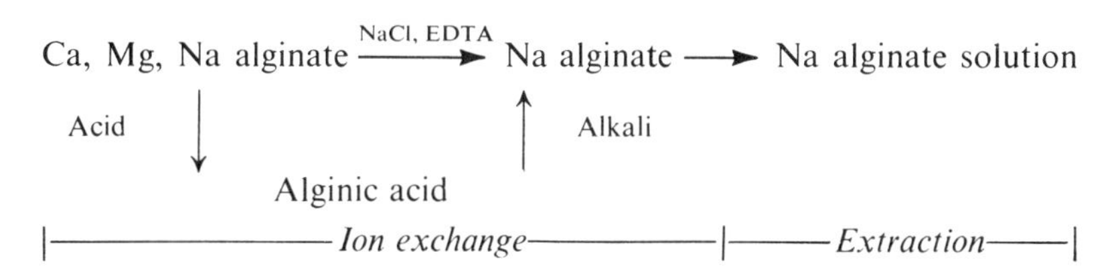

Figure 2.2 Extraction of alginate

Molecular weights of alginate preparations depend upon the method of preparation. The correlation between intrinsic viscosity and molecular weight was established by light-scattering studies[100] as

$$[\eta]_{(0\cdot 1\ M\ NaCl)} = 2.0 \times 10^{-5}\ M_w$$
$$M_w = 5 \times 10^4 \times [\eta]\ dl/g\ (0.1\ M\ NaCl)$$

and molecular weights of the order of 1–1.5 $\times$ 10^6 are commonly obtained for laboratory preparations; under particularly carefully controlled conditions mol. wt. as high as 3 $\times$ 10^6 have been obtained.

The structure of the alginate molecule is that a linear chain of 1,4- linked uronic acid residues, as shown by methylation of the carboxyl-reduced polysaccharide[101, 102]. An apparent contradiction between this structure and a periodate consumption of 0.45–0.5 mol per anhydrohexuronic acid residue[103] has been explained by the formation of intramolecular hemiacetal linkages[104] between the aldehyde groups formed by the oxidation and the neighbouring unoxidised units. A major problem in alginate chemistry is the distribution of the two types of monomers between the polymer molecules and along the polymer chain. Heterogeneity of ordinary alginate samples was demonstrated by fractionation experiments, which at the same time indicated that alginate was not a mixture of polymannuronic and polyguluronic acid[18]. Heterogeneous acid hydrolysis of alginic acid from *Laminaria digitata* (Laminariales) led to solubilisation of *ca.* 30% of the sample, while the remaining insoluble material could be separated into fractions approaching a homopolymeric composition, and with number average degrees of polymerisation of 20–30[105]. The oligouronides formed by the partial heterogenous hydrolysis could be separated by free boundary electrophoresis in a medium containing both sodium and calcium ions[25] (based on the different ion exchange properties of the two uronic acid residues, see later, and marked differences between different species were observed[106]. The part of the alginate sample which was solubilised during the partial hydrolysis gave rise mainly to diuronides containing both monomers on further hydrolysis[25], thus indicating a predominantly alternating sequence in this part of the molecule. The alternating structure was confirmed by a study of the distribution of oligomers of different molecular weights[107] and from the yields of free monomers[108] after partial hydrolysis. The picture of alginate which emerges from these studies is that of a linear copolymer where the two types of monomers occur in three different block structures, homopolymeric blocks of D-mannuronic acid residues, homopolymeric blocks of L-guluronic acid residues, and blocks with an alternating structure. The relative amounts of the three block-structures may vary from one species to another and also between different tissues of the same species[26,106] and is closely correlated to properties of alginates such as solubility in acid or calcium chloride solutions[106]. The simplest statistical description being in accordance with these observations is based on a model where the probability of a monomer being a mannuronic or guluronic acid residue depends upon the nature of the neighbour and nearest-neighbour in the polymer chain (a penultimate model)[28]. Even if homopolymeric and alternating blocks with number average degrees of polymerisation of 20–30 have been prepared after partial hydrolysis, the block-lengths in the native undegraded alginate molecules and the distribution of block lengths are unknown and a fully satisfactory statistical description of the alginate molecule can therefore not yet be given. Enzymes degrading alginates by β-elimination, leading to unsaturated degradation products, have been described from bacteria[109,110] and marine invertebrates[111,112]. By utilising an alginate lyase with specificity for mannuronide linkages, isolated from a marine mollusc[113] and another alginate lyase with specificity for guluronide linkages, isolated from a bacteria[114], enzymatic degradation has been used in the study of the structure of alginate[115] with results in general agreement with the picture outlined above.

X-Ray examinations of alginate preparations with known uronic acid composition have given results indicating that in acid form the D-mannuronic acid units occur in the $^4C_1$ ($C1$) and the L-guluronic acid units in the $^1C_4$ ($1C$) conformation, both with a twofold screw axis[98,116]. Less clear diagrams are obtained for salts of alginic acid, but the results indicate the same conformations as in the acid form for sodium and ammonium alginate, with the difference that the mannuronate units form a threefold screw axis[117].

2.7.3.2 Fucose-containing polysaccharides

The presence of a sulphated L-fucan, fucoidan, in Phaeophyta has been reported by a number of investigators[5]. Fucoidan has usually been obtained by extraction with dilute acid or from exudates. Based on methylation[118] and acetolysis[119], a 1,2-linked fucan 4-sulphate has been proposed as the structure of fucoidan. The presence of sulphate groups at C-4 has been confirmed by the isolation of L-fucose 4-sulphate from fucoidan prepared from *Pelvetia wrightii* (Fucales)[120].

In 1966 the presence in *Ascophyllum nodosum* (Fucales) of fucose-containing polysaccharides of a more complex composition was reported[121]. In the usual alginate extraction procedure, the seaweed material is extracted successively with dilute acid and dilute alkali. When alginate is precipitated from the alkaline extract by acidification, a mixture of fucose-containing polysaccharides remains in solution. In free boundary electrophoresis this mixture gave three distinct peaks. (Figure 2.3a). By fractional precipitation, an electrophoretically homogeneous fraction (ascophyllan) was obtained (Figure 2.3b) containing L-fucose, D-xylose, D-glucuronic acid and sulphate half-ester in approximately equimolar proportions, and, in addition, *ca.* 10% protein. The same constituents were present in the other components of the mixture, but in different proportions and with fucose as the quantitatively dominating monosaccharide unit. Partial hydrolysis of ascophyllan removed the main part of the neutral sugars and the sulphate groups, leaving a non-dialysable fraction consisting of *ca.* 70% glucuronic acid residues. From the partial hydrolysate, the disaccharide D-xylose $\beta 1 \rightarrow 3$L-fucose was isolated, demonstrating that the two neutral sugars occur in the same part of the molecule[122].

Preparations of a similar composition have been obtained from the residue after alginate extraction from *Ascophyllum nodosum* (Fucales) and *Laminaria hyperborea* (Laminariales)[6]. Partial hydrolysis[123] and methylation[124] indicated the presence of the following structural elements in these preparations: $1 \rightarrow 4$ linked D-xylose, $1 \rightarrow 2$ and $1 \rightarrow 3$ linked L-fucose, partly 4-sulphated, D-glucuronic acid $\beta 1 \rightarrow 3$ L-fucose, L-fucose $\alpha 1 \rightarrow 4$ D-xylose in addition to D-xylose $\beta 1 \rightarrow 3$ L-fucose. Partial hydrolysis followed by dialysis gave a degraded non-dialysable fraction containing fucose and glucuronic acid as the major constituents. The preparation was described as a glucuronoxylofucan, different from ascophyllan. It has, however, not been examined by electrophoresis and in view of the complex electrophoretic behaviour of an unfractionated extract described previously[121], it seems difficult to exclude the possibility that this preparation may be a mixture of polysaccharides.

The fucose-containing polysaccharides from *Ascophyllum nodosum* have been further investigated by extraction of the plant material with very dilute acid (pH 2)[7]. Electrophoretic examination gave one peak moving as an anion at pH 2 (Figure 2.3c) but after a very mild hydrolysis (0.02 M HCl, 80 °C, 1 h), three distinct peaks appeared (Figure 2.3d). The components corresponding to the three peaks were identified by fractional precipitation followed by electrophoresis as alginic acid (boundary 1), a sulphated fucan containing some galactose units ('fucoidan') (the fastest moving boundary) and a sulphated glucuronoxylofucan of the ascophyllan type containing small amounts

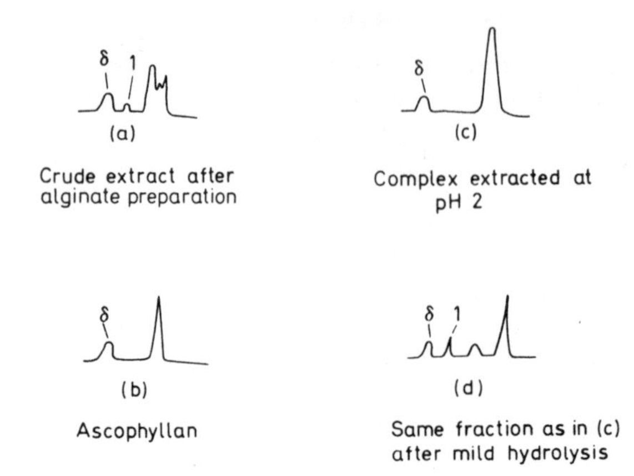

Figure 2.3 Electrophoresis of fucose-containing polysaccharides from *Ascophyllum nodosum*. Ascending boundaries at pH 2. The stationary boundary is marked δ, boundary 1 corresponds to alginate. For details see text

of mannose. The occurrence of a native complex molecule comprising a sulphated fucan or galactofucan (fucoidan), glucuronoxylofucans (ascophyllan), alginate and probably some protein is thus strongly indicated. The presence of free fucoidan in *Ascophyllum* seems doubtful, but free fucoidan may occur in other species[7]. The fact that constituents other than fucose and sulphate groups often have been reported in fucoidan[5] may be connected with different degrees of degradation of the native complex during preparation. The presence of fucoidan fractions with and without galactose in *Pelvetia wrightii* (Fucales) has recently been reported[125]. In a recent work, the family concept of the fucose-containing polysaccharides in Phaeophyta was stressed[126], a concept which is coherent with the existence of a labile complex molecule giving rise to different degradation products of which fucoidan and ascophyllan are two fairly well-defined members.

In addition to *Ascophyllum nodosum* and *Laminaria hyperborea*, *Fucus vesiculosus*[127], *Sargassum pallidium*[128] and *Pelvetia wrightii*[129] (Fucales) also give rise to glucuronoxylofucans, and glucoproteins of a related but possibly more complex composition are reported from 13 species of Phaeophyta[130]. The present evidence, even if admittedly scanty, thus indicates that fucose-containing polysaccharides of a complex composition are widespread among the Phaeophyta.

2.8 RHODOPHYTA (RED ALGAE)

2.8.1 General

The division Rhodophyta comprises mainly marine, in most cases multicellular organisms. It is divided into two main groups, Bangiophyceae and

Florideophyceae. Among the differences between the two is diffuse growth and lack of well defined pit connections between the cells in the former and growth from apical cells and well-marked pits joining the cytoplasma in adjacent cells in the latter.

2.8.2 Fibrillar components of the wall

Myers and Preston[131] investigated in 1959 'α-cellulose'[31,132] from *Rhodymenia palmata* (Florideophyceae, Rhodymeniales). They found a network of unorientated microfibrils which could be orientated under stress. Chemical analysis gave about equal amounts of xylose and glucose residues and they concluded that the microfibrils consisted either of separate molecular chains of glucose and xylose residues or that each chain was formed of both residues. Dennis and Preston[133] succeeded by treatment with alkali, followed by heating with strong acid (1.25 M H_2SO_4, 100 °C, 24 h) in reducing the walls to a suspension which could be separated into an insoluble fraction giving mainly glucose and a soluble fraction giving mainly xylose on hydrolysis. Frei and Preston[17] reported that Rhodophyta of the class Florideophyceae, in general, give x-ray diagrams of the cellulose I type, even if both amounts and degree of crystallinity were low.

Recent work has provided information about the chemical structure of the water insoluble glucan and xylan in Florideophyceae. Turvey and Williams[134] used sequential extraction of dried red algae, and after removal of xylans soluble in acid, water and 1 M alkali they succeeded in isolating from *Rhodymenia palmata* a fraction, soluble in 3 M NaOH, which by methylation was identified as 1,4-linked xylan with only traces of 1,3-links present. Even if the results do not prove the existence of xylan in the microfibrils, it demonstrates the presence of a sparingly soluble xylan fraction, chemically different from the main part of the xylan (see later). Two other members of Florideophyceae: *Laurencia pinnatifida* (Ceramiales) and *Rhodochorton floridulum* (Nemalionales) were also investigated, but a similar fraction of 1,4-xylan was not found.

The glucan from the residue after extraction of *Rhodymenia pertusa* was investigated by methylation, gas–liquid chromatography and mass spectrometry of the methylated product after hydrolysis, and n. m. r. of the methylated polymer[135]. The results were in agreement with a 1,4-β-glucan, and the presence of cellulose in this group of red algae seems thus well established.

Porphyra umbilicalis (Bangiophyceae, Bangiales) consists of sheets, one cell-layer thick surrounded by a cuticle. The cells and the cuticle can be mechanically separated after treatment with dilute acid[136]. The two preparations gave different x-ray diagrams, none of them corresponding to cellulose. The cell walls were fibrillar, gave by x-ray analysis the same spacings as found for green algae shown to contain β-1,3-linked xylan (see above) and gave xylose and small amounts of glucose on hydrolysis. The cuticles were granular, gave a mannan type of x-ray diagram and produced mannose and minor amounts of glucose on hydrolysis. Chemical evidence of 1,3-linked xylan occurring in a fibrillar form in *Porphyra umbilicalis* were later provided by the sequential extraction experiments of Turvey and Williams[134]. Results similar to those obtained for *Porphyra umbilicalis* were also obtained for *Bangia fusco-purpurea*[136] and microfibrils consisting of 1,3-xylan may be a characteristic feature of Bangiophyceae.

2.8.3 Matrix polysaccharides

2.8.3.1 Xylans

Water extraction of *Rhodymenia palmata* removes a xylan, shown to contain β-1,3- and β-1,4-linkages in the same molecule[5]. Bjørndal *et al.*[137] used enzymatic degradation and isolated tetra-, penta- and hexa-saccharides with one β-1,3-linkage in each oligosaccharide. The authors favoured a random distribution of the two linkage types. Two fractions were investigated, one water soluble and one acid soluble. Both contained predominantly β-1,4-linkages (*ca.* 66%). Turvey and Williams[134] isolated four xylan fractions by sequential extraction; the three most soluble ones contained both 1,3- and 1, 4-linkages (75–80%). Also from *Laurencia pinnatifida* and *Phorphyra umbilicalis* xylan fractions could be isolated which contained 1,3- and 1,4-linkages in ratios of *ca.* 1:4. In *Rhodochorton floridulum*, similar 1,3 and 1,4-linked xylans were present, but methylation indicated short chains with considerable branching and the possibility of the xylan occurring as short side-chains on a heteropolysaccharide was suggested. *Chaetangium fastigiatum* (Florideophyceae, Nemaliales) contained a water soluble xylan with β-1,3; β-1,4 linkages in the ratio 1:3, in an amount of *ca.* 30% of the dry matter[138].

Xylans thus appear to be widespread in the Rhodophyta, both as fibrillar components of the wall, and as a soluble compound, probably occurring as a wall matrix substance. This is one of the few instances in the algae where a quantitatively dominating matrix component (at least in *Rhodymenia palmata*) is a neutral polysaccharide. The difference in solubility between the polymers with only one type of linkage (either β-1,3 (Bangiophyceae) or β-1,4 (Florideophycea)) and with both linkages in the same molecule is remarkable. In several cases fractions with different solubility, but with approximately the same proportion between the two linkage types have been isolated[134,137]. It can be assumed that a blockwise distribution of the linkage types would lead to a decreased solubility compared to a random distribution, and a more detailed knowledge of the fine structure of the Rhodophyta xylans and their biosynthesis might reveal valuable information about the correlation between structure and physical properties of polysaccharides and the biochemical control of the properties of the cell wall.

2.8.3.2 Galactans

Most Rhodophyta contain some type of galactan, usually sulphated. There are probably a few exceptions; sulphated galactans have not been reported from *Rhodymenia palmata*, which is particularly rich in water soluble 1,3–1,4 linked xylan. Water-soluble xylan and sulphated galactans may, however, occur in the same organism (e.g. *Chaetangium fastigiatum*[138], *Porphyra umbilicalis*[134, 139]). A sulphated galactan is also reported from *Rhodymenia pertusa*[135].

The Rhodophyta galactans are the most intensively investigated group of algal polysaccharides, a fact which may be due to the commercial importance of some of these compounds. Most investigations have either followed the usual approach; to isolate the galactan fraction and determine its composition and structure, or the investigator has studied in detail the chemical structure of a highly purified preparation without being particularly concerned about how large a part of the total galactan fraction this preparation accounts for. The latter approach has provided some valuable landmarks in what may appear as a rather confusing wilderness of more or less closely related polysaccharides, but which probably more fruitfully should be regarded as one, or possibly two, families of polysaccharides with a more or less continuous variation in chemical composition.

(a) *Backbone structure*—The algal polysaccharide with the most ancient history is agar, which in the form of a dry extract was a commercial product in Japan from the seventeenth century. Appropriately enough, a Japanese group headed by Araki made the most important progress in agar chemistry, by determining the basic chemical structure of a fraction of agar named agarose, and this polysaccharide was the first to reveal some of the basic features of Rhodophyta galactans. The agarose molecule is an alternating copolymer of 3-linked β-D-galactose and 4-linked 3,6-anhydro-α-L-galactose,

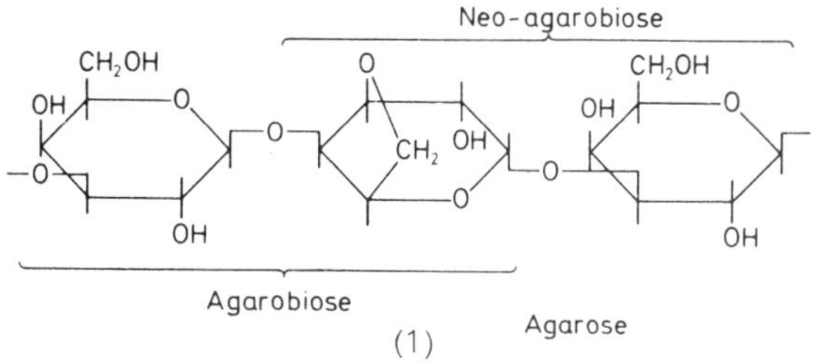

Neo-agarobiose

Agarobiose

Agarose

(1)

formula (1). The experiments leading to this formula has been reviewed by Araki[139a]. Agarose was separated from the rest of the agar by acetylation and extraction of the agarose acetate by chloroform. Other methods for preparation of agarose from agar have since been introduced[140-143], most of them, as the method of Araki, essentially being a separation into charged ('agaropectin') and uncharged ('agarose') components. The main structure of agarose was elucidated by the isolation of disaccharides; agarobiose (β-D-galactopyranosyl (1→4) 3,6-anhydro-L-galactose) isolated after partial acid degradation, and neoagarobiose (3,6-anhydro-α-L-galactopyranosyl (1→3) D-galactose) after enzymatic degradation. The structure of the disaccharides was determined by methylation.

The structure of agarose should be regarded as an idealised formula and does not represent the structure of all the molecules in the agarose fraction. Before this is discussed further, however, other prominent members of the galactan family will be presented. One of them is porphyran, the galactan fraction of *Porphyra umbilicalis*. Porphyran contains D-galactose, 3,6-anhydro-L-galactose, 6-*O*-methyl-D-galactose and L-galactose-6-sulphate[139, 144]. The relative proportion of the components varied widely[145], but the ratio between the D- and L-isomers was always close to one. By alkali-treatment[20] or treatment with an enzyme preparation from *Porphyra*[146], the L-galactose 6-sulphate could be transformed to 3,6-anhydro-L-galactose. Isolation of disaccharides after partial hydrolysis showed that the L-galactose derivatives were 4-linked and the D-galactose and 6-*O*-methyl-D-galactose were 3-linked[147]. The relationship to agarose was thus obvious and was further confirmed by alkali treatment and methylation of porphyran[148, 149]. This product gave rise to methylated agarobiose in good yield (62%) by partial methanolysis. The chemical evidence has been corroborated by enzymatic studies. Enzyme preparations from *Cytophaga* sp. were found to degrade both agarose and porphyran[150, 151]. An extracellular agarase preparation[152] was found to be particularly convenient, and the effect of this preparation on agarose, porphyran and alkali-treated porphyran was compared[153]. Neo-agarobiose and higher oligosaccharides of the same structure were isolated, and the two porphyran preparations gave, in addition, degradation products of the same structure, but with some of the D-galactose units carrying 6-*O*-methyl groups. The presence of a methyl group decreased the rate of hydrolysis of the glycosidic linkage, while the presence of sulphate completely inhibited the enzyme action. After exhaustive enzyme degradation, 70% of the native and 45% of the alkali-modified porphyran could be precipitated with ethanol. The authors concluded that the results indicate a random distribution of 6-*O*-methyl groups in porphyran, but possibly a blockwise distribution of 6-sulphate groups. The high amount of enzyme-resistant polysaccharide in the alkali-treated porphyran was supposed to be caused by the amount of sulphate (1.8% of the polymer weight) which was not removed by the alkali-treatment. A small amount of alkali-resistant sulphate were also observed in the chemical studies[149] and may correspond to sulphate half-ester groups located in positions other than the C-6 of the 4-linked units.

The second main group of Rhodophyta galactans are the carrageenans, which have been used in the household in certain parts of Ireland and the American east coast for centuries and which are now commercial products of some importance. The carrageenans differ from the agar family of polysaccharides in not containing the L-isomer of galactose and in carrying more sulphate groups. Leaving for the moment the location of sulphate groups other than at C-6 in the 4-linked units (precursors of 3,6-anhydro-derivatives) for later discussion, we shall first describe the elucidation of the backbone structure of the carrageenans. As with agar, the separation into two components, in this case by fractional precipitation in 0.25% potassium chloride solution[154], meant a major breakthrough in the study of the chemistry of the carrageenans. The insoluble fraction was named κ-carrageenan, and was already in 1955 proposed to have an alternating structure of 3-linked β-D-galactose and 4-linked 3,6-anhydro-α-D-galactose[155], formula (2) based, among other evidence, on the isolation of the disaccharide carrabiose (β-D-galactopyranosyl (1$\rightarrow$4)-3,6-anhydro-D-galactose) in good yield. The polysaccharide also carry sulphate half-ester groups in an amount somewhat in excess of one sulphate group per disaccharide unit. The amount of galactose for most samples is also slightly higher than that corresponding to the structure suggested above. Several suggestions have been put forward[155, 156] but it is now

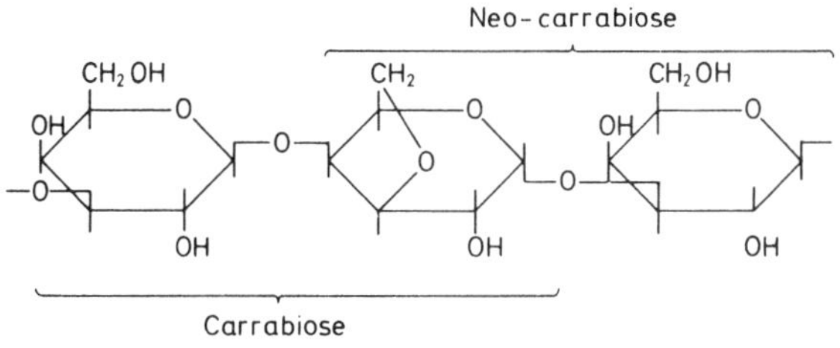

Neo-carrabiose

Carrabiose

Desulphated κ-carrageenan

(2)

generally accepted that this is due to a certain amount of 4-linked D-galactose 6-sulphate, which by alkali-treatment may be transformed to the 3,6-anhydro-derivative[157-159]. Enzymatic studies have supported the chemical evidence; hydrolysis of a κ-carrageenan fraction by an enzyme prepared from *Pseudomonas carrageenovora* led to the isolation of a sulphated neo-carrobiose[160] (α-3,6-anhydro-D-galactopyranosyl (1→3)-D-galactose), sulphated oligosaccharides and *ca.* 20% enzyme-resistant polysaccharide. By alkali-treatment of the latter fraction, 75% was rendered available for enzyme degradation[161].

The material remaining in solution after the potassium chloride fractionation was called the λ-fraction[154]. It is a highly sulphated galactan, usually[162] with a low content of 3,6-anhydro-D-galactose. The close relationship between the κ- and the λ-fraction was clearly demonstrated by Rees[163], by alkali treatment of the λ-fraction. This led to release of sulphate and an increasing 3,6-anhydrogalactose content, and allowed the preparation of carrabiose from the alkali-treated fraction by partial mercaptolysis. Methylation, before and after desulphation, carried out on fractions prepared from *Chondrus crispus*, showed that the polymer contained about equal amounts of 1,3- and 1,4-linked galactose units with the 4-linked unit 6-sulphated[163, 164]. Carrabiose was prepared from the alkali modified fraction by methanolysis in 70% yield[157] and acetolysis gave products consistent within an alternating structure[165].

It seems, thus, to be a common feature of Rhodophyta galactans that the chain is built of β-1,3- and α-1,4-linked galactose units, arranged alternately, where the 1,4-linked units either occur as the 3,6-anhydro derivative or it is 6-sulphated and thus may be transformed to the 3,6-anhydro derivative. In the agar-porphyran family the 4-linked units are L-galactose derivatives, while in the carrageenan type only the D-isomer of galactose occur.

There are, however, exceptions to this rule. In several cases where both D- and L-isomers of galactose are present, the D-isomers are in excess[162, 166-168]. Traces of L-galactose have also been reported from typical carrageenan plants, as *Gigartina tenella* (Gigartinales)[169]. In other cases different amounts of 3- and 4-linked units have been indicated[170-172]. These exceptions from the general backbone structure of the Rhodophyta galactans have been reported particularly frequently in the order Cryptonemiales. In most cases, however, no criteria of homogeneity of the polysaccharide fraction have been given, and the possibility that some of these polysaccharide preparations are mixtures should be taken into account.

(b) *Substitution*—Much of the complexity of Rhodophyta galactans is caused by the high degree of substitution characteristic of these polysaccharides. Three types of substituents occur: sulphate half-ester groups, *O*-methyl groups and pyruvic acid bound as acetal to galactose units (forming 4,6-*O*-(1-carboxy-ethylidene)-D-galactose units).

The latter type of substituent was found in agaropectin[139a, 173] (the charged fraction of agar) from *Gelidium amansii* and *G. subcostatum* (Gelidiales) and is also a constituent of agar of a number of other species of Gelidiales and of *Gracilaria* species (Gigartinales)[174, 175].

The presence of 6-*O*-methyl-D-galactose in porphyran has been discussed above. Araki[139a, 177] showed the presence of 6-*O*-methyl-D-galactose also in agarose, e.g. 1.4% in agarose from *Gelidium amansii* (the agarose used for the original structural work). Higher degrees of 6-*O*-methyl substitution are common for agarose both from *Gelidium*[139a] and *Gracilaria* species[139a, 176, 175]. Methylation at other positions occurs frequently[178]; particularly highly methylated galactans have been reported from members of the Grateloupiaceae family (Cryptonemiales)[166, 179-182]. *O*-Methyl substitution has been reported in all positions where a free hydroxyl group occurs in a polysaccharide with the agarose–porphyran type of repeating structure. That this repeating structure is not universal is indicated by the isolation of 4-*O*-methyl-L-galactose[139a, 166, 177]. The occurrence of *O*-methyl groups seems to be confined to galactans containing L-galactose residues.

Sulphate substitution at positions other than at C-6 of the 4-linked residues are alkali stable and will influence the properties of both native and alkali-treated galactans. Sulphate substitution of this type has been reported for a number of galactans containing L-galactose residues[170, 175, 176, 178, 181]. It is, however, the carrageenan type of galactans which are most heavily sulphated and where this type of substitution is of particular importance. Early studies indicated that κ-carrageenan was sulphated at C-4 of the 3-linked galactose units[5]. Painter[183] reported in 1965, however, in autohydrolysates from κ-carrageenan (*Chondrus crispus*, Gigartinales), the presence of four different mono-sulphate components; D-galactose 2-sulphate, D-galactose 4-sulphate, D-galactose 6-sulphate and 3,6-anhydro-D-galactose 2-sulphate; i.e. substitution at all free hydroxyl groups of the polymer. Methylation studies[157, 158] on a κ-carrageenan fraction from the same species indicated that, after having transformed 4-linked galactose units sulphated at C-6 to 3,6-anhydrogalactose by alkali treatment, virtually all galactose units were 4-sulphated, and one out of seven 3,6-anhydro units were 2-sulphated. Qualitatively similar results were obtained with a κ-carrageenan fraction from *Gigartina tenella*, using a method where sulphate groups were replaced by methyl groups[159]. Comparing extracts from different plants by means of oxidative hydrolysis[158] of the methylated products and infrared spectroscopy[184], a considerable variation in the degree of sulphate substitution at C-2 in the 3,6-anhydrogalactose units was observed[185], with *Euchema cottonii* and *E. spinosum* (Gigartinales) as the two extremes with $<5\%$ sulphated and $<5\%$ unsulphated respectively.

Originally κ-carrageenan was defined as the fraction precipitated at a certain potassium chloride concentration (0.25 %). It has become customary to assign a certain chemical structure to the different carrageenan fractions Thus, κ-carrageenan is usually defined by formula (3)[204, 205], with $R^1 = SO_3H$

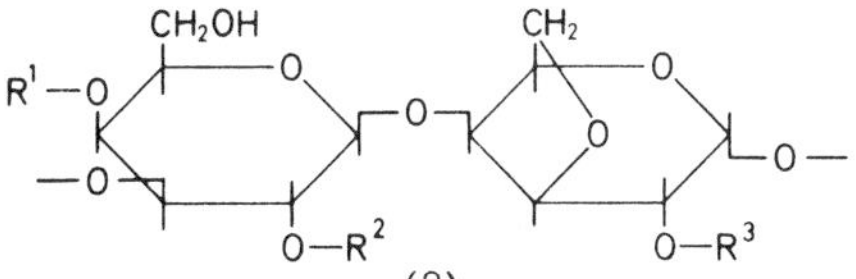

(3)

$R^2 = H$ and $R^3 = H$ (although sometimes another definition is used[5, 186], allowing a certain amount of $R^3 = SO_3H$). Based on the *Euchema spinosum* galactan, a new carrageenan fraction, ι-carrageenan, was defined with $R^1 = SO_3H$, $R^2 = H$ and $R^3 = SO_3H$.

The fraction which was soluble in 0.25 % potassium chloride solution, originally defined as the λ-fraction, was studied by methylation[163, 164]. The 4-linked galactose units were sulphated at positions 2 and 6, while the 3-linked units were usually sulphated at position 2 and to a smaller extent at position 4. Based on these observations, the λ-fraction was re-defined[164] as molecules where the 4-linked units occur as 2,6-disulphate and the 3-linked units are sulphated at C-2. By alkali treatment, this molecule should be transformed to a molecule described by the formula above with $R^1 = H$, $R^2 = SO_3H$ and $R^3 = SO_3H$, i.e. different from both κ- and ι-carrageenan.

After alkali treatment of the fraction soluble in 0.25 % potassium chloride solution, the material could be separated into a soluble and an insoluble component[187]. Methylation indicated that the soluble component corresponded to the expected transformation product of the λ-carrageenan described above, while the insoluble component was identical to κ-carrageenan. The precursor of κ-carrageenan, present in the originally soluble fraction, was called μ-carrageenan. To complete the picture, the term ν-carrageenan was introduced as the theoretical precursor of ι-carrageenan[188].

This leaves us with the following idealised set of precursors and 'finished molecules' in the carrageenan family:

Precursor	*Finished molecule*	
μ	κ	$R^1 = SO_3H$, R^2: H, R^3: H
ν	iota	$R^1 = -SO_3H$, R^2: H, R^3: $-SO_3H$
λ	alkali treated λ	$R^1 = H$, R^2: $-SO_3H$, R^3: $-SO_3H$

Naturally-occurring carrageenans, as extracted from algal samples, are not only mixtures of precursor and 'finished molecules', but also contain molecules of an intermediate composition. This was clearly demonstrated in a study of the solubility of the polysaccharide at varying potassium chloride concentrations before and after alkali-treatment[189, 190], which indicated that the samples, before alkali-treatment, consisted of a more or less continuous distribution of molecules with varying 3,6-anhydrogalactose content. Carrageenans from different plants varied not only in the 3,6-anhydrogalactose content of the total sample, but also in the distribution of the 3,6-anhydrogalactose units between the polymer molecules. Samples with closely similar 3,6-anhydrogalactose content, therefore, had different gelling properties depending on whether the composition distribution was wide or narrow.

Less is known about the distribution of sulphate at positions other than C-6, e.g. whether polymer molecules of pure 'ι' type and pure 'κ' type exist in an ordinary carrageenan sample, or whether the ι- and κ-structural elements (i.e. sulphate substitution or free hydroxyl group at C-2 in the 4-linked unit) occur in the same molecule. In the latter case, it is again a question of random or block-wise distribution of the ι- and κ type. Fractions with varying proportions of 3,6-anhydrogalactose and 3,6-anhydrogalactose 2-sulphate have been prepared from *Chondrus crispus*[184], making a random distribution unlikely. Based on physical properties, it has been suggested that preparation from plants with about equal amounts of 2-sulphated and unsubstituted 3,6-anhydrogalactose units (e.g. *Agardhiella tenera*, Gigartinales) contain the structural elements in the same molecules[188]. On the other hand, 'ι-carrageenan segments' have been prepared from *Agardhiella tenera* by Smith degradation, and 6-sulphate elimination[191]. No details of molecular weight or composition were given, and the distribution of the ι- and κ-structural elements along the chain were not discussed. The results may, however, be interpeted as indicating a blockwise distribution.

The existence of galactans related to carrageenan but with a different degree of sulphate substitution may be exemplified by the galactan from *Furcellaria fastigiata* (Gigartinales) which both chemically and in physical properties resembles κ-carrageenan but contains significantly less sulphate[5,193].

(c) *The family concept*—Much is lacking before a satisfactory knowledge of the sulphate distribution in carrageenan samples is achieved and either careful fractionation studies combined with controlled degradation or studies of the factors controlling the biochemical sulphation and de-sulphation of the galactans seem to the author to be the techniques most likely to provide further insight in the carrageenan chemistry. So far, the carrageenans should be regarded as a family of polysaccharides, where the structural elements indicated by the different idealised types (ι, κ, λ etc.) occur, where the relative amounts of these elements may vary widely from one algal sample to another and where little is known about the distribution of these different structural elements between the polymer molecules or along the polysaccharide chain.

The family concept, rather than the older distinction between well-defined separate polysaccharides, has also found strong support within the agar type of polysaccharides. By fractionation of a commercial agar preparation (Difco Bacto agar, probably prepared from *Gelidium cartelagenium*) on a DEAE Sephadex column, a fraction containing only uncharged substituents was eluted with water ('agarose'), and a continuous distribution of polysaccharides with increasing charge was eluted by increasing sodium chloride concentrations[143]. No sharply defined fractions were suggested by the elution curve, but fractions rich in pyruvate were eluted at intermediate salt concentrations while fractions richer in sulphate and with a lower pyruvate content were eluted at higher salt concentrations. Agarase degradation[192] gave high yields of oligosaccharides with pyruvate substitution, while parts of the molecule rich in sulphate groups were not degraded. The result, thus, indicates that the two charged substituents tend to occur in different molecules of different parts of the chain molecules. Agar preparations from eight different species were compared and the results were in all cases in qualitative agreement with those described above[174].

2.9 SOME PHYSICAL-CHEMICAL PROPERTIES OF RHODOPHYTA GALACTANS AND ALGINATES

The polysaccharides forming the matrix substances of the cell walls of algae are with few exceptions polyanions. Being located outside of the cell membrane, the polyanions must be expected to be in ion-exchange equilibrium with the surrounding water. In the natural environment these substances usually form more or less firm gels. Ion-exchange properties and gel-forming ability are therefore properties of fundamental importance for the biological function of cell-wall polysaccharides.

In the case of two groups of compounds, the alginates of Phaeophyta and the Rhodophyta galactans, experimental results have been obtained which throw some light upon the correlation between the chemical structure and the biological function of these compounds.

Rhodophyta galactans show a close correlation between chemical structure and gel-forming ability. It is well known by all workers in the field that properties like gel strength, setting and melting temperatures, elasticity, brittleness, transparency etc. vary widely[5, 188, 194, 195]. Due to the lack of well-established methods for characterising gel properties, however, only few quantitative data are given. The qualitative evidence available strongly indicates that the regularity of the repeating structure of 3-linked galactose units and 4-linked 3,6-anhydrogalactose units is essential for giving a high gel strength. This means that transformation of 4-linked galactose 6-sulphate to 3,6-anhydrogalactose, which may occur enzymatically or by treatment with alkali, gives products with increased gel-forming ability. Such a change has been reported both in the carrageenan[184, 188, 190] and the agar family[175, 176]. The effect of additional sulphate groups is less well known, but it is suggested[194] that sulphate groups would prevent association of long-chain segments, and that this may explain the change from an opaque brittle gel of the sulphate-free agarose to the transparent, elastic gel of the ι-carrageenan, which has the highest sulphate content, with κ-carrageenan in between both in properties and sulphate content. The fact that alkali-treated λ-carrageenan does not form precipitates or gels in the presence of potassium ions indicates that the localisation of the sulphate groups is important.

An obvious effect of the sulphate groups is that the carrageenans, also after alkali treatment, are polyelectrolytes and that their properties, such as gel strength, therefore depend upon the ionic strength and the type of ions present in the medium[5, 196, 197]. Among the monovalent cations, potassium, rubidium, caesium and ammonium ions give higher gel strengths than sodium and lithium ions, and divalent cations do not have a stronger gel-forming ability than monovalent ions[197]; in marked contrast to alginates (see later). An explanation of the different effects of the monovalent cations on gel strength was attempted by Bailey[156]. Based on x-ray diagrams and infrared spectra, he proposed a model where the radii oft he hydrated lithium and sodium ions were too large to allow a close packing of the carrageenan molecules, while cations with smaller radii in the hydrated state fitted into the packing arrangement, leading to precipitation or gel formation. This model, has, however, been refuted by more recent work. A point of crucial importance for the understanding of the effect of the different cations on the gel formation of the carrageenans is the relative affinity of the cations to the carrageenan polyanion. Measurements with ion-sensitive electrodes have suggested that, in contrast to their effect on gel formation, no great difference exists in the affinity of potassium and sodium ions to carrageenan. In one case, the percentages of ion pairs for an unfractionated carrageenan sample were found to be 38.3 and 36.5 for potassium and sodium ions, respectively[22], while a more detailed investigation showed a somewhat lower activity coefficient for sodium than potassium ions in the presence of both λ- and κ-carrageenan[199]. Selectivity measurements, carried out by the dialysis technique used for alginate[200], gave selectivity coefficients, $k^{\mathrm{K}}_{\mathrm{Na}}$, of 1.2 for carrageenan from *Gigartina acicularis* and 1.3 for whole, dead tissue of *G. stellata*[201]. Similar selectivity coefficients, indicating only minor differences in affinity to potassium and sodium ions, have been found for animal mucopolysaccharides[202]. The difference in precipitating and gel-forming ability of sodium and potassium ions is thus not due to a difference in the degree of ion-pair formation between the cations and the sulphate half-ester groups, and it has been suggested that the difference may be caused by the two types of ion pairs having different affinities to the solvent molecules[22]. A recent study of the sol-gel transition[203], carried out by determining the melting and setting temperature by light-scattering measurements, showed that the transition temperature varied with the square root of the electrolyte concentration and that the relative effect of the different cations followed an inverted Hofmeister series. The authors conclude that electrostatic effects are predominant and that specific interactions between the cations and the polymer molecules are not important for gel formation, a conclusion which agrees well with the results described above.

A theory about the structure of the junctions formed between the carrageenan molecules in the gels has been proposed by Rees and his co-workers. x-Ray studies were performed on κ- and ι-carrageenans in the form of fibres, stretched during the setting of the gel and dried[204]. The diagrams obtained compared well with those of Bailey[156]. The best diagrams were obtained for ι-carrageenan in the potassium form. Several single and double helical models were in general agreement with the x-ray pattern. Based on model building, a double helical model was selected as the most plausible. In this model, hydrogen bonds between *O*-2 in the galactose units in one chain and *O*-6 in galactose units in the other chain are supposed to stabilise the double helix. Unpublished results of deuterium-exchange experiments and perpendicular dichroism in the infrared are quoted as evidence of such hydrogen bonds[204]. Changes in optical rotation with the sol–gel transition of aqueous κ-carrageenan were observed and interpreted as a change from random coils to a structure with double helical junctions[205]. Working with ι-carrageenan fragments prepared by Smith degradation of carrageenan from

Agardhiella tenera, a similar change in optical rotation with the temperature was observed without any gel formation taking place[206]. Theoretical calculations[207] indicated that a change in optical rotation of the same magnitude should be expected to take place with a change from random coil to double helix. The model thus implies the existence of double helical dimers in solution at ordinary room temperature.

Based on these experimental results, the gel formation of carrageenan is described as the formation of double helices by chain segments which cross-link the chains to a three-dimensional network, and where the double helices in the next stage of the gel formation (leading to syneresis) assemble into aggregates[186, 205]. An important feature of the theory is the effect of the 4-linked galactose 6-sulphate groups. As discussed above, it is empirically well known that the transformation of these groups into 3,6-anhydrogalactose units increases the gel strength. Model building showed that the replacement of 3,6-anhydrogalactose units with galactose 6-sulphate would disrupt the double helix, leading to 'kinks' which would break the junctions. This presence of kinks is described[184, 186] as decreasing the gel strength, with as few as one D-galactose 6-sulphate in every 200 residues having a dramatic effect on gel strength. On the other hand, the kinks are regarded as essential for gel formation by breaking the helices, so that each polysaccharide chain can form junctions with more than one partner, thereby forming a three-dimensional network instead of a collection of isolated chain pairs[208].

In several review articles[186, 194, 208], Rees has discussed this qualitative gel theory. Based on the observation that model building did not exclude the possibility of double helices for a number of other polysaccharides[205] such as hyaluronic acid, chondroitin sulphate and other animal mucopolysaccharides, agarose, μ-carrageenan and related algal galactans, the double helix type of junction was also proposed as occurring in gels formed by these polysaccharides. Recent x-ray evidence does not support this assumption in the case of hyaluronic acid[210].

As discussed above, alginic acid is a linear block copolymer of D-mannuronic and L-guluronic acids. The shape of the alginate molecule in solution was studied by light scattering and viscometry of alginates prepared by homogeneous degradation of a sample isolated from *Laminaria digitata*[100]. In 0.1 M sodium chloride, the molecule behaved as an extended random coil, characterised by a proportionality between the radius of gyration and the square root of the molecular weight, $R_{GW} = \text{Const } M_W{}^{0.5}$, and with a Kuhn statistical segment Am of 340 Å. By determining the viscosity at different ionic strengths and extrapolating[211], it was found that the molecule was also highly extended at infinite ionic strength ($Am \approx 150$ Å). Based on the use of Burchard–Stockmayer–Fixman extrapolation, it was concluded that the stiffness of the alginate molecule is due to a high degree of mechanical inflexibility of the chain and not to the interaction between alginate and water. This is in agreement with results obtained by using an empirical method for determining the relative stiffness of unperturbed polyelectrolytes[212]. Using this method on alginate partially oxidised with periodate, the stiffness of the alginate molecule was found to be very much reduced by the change of some of the pyranoid rings into a polymer segment containing three contiguous single bonds[213]. Due to the formation of hemi-acetal linkages[104], rotation about the glycosidic linkages preceding and succeeding the oxidised unit is precluded. This loss of rotation around two glycosidic linkages and gain of three consecutive single bonds leads to a marked decrease in stiffness and is thus a direct experimental proof of the hindered rotation around the glycosidic bond[213]. By investigating fractions prepared from alginates from *Macrocystis pyrifera* (Laminariales), Brucker *et al.*[214] found evidence for L-guluronate rich polymers being more extended than D-mannuronate rich fractions in 0.1 M NaCl solution. Smidsrød *et al.*[215] studied alginates more well defined with regard to the amounts of the three block types and concluded, based on light scattering and viscosity data, that the relative extension of the three types of blocks increased in the order

'MG' blocks $<$ 'MM' blocks $<$ 'GG' blocks

both in 0.1 M NaCl and in the unperturbed state.

Statistical mechanical calculations of unperturbed dimensions, using potential functions for non-bonded interaction between monomer residues, have been carried out for polymannuronic and polyguluronic acids[216] and for the alternating copolymer of guluronic and mannuronic acid units[217]. The results gave the same order of increasing stiffness as given above. It was assumed in the calculations that the mannuronic acid units were in the $^4C_1$ and the guluronic acid units in the $^1C_4$ conformation, in agreement with x-ray evidence (see above).

It is well known that alkali metal salts of alginic acid are soluble in water, while divalent metal ions, with the exception of magnesium ions, lead to the formation of gels or precipitates[5, 18]. At alkali chloride concentrations[18] above 1 M and magnesium chloride concentrations[23] between 0.1 and 1 M, however, alginate is only partially soluble. On the other hand, soluble calcium alginate has been prepared at very low ionic strength[218].

The interaction between alginate and divalent cations has been examined by dialysing sodium alginate solutions against large volumes of salt solution of suitable composition, then against water and finally determining the ionic composition of the alginate[200]. In alginate gels, the guluronic acid units have a much higher affinity for calcium than magnesium ions, while the mannuronic acid units have about the same affinity to the two ions[200]. By assigning a selectivity coefficient to each of the two types of monomers, the selectivity coefficients of alginates with different compositions and the variation of the selectivity coefficient with the molar fraction of calcium ions bound to the alginate (X_{Ca}) could be calculated. Satisfactory agreement with experimental observations was obtained, except for low values of X_{Ca}, where the alginate was partially soluble. Separating the soluble and insoluble material and analysing them made it possible to determine the selectivity coefficients of the soluble and insoluble phases separately[219]. Marked differences were observed, showing that the ion selectivity of alginates was different in the gel and the sol state. The selectivity coefficient of the guluronic acid units in alginate in the sol state (k^{Ca}_{Mg}) was *ca.* 7[219, 220], while that of the mannuronic acid units was close to 1. This is in agreement with determinations of the activity coefficients of calcium ions in solutions of calcium polymannuronate and polyguluronate as 0.28 and 0.08, respectively[218]

This difference in affinity for calcium ions may be either of electrostatic nature and caused by the differences in charge density or may be due to stereochemical differences allowing a chelate formation involving the hydroxyl groups in the case of calcium polyguluronate. The latter explanation seems to be in better agreement with observations published recently. The high selectivity coefficient k_{Mg}^{Ca} of the guluronic acid units in the soluble state is an unusual feature of polyanions[221], indicating that stereochemical details of the polyguluronate molecule are of importance. Acetylation of the hydroxyl groups of polyguluronic acid reduced the selectivity coefficient to 1, while partial reduction (42%) of the carboxyl groups only reduced the selectivity coefficient in the sol state to 6[219].

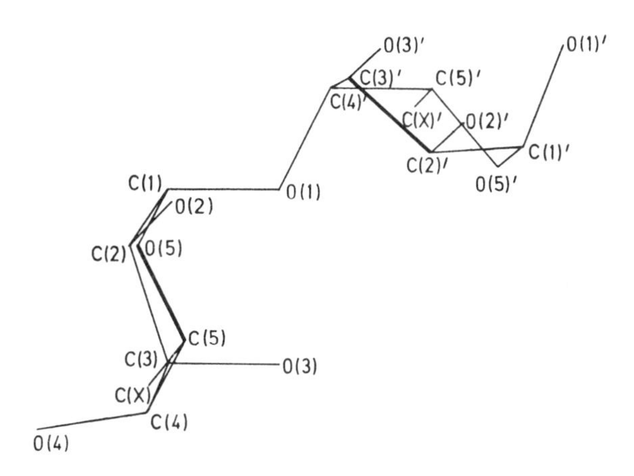

Figure 2.4 Dimer of L-guluronic acid in the $^1C_4$ conformation

Figure 2.4 shows a L-guluronic acid dimer in the $^1C_4$ conformation, with the torsion angles of the single bonds forming the glycosidic linkages so that no overlap of van der Waals radii occurs[216]. Two different proposals for the formation of chelate bonds to calcium ions have been put forward. Rees[208] proposed that the calcium ions bound to the carboxyl group of the non-reducing unit interact with O-2′ and O-5 (marks indicating the unit at the reducing end). Smidsrød *et al.*[220] assumed that calcium ions bound to the carboxyl group of the reducing unit interact in the cavity formed between the rings with O-5′, O-2, O-3 and the bridge oxygen. N.M.R. studies, employing the chemical shift of the H-1 of the α-anomers caused by addition of europium or calcium ions, indicated binding sites in galacturonic acid involving the carboxyl group, O-4 and the ring oxygen and binding sites in methyl α-D-guloside involving O-1, O-2 and O-3[222,223]. This result may be interpreted as favouring the latter model[222], as the binding site in this model is composed of one binding site similar to that of galacturonic acid and another similar to that of the α-D-guloside.

In a polysaccharide gel, parts of the chain molecules form junctions with one another while parts of the same chain molecules are interacting with the solvent molecules, probably being much in the same state as in solution. The difference in selectivity between the soluble and insoluble fraction of polyguluronate fragments indicates a difference in the binding of calcium to isolated parts of the chain molecules and to the junctions binding the chains together in the gel[219]. Two different types of binding sites for calcium ions should thus be expected. Not much is known about the structure of the junctions. Rees describes in a review article[186] the junctions in calcium alginate gels as microcrystallites, implying that a number of consecutive units along the chain are joined together by calcium ions and that several chain molecules take part in the same junctions. The results of the fractionation of polyguluronate fragments in the region of low X_{Ca} has been compared by Smidsrød and Haug[219] with theoretical models for ion binding and found to indicate that the formation of insoluble fragments involve a near-neighbour autoco-operative effect in the binding of calcium ions. This experimental result thus suggests that calcium ions are selectively bound in long sequences between the polyguluronate chains in the gel. Experiments with partially carboxyl-reduced alginate samples support the assumption of autoco-operatively formed sequences of calcium ions, as reduction of 40% of the carboxyl groups destroyed the high selectivity associated with the autoco-operative interchain linkages, while leading to only a slight decrease of the selectivity in solution. Observations indicated that these interchain linkages were very stable kinetically[219].

Recently a method for characterising the mechanical properties of alginate gels has been introduced[224, 225]. By dialysing solutions of sodium alginate contained in small cylinders covered with cellophane membranes against calcium chloride solutions, cylindrical pellets of gel were prepared which could be used for determination of the modulus of stiffness. By examining the correlation between the modulus of stiffness and the molecular weight, the results indicated that the distance between the junctions may be of the same order of magnitude as the Kuhn segments. The modulus of stiffness also depended upon the uronic acid composition of the alginate and the type of divalent metal ion used, in all cases increasing with increasing affinity of the polyuronate for the metal ion. Electron micrographs of gels, prepared by successive dialysis against calcium nitrate and lead nitrate solutions, revealed a randomly cross-linked network of extended threads of a thickness suggesting the presence of single molecular chains of lead alginate[226]. The distances between the junctions varied between 100 and 1000 Å, in good agreement with the results discussed above. Microcrystallites in the sense of many chain molecules taking part in the same junction were not observed.

Returning to the biological situation, the uronic acid composition of the alginate surrounding the cells in brown algae determines the ion-exchange properties of the gel and its mechanical strength. The magnesium, calcium and strontium content of brown algae have been determined, and the selectivity coefficients k^{Ca}_{Mg} and k^{Sr}_{Mg} calculated, regarding the plants as ion-exchange materials suspended in sea water[227]. A close correlation to the selectivity coefficients of the alginates present in the plants were observed, indicating that alginate in the plants must be in ion-exchange equilibrium with sea water and that a major part of the alkali earth ions in brown algae are bound to alginates. Little is known about a possible correlation between the strength of brown algal tissue and alginate composition. It is interesting, however, that the only known occurrence of an alginate with a composition approaching polymannuronic acid is in the medulla of the receptacles of certain species in the order Fucales[26] where it forms a viscous solution or a very soft gel, while the most guluronic rich alginate is found in the old stipes of *Laminaria hyperborea* which have a very rigid structure.

2.10 BIOSYNTHESIS

The biosynthesis of a polysaccharide involves a series of steps; the formation of the proper precursors (usually sugar nucleotides), the polymerisation reaction and finally possible modifications of the polymer chain by substitution or other reactions. A satisfactory description of the complete biosynthetic pathway has not been given for any algal cell-wall polysaccharide.

For the red alga *Porphyra perforata* (Bangiophycea, Bangiales), the following sugar nucleotides have been reported[228]: UDP-D-glucose, UDP-D-galactose, UDP-D-glucuronic acid, GDP-D-mannose and GDP-L-galactose. The latter is of particular interest, as L-galactose is a characteristic component of the polysaccharide porphyran present in *Porphyra* (see above). L-Galactose has also recently been reported in *Chlorella pyrenoidosa*[62] (Chlorophyta, Chlorococcales), and it has been shown that by incubating an enzyme extract from this species with labelled mannose in the form of GDP-D-mannose, labelled L-galactose 1-phosphate was formed[229]. It is reasonable to assume that in the intact algal tissue the useful product for further enzymic reactions would have been GDP-L-galactose[229]. An enzyme performing the related transformation of UDP-D-glucose to UDP-L-rhamnose was previously reported, also from *Chlorella pyrenoidosa*[230] and evidence was presented indicating that the reaction proceeded through the formation of the intermediate UDP-6-deoxy-D-xylo-4-hexulose, as for higher plants.

In brown algae the only study of the sugar nucleotides was carried out by Lin and Hassid on *Fucus gardneri*[231]. They isolated GDP-D-mannuronic acid and small amounts of another acidic nucleotide, indicated to be the L-guluronic acid derivative. In addition, chromatographic evidence of the presence of a number of neutral sugar nucleotides was presented. They also provided evidence for the presence of hexokinase, phosphomannomutase, D-mannose 1-phosphate guanylyl transferase and GDP-D-mannose dehydrogenase, i.e. a set of enzymes providing a pathway from mannose to a precursor for polymannuronic acid[232]. An enzyme providing the epimerisation of GDP-D-mannuronic acid to GDP-L-guluronic acid was not found. Using GDP-D-[^{14}C]mannuronic acid, they were able to demonstrate the transfer of mannuronic acid to a polyuronide fraction by a cell-free extract of *Fucus gardneri*[232].

Lin and Hassid's work still presents the most detailed study of the biosynthetic pathway of an algal cell-wall polysaccharide. So far, the evidence indicates that the pathways are of the same type as described for higher plants. A characteristic feature of many algal polysaccharides is their high degree of substitution. Very little is known about the substitution reactions taking place with algal polysaccharides, but analogy with higher plants and the fact that no substituted precursors have been observed, suggest that substitution may take place at the polymer level[228]. This is also suggested by the very rapid incorporation of sulphate into the carrageenan of *Chondrus crispus*[233] and into the capsular polysaccharide of the unicellular red alga *Porphyridium aerugineum*[234].

Two particularly interesting types of polymer modification reactions have been reported for algal polysaccharides. From *Porphyra umbilicalis* an enzyme extract was prepared which was able to eliminate sulphate from the sulphated polysaccharide porphyran and at the same time increase the amount of 3,6-anhydro-L-galactose units[146]. The reaction was essentially irreversible and indicated the presence in the plant of a L-galactose 6-sulphate alkyltransferase (cyclising). A corresponding enzyme preparation performing the elimination reaction in the D series has been prepared from *Gigartina stellata*[235]. The transformation of a 4-linked galactose 6-sulphate unit into a 3,6-anhydrogalactose unit increases the gel-forming ability of the polymer, according to the double helix theory of Rees by decreasing the number of 'kinks'. Some of the Rhodophyta thus apparently have an enzyme which may increase the gel strength of the cell wall matrix.

The other type of enzyme system capable of performing a polymer modification, has not been demonstrated to be present in algae, but is able to accept algal alginates as substrates. Two groups of bacteria have been shown to produce extracellular alginate[236, 237] which apparently is only distinguishable from algal alginates in containing some acetyl groups[26, 237, 238]. From one of these bacteria, *Azotobacter vinelandii*, an extracellular enzyme was prepared which could convert polymannuronic acid isolated from *Ascophyllum nodosum*[26] into a block copolymer of D-mannuronic and L-guluronic acid[238, 239]. When carrying out the epimerisation reaction in tritiated water, tritium was incorporated into the polymer and 90% of the activity was found in the L-guluronic acid units[240]. The enzyme capable of this transformation has been described as a polymannuronic acid C-5 epimerase and the first step in the reaction has been suggested to be an abstraction of H-5. The reverse reaction has not been demonstrated. This enzyme acts at the polymer level, and above a degree of polymerisation of 15, the activity appeared independent of the degree of polymerisation, while below DP 10 the activity was very low or absent[241]. A very sharp drop in activity thus occurs between DP 15 and 10 of the substrate.

The results indicate that in bacteria the biosynthetic pathway of alginate is via polymannuronic acid, involving epimerisation at the polymer level. Whether this mechanism also operates in brown algae is not known, and the isolation by Lin and Hassid of a nucleotide identified as GDP-L-guluronic acid[231] might indicate a more conventional pathway. ^{14}C-incorporation studies, involving the separation of the alginate into the three block types[242], gave results more easily explained by assuming an epimerisation of D-mannuronic to L-guluronic acid units at the polymer level, but did not furnish proof of this pathway.

Assuming the epimerisation at polymer level to take place also in algae, alginate provides another example of an enzymic modification of a matrix polysaccharide in algae in the direction of increased gel strength. Recent work has shown that epimerisation at the polymer level is not confined to alginate, but takes place also in heparin where epimerisation of D-glucuronic to L-iduronic acid units in the polymer has been demonstrated[243].

Note added in proof

Several significant contributions have appeared after the manuscript was finished in January 1973.

The green alga *Acetabularia crenulata* (Dasycladales), which is unicellular, but macroscopic, was shown to contain a water soluble, highly branched, sulphated polysaccharide containing rhamnose, glucuronic acid, xylose, galactose and 4-*O*-methylgalactose[244]. The polysaccharide appears thus to be related to the *Ulva* type[59,60], but contains in addition galactose, as does the sulphated polysaccharide of the unicellular *Chlorella*[62].

The widespread occurrence of fucose-containing polysaccharides of the sulphated fucan-sulphated glucuronoxylofucan type in Phaeophyta was confirmed by the study of three new species, *Himantalia lorea*, *Bifurcaria bifurcata* (Fucales) and *Padina pavona* (Dictyotales)[245,246].

The red alga *Nemalion vermiculare* (Nemalionales) contained in addition to a water soluble, neutral xylan of the usual Rhodophyta type[137] also a sulphated α 1,3 linked mannan[247]. The latter type of polysaccharide is new in algae. In the chemistry and biology of the carrageenans, a particularly interesting observation has been published by two canadian groups. Sporophytes and gametophytes of *Chondrus crispus* (being morphologically similar) were shown to contain carrageenans of widely different composition[248,249]. The work carried out so far strongly suggests that the sporophytes contain mainly or exclusively λ-carrageenan, while the gametophytes contain κ-carrageenan, 'unfinished' κ-carrageenan (μ-carrageenan) and another, so far not further characterised fraction[249]. This observation opens up a new approach both in the carrageenan chemistry and in the study of the biology of the algal polysaccharides in general.

References

1. Silva, P. C. (1962). *Physiology and Biochemistry of Algae* (R. A. Lewin, editor.), 827 (New York: Academic Press)
2. Christensen, T. (1962). *Botanik II* (Köbenhavn: Munksgaard)
3. Stanier, R. Y., Kunisawa, R., Mandel, M. and Cohen-Bazire, G. (1971). *Bacteriol. Rev.*, **35,** 171
4. Lewin, R. A. (1962). *Physiology and Biochemistry of Algae* (New York: Academic Press)
5. Percival, E. and McDowell, R. H. (1967). *Chemistry and Enzymology of Marine Algal Polysaccharides* (London: Academic Press)
6. Percival, E. (1967). *Chem. Ind. (London)*, 511
7. Larsen, B., Haug, A. and Painter, T. (1970). *Acta Chem. Scand.*, **24,** 3339
8. Baardseth, E. (1966). *5th International Seaweed Symposium*, 19 (Oxford: Pergamon Press)
9. McCully, M. E. (1970). *Ann. N. Y. Acad. Sci.*, **175,** 702
10. Vreeland, V. (1970). *J. Histochem. Cytochem.*, **18,** 371
11. Mühlethaler, K. (1967). *Ann. Rev. Plant. Physiol.*, **18,** 1

12. Lamport, D. T. A. (1970). *Ann. Rev. Plant. Physiol.*, **21,** 235
13. Cleland, R. (1971). *Ann. Rev. Plant. Physiol.*, **22,** 197
14. Northcote, D. H. (1972). *Ann. Rev. Plant. Physiol.*, **23,** 113
15. Shafizadeh, F. and McGinnis, G. D. (1971). *Advan. Carbohydr. Chem. and Biochem.*, **26,** 297
16. Kreger, D. R. (1962). *In Physiology and Biochemistry of Algae* (R. A. Lewin, editor), 315, (New York: Academic Press)
17. Frei, E. and Preston, R. D. (1961). *Nature* (*London*) **192,** 939
18. Haug, A. (1964). *Composition and Properties of Alginates*, Report no. 30 (Trondheim: Norwegian Institute of Seaweed Research)
19. Haug, A., Larsen, B. and Smidsrød, O. (1967). *Acta Chem. Scand.*, **21,** 2859
20. Rees, D. A. (1961). *J. Chem. Soc.*, 5168
21. Nevo, Z. and Sharon, N. (1969). *Biochem. Biophys. Acta*, **173,** 161
22. Smidsrød, O. and Haug, A. (1967). *J. Polymer Sci.*, **C 16,** 1587
23. Haug, A. and Smidsrød, O. (1968). *Chem. Soc. Spec. Publ. No. 23*, 273
24. Larsen, B. and Haug, A. (1963). *Acta Chem. Scand.*, **17,** 1646
25. Haug, A., Larsen, B. and Smidsrød, O. (1967). *Acta Chem. Scand.*, **21,** 691
26. Haug, A., Larsen, B. and Baardseth, E. (1969). *6th International Seaweed Symposium*, 443. (Madrid: Direccion General de Pesca Maritima)
27. Painter, T., Smidsrød, O., Larsen, B. and Haug, A. (1968). *Acta Chem. Scand.*, **22,** 1637
28. Larsen, B., Painter, T., Haug, A. and Smidsrød, O. (1969). *Acta Chem. Scand,*, **23,** 355
29. Gibbons, R. A. (1963). *Nature* (*London*), **200,** 665
30. Haug, A., Larsen, B., Smidsrød, O. and Painter, T. (1969). *Acta Chem. Scand.*, **23,** 2955
31. Cronshaw, J., Myers, A. and Preston, R. D. (1958). *Biochem. Biophys. Acta*, **27,** 89
32. Preston, R. D. and Cronshaw, J. (1958). *Nature* (*London*), **181,** 248
33. Manley, R. St. J. (1964). *Nature* (*London*), **204,** 1155
34. Nieduszynski, I. A. and Atkins, E. D. T. (1970). *Biochem. Biophys. Acta*, **222,** 109
35. Blackwell, J., Vasko, L. D. and Koenig, J. L. (1970). *J. Appl. Phys.*, **41,** 4375
36. Marx-Figini, M. (1969). *Biochem. Biophys. Acta*, **177,** 27
37. Marx-Figini, M. (1969). *J. Polymer Sci.*, **C 28,** 57
38. Marx-Figini, M. (1971). *Biochem. Biophys. Acta*, **237,** 75
39. Northcote, D. H., Goulding, K. J. and Horne, R. W. (1958). *Biochem. J.*, **70,** 391
40. Barnett, J. K. and Preston, R. D. (1969). *Proc. Roy. Microscop. Soc.*, **4,** 135
41. Horne, R. W., Davies, R. D., Norton, K. and Gurney-Smith, M. (1971). *Nature London*), **232,** 493
42. Mackie, I. M. and Percival, E. (1959). *J. Chem. Soc.*, 1151
43. Miwa, T., Iriki, V. and Suzuki, T. (1961). *Colloques. Int. Centr. Nat. Rech. Scient.*, **103,** 135
44. Frei, E. and Preston, R. D. (1964). *Proc. Roy. Soc.*, (*London*), **B 160,** 293
45. Mackie, W. (1969). *Carbohydr. Res.*, **9,** 247–9
46. Mackie, W. and Sellen, D. B. (1971). *Biopolymers*, **10,** 1
47. Atkins, E. D T., Parker, K. D. and Preston, R. D. (1969). *Proc. Roy. Soc.*, (*London*), **B 173,** 209
48. Love, J. and Percival, E. (1964). *J. Chem. Soc.*, 3345
49. Frei, E. and Preston, R. D. (1968). *Proc. Roy. Soc.*, (*London*), **B 169,** 127
50. Mackie, W. and Sellen, D. B. (1969). *Polymer*, **10,** 621
51. Fisher, I. S. and Percival, E. (1957). *J. Chem. Soc.*, 2666
52. Steward, F. C., Lyndon, R. F. and Barber, J. T. (1965). *Amer. J. Botany*, **52,** 155
53 Hirst, E., Mackie, W. and Percival, E. (1965). *J. Chem. Soc.*, 2958
54. Johnson, P. G. and Percival, E. (1969). *J. Chem. Soc. C*, 906
55. Bourne, E. J., Johnson, P. G. and Percival, E. (1970). *J. Chem. Soc. C*, 1561
56. Percival, E and Young, M. (1971). *Phytochemistry*, **10,** 807
57. Mackie, I. M. and Percival, E. (1961). *J. Chem. Soc.*, 3010
58. Love, J. and Percival, E. (1964). *J. Chem. Soc.*, 3338
59. Haq, Q. N. and Percival, E. (1966). *5th International Seaweed Symposium*, 261 (Oxford: Pergamon Press)
60. Haq, Q. N. and Percival, E. (1966). *Some Contemporary Studies in Marine Science* (H. Barnes, editor), 355 (London: George Allen and Unwin Ltd.)
61. Olaitan, S. A. and Northcote, D. H. (1962). *Biochem. J.*, **82,** 509

62. White, R. C. and Barber, G. A. (1972). *Biochem. Biophys. Acta*, **264,** 117
63. Manton, I. (1967). *J. Cell. Sci.*, **2,** 411
64. Manton, I. (1969). *Proc. Roy. Soc., (London)*, **B 172,** 1
65. Green, J. C. and Jennings, D. H. (1967). *J. Exp. Bot.* **18,** 359
66. Throndsen, J. (1971). *Norw. J. Bot.*, **18,** 47
67. Brown, R. M., Franke, W. W., Kleinig, H., Falk, H. and Sitte, P. (1969). *Science*, **166,** 894
68. Brown, R. M., Franke, W. W., Kleinig, H., Falk, H. and Sitte, P. (1970). *J. Cell. Biol.*, **45,** 246
69. Herth, W., Franke, W. W., Stadler, J., Bittiger, H., Keilich, G. and Brown, R. M. (1972). *Planta*, **105,** 79
70. Schneff, E., Deichgräber, G. and Koch, W. (1968). *Arch. Michrobiol.*, **63,** 15
71. Kramer, D. (1970). *Z. Naturforsch.*, **25B,** 1017
72. Fritsch, F. E. (1961). *The Structure and Reproduction of the Algae* (Cambridge: The University Press)
73. Round, F. E. (1965). *The Biology of the Algae.* (London: Edward Arnold Ltd.)
74. Reimann, B. E. F., Lewin, J. C. and Volcani, B. E. (1965). *J. Cell. Biol.*, **24,** 39
75. Reimann, B. E. F., Lewin, J. C. and Volcani, B. E. (1966). *J. Phycol.*, **2,** 77
76. Reimann, B. E. F. and Volcani, B. E. (1968). *J. Ultrastruct. Res.*, **21,** 182
77. Stosch, H. A. von and Reimann, B. E. F. (1970). *Nova Hedwigia Beiheft*, **31,** 1
78. Coombs, J. and Volcani, B. E. (1968). *Planta*, **80,** 264
79. Lewin, J. C., Reichmann, B. E., Busby, W. F. and Volcani, B. E. (1966). *Cell Synchrony*, 169
80. Coombs, J. and Volcani, B. E. (1968). *Planta*, **82,** 280
81. Lewin, J. C., Lewin, R. A. and Philpott, D. E. (1958). *J. Gen. Microbiol.*, **18,** 418
82. Ford, C. W. and Percival, E. (1965). *J. Chem. Soc.*, 7042
83. Lewin, J. C. (1955). *J. Gen. Microbiol.*, **13,** 162
84. Lewin, R. (1958). *Limn. and Oceanogr.*, **3,** 111
85. Huntsman, S. A. and Sloneker, J. H. (1971). *J. Phycol.*, **7,** 261
86. Myklestad, S., Haug, A. and Larsen, B. (1972). *J. Exp. Mar. Biol. Ecol.*, **9,** 137
87. Allen, G. G., Lewin, J. and Johnson, P. G. (1972). *Bot. Marina*, **15,** 102
88. McLachlan, J. and Craigie, J. S. (1966). In: *Some Contemporary Studies in Marine Science* (H. Barnes, editor), 511 (London: George Allen and Unwin Ltd.)
89. Dweltz, N. E. and Colvin, J. R. (1968). *Can. J. Chem.*, **46,** 1513
90. Dodge, J. D. (1971). *Bot. Rev.*, **37,** 481
91. Dodge, J. D. and Crawford, R. M. (1970). *Bot. J. Limn. Soc.*, **63,** 53
92. Dodge, J. D. (1965). *J. Marine Biol. Assoc. UK*, **45,** 607
93. Venkataraman, G. S. and Mehta, S. C. (1960). *Lloydia*, **23,** 115
94. Swift, E. and Remsen, C. C. (1970). *J. Phycol.*, **6,** 79
95. Percival, E. G. V. and Ross, A. G. (1948). *Nature (London)*, **162,** 895
96. Frei, E. and Preston, R. D. (1962). *Nature (London)*, **196,** 130
97. Black, W. A. P. (1950). *J. Marine Biol. Assoc. UK*, **29,** 379
98. Atkins, E. D. T., Mackie, W. and Smolko, E. E. (1970). *Nature (London)*, **225,** 626
99. Fischer, F. G. and Dörfel, H. (1955). *Hoppe-Zeiler's Z. Physiol. Chem.*, **302,** 186
100. Smidsrød, O. and Haug, A. (1968). *Acta Chem. Scand.*, **22,** 797
101. Hirst, E. and Rees, D. A. (1965). *J. Chem. Soc.*, 1182
102. Rees, D. A. and Samuel, J. W. B. (1967). *J. Chem. Soc. C*, 2295
103. Drummond, D. W., Hirst, E. and Percival, E. (1962). *J. Chem. Soc.*, 1208
104. Painter, T. and Larsen, B. (1970). *Acta Chem. Scand.*, **24,** 813
105. Haug, A., Larsen, B. and Smidsrød, O. (1966). *Acta Chem. Scand.*, **20,** 183
106. Haug, A., Myklestad, S., Larsen, B. and Smidsrød, O. (1967). *Acta Chem. Scand.*, **21,** 768
107. Larsen, B., Smidsrød, O., Haug, A. and Painter, T. (1969). *Acta Chem. Scand.*, **23,** 2375
108. Larsen, B., Smidsrød, O., Painter, T. and Haug, A. (1970). *Acta Chem. Scand.*, **24,** 726
109. Preiss, J. and Ashwell, G. (1962). *J. Biol. Chem.* **237,** 309
110. Preiss, J. and Ashwell, G. (1962). *J. Biol. Chem.*, **237,** 317
111. Tsujéno, I. and Saito, T. (1962). *Agr. Biol. Chem. (Japan)*, **26,** 115
112. Nakada, H. I. and Sweeny, P. C. (1967). *J. Biol. Chem.* **242,** 845
113. Nisizawa, K., Fujibayashi, S. and Kashiwabara, Y. (1968). *J. Biochem. (Tokyo)*, **64,** 25
114. Kashiwabara, Y., Suzuki, H. and Nisizawa, K. (1969). *J. Biochem. (Tokyo)*, **66,** 503

115. Fujibayashi, S., Habe, H. and Nisizawa, K. (1969). *J. Biochem.*, **67,** 37
116. Atkins, E. D. T., Mackie, W., Parker, K. D. and Smolko, E. E. (1971). *J. Pol. Sci. B*, **9,** 311
117. Mackie, W. (1971). *Biochem. J.*, **125,** 89P
118. Conchie, J. and Percival, E. G. V. (1950). *J. Chem. Soc.*, 827
119. O'Neill, A. N. (1954). *J. Amer. Chem. Soc.*, **76,** 5074
120. Anno, K., Seno, N. and Ota, M. (1970). *Carbohydr. Res.*, **13,** 167
121. Larsen, B., Haug, A. and Painter, T. J. (1966). *Acta Chem. Scand.*, **20,** 219
122. Larsen, B. (1967). *Acta Chem. Scand.*, **21,** 1395
123. Percival, E. (1968). *Carbohydr. Res.*, **7,** 272
124. Percival, E. (1971). *Carbohydr. Res.* **17,** 121
125. Anno, K. and Uemura, K. (1972). *8th International Seaweed Symposium*, 439 (Tokyo: University of Tokyo Press)
126. Bidwell, R. G. S., Percival, E. and Smestad, B. (1972). *Can. J. Bot.*, **50,** 191
127. Bourne, E. J., Brush, P. and Percival, E. (1969). *Carbohydr. Res.*, **9,** 415
128. Ovodov, Y. S., Khomenko, V. A. and Guseva, T. F. (1970). *Khim. Prir. Soedin*, **6,** 285
129. Ovodov, Y. S. and Pavlenko, A. F. (1970). *Khim. Prir. Soedin*, **6,** 400
130. Ovodov, Y. S. and Khomenko, V. A. (1969). *Khim. Prir. Soedin*, **6,** 73
131. Myers, A. and Preston, R. D. (1959). *Proc. Roy. Soc.*, (*London*), **B, 150,** 447
132. Roelofsen, P. A. and Houwink, A. L. (1953). *Acta Bot. Neerl.*, **2,** 218
133. Dennis, D. T. and Preston, R. D. (1961). *Nature* (*London*), **191,** 667
134. Turvey, J. R. and Williams, E. L. (1970). *Phytochemistry*, **9,** 2383
135. Whyte, J. N. C. (1971). *Can. J. Chem.*, **49,** 1302
136. Frei, E. and Preston, R. D. (1964). *Proc. Roy. Soc.*, (*London*), **B, 160,** 314
137. Bjørndal, H., Eriksson, K.-E., Garegg, P. J., Lindberg, B. and Swan, B. (1965). *Acta Chem. Scand.*, **19,** 2309
138. Cerezo, A. S., Lezerovick, A., Labriola, R. and Rees, D. A. (1971). *Carbohydr. Res.*, **19,** 289
139. Peat, S., Turvey, J. R. and Rees, D. A. (1961). *J. Chem. Soc.*, 1590
139a. Araki, C. (1966). *5th International Seaweed Symposium*, 3 (Oxford: Pergamon Press)
140. Hjertén, S. (1962). *Biochem. Biophys. Acta*, **62,** 445
141. Barteling, S. J. (1969). *Clin. Chem.*, **15,** 1003
142. Egorov, A. M., Vakhabov, A. Kh. and Chernyak, V. Ya. (1970). *J. Chromatogr.*, **46,** 143
143. Duckworth, M. and Yaphe, W. (1971). *Carbohydr. Res.*, **16,** 189
144. Nunn, J. R. and von Holdt, M. M. (1957). *J. Chem. Soc.*, 1094
145. Rees, D. A. and Conway, E. (1962). *Biochem. J.*, **84,** 411
146. Rees, D. A. (1961). *Biochem. J.*, **81,** 347
147. Turvey, J. R. and Williams, T. P. (1964). *4th International Seaweed Symposium*, 370 (Oxford: Pergamon Press)
148. Anderson, N. S., Dolan, T. C. S. and Rees, D. A. (1965). *Nature* (*London*), **205,** 1060
149. Anderson, N. S. and Rees, D. A. (1965). *J. Chem. Soc.*, 5880
150. Turvey, J. R. and Christison, J. (1967). *Biochem. J.*, **105,** 311
151. Turvey, J. R. and Christison, J. (1967). *Biochem. J.*, **105,** 317
152. Duckworth, M. and Turvey, J. R. (1969). *Biochem. J.*, **113,** 139
153. Duckworth, M. and Turvey, J. R. (1969). *Biochem. J.*, **113,** 687
154. Smith, D. B. and Cook, W. H. (1953). *Arch. Biochem. Biophys.*, **45,** 232
155. O'Neill, A. N. (1955). *J. Amer. Chem. Soc.*, **77,** 6324
156. Bayley, S. T. (1955). *Biochem. Biophys. Acta*, **17,** 194
157. Anderson, N. S. and Rees, D. A. (1966). *5th International Seaweed Symposium*, 243 (Oxford: Pergamon Press)
158. Anderson, N. S., Dolan, T. C. S. and Rees, D. A. (1968). *J. Chem. Soc. C*, 596
159. Hirase, S. and Watanabe, K. (1972). *Bull. Chem. Soc. Jap.*, **45,** 1529
160. Weigl, J., Turvey, J. R. and Yaphe, W. (1966). *5th International Seaweed Symposium*, 329 (Oxford: Pergamon Press)
161. Weigl, J. and Yaphe, W. (1966). *Can. J. Microbiol.*, **12,** 939
162. Black, W. A. P., Blakemore, W. R., Colquhoun, J. A. and Dewar, E. T. (1965). *J. Sci. Fd. Agric.*, **16,** 573
163. Rees, D. A. (1963). *J. Chem. Soc.*, 1821
164. Dolan, T. C. S. and Rees, D. A. (1965). *J. Chem. Soc.*, 3534

165. Lawson, C. J. and Rees, D. A. (1968). *J. Chem. Soc., C*, 1301
166. Allsobrook, A. J. R., Nunn, J. R. and Parolis, H. (1969). *6th. International Seaweed Symposium*, 417 (Madrid: Direccion General de Pesca Maritima)
167. Hirase, S., Araki, C. and Watanabe, K. (1967). *Bull. Soc. Chem. Jap.*, **40,** 1445
168. McKenzie, M. E. (1965). *Fortschr. Chem. Org. Naturstoffe*, (S. Peat and J. R. Turvey, editors), **23,** 1
169. Hirase, S. and Watanabe, K. (1967). *Bull. Chem. Soc. Jap.*, **40,** 1442
170. Turvey, J. R. and Simpson, P. R. (1966). *5th International Seaweed Symposium*, 323 (Oxford: Pergamon Press)
171. Barry, V. C. and McCromick, J. E. (1957). *J. Chem. Soc.*, 2777
172. Rees, D. A. (1961). *J. Chem. Soc.*, 5168
173. Hirase, S. (1957). *Bull. Chem. Soc. Jap.*, **30,** 68, 70, 75
174. Young, K., Duckworth, M. and Yaphe, W. (1971). *Carbohydr. Res.*, **16,** 446
175. Duckworth, M., Hong, K. C. and Yaphe, W. (1971). *Carbohydr. Res.*, **18,** 1
176. Hong, K. C., Goldstein, M. E. and Yaphe, W. (1969). *6th International Seaweed Symposium*, 473 (Madrid: Direccion General de Pesca Maritima)
177. Araki, C., Arai, K. and Hirase, S. (1967). *Bull. Chem. Soc. Jap.*, **40,** 959
178. Bowker, D. M. and Turvey, J. R. (1968). *J. Chem. Soc. C*, 983
179. Hirase, S., Araki, C. and Watanabe, K. (1967). *Bull. Chem. Soc. Jap.*, **40,** 1445
180. Nunn, J. R. and Parolis, H. (1968). *Carbohydr. Res.*, **9,** 265
181. Nunn, J. R. and Parolis, H. (1968). *Carbohydr. Res.*, **6,** 1
182. Nunn, J. R. and Parolis, H. (1968). *Carbohydr. Res.*, **8,** 361
183. Painter, T. J. (1966). *5th International Seaweed Symposium*, 305 (Oxford: Pergamon Press)
184. Anderson, N. S., Dolan, T. S. C., Penman, A., Rees, D. A., Mueller, G. P., Stancioff, D. J. and Stanley, N. F. (1968). *J. Chem. Soc. C*, 602
185. Mueller, G. P. and Rees, D. A. (1968). *Transactions of Drugs from the Sea Symposium*, 241. (Washington D.C.: Marine Technological Society)
186. Rees, D. A. (1969). *Advan. Carbohydr. Chem Biochem.*, **24,** 267
187. Anderson, N. S., Dolan, T. C. S., Lawson, C. J., Penman, A. and Rees, D. A. (1968). *Carbohydr. Res.*, **7,** 468
188. Stancioff, D. J. and Stanley, N. F. (1969). *6th International Seaweed Symposium*, 595. Madrid: Direction General de Pesca Maritima)
189. Pernas, A. J., Smidsrød, O., Larsen, B. and Haug, A. (1967). *Acta Chem. Scand.*, **21,** 98
190. Smidsrød, O., Larsen, B., Pernas, A. J. and Haug, A. (1967). *Acta Chem. Scand.*, **21,** 2585
191. McKinnon, A. A., Rees, D. A. and Williamson, F. B. (1969). *Chem. Commun.*, 701
192. Duckworth, M. and Yaphe, W. (1971). *Carbohydr. Res.*, **16,** 435
193. Painter, T. J. (1960). *Can. J. Chem.*, **38,** 112
194. Rees, D. A. (1972). *Chem. Ind.*, 630
195. Percival, E. (1972). *J. Sci. Fd. Agric.*, **23,** 933
196. Zabik, M. E. and Aldrich, P. J. (1965). *J. Food Sci.*, **30,** 795
197. Zabik, M. E. and Aldrich, P. J. (1968). *J. Food Sci.*, **33,** 371
199. Podlas, T. J. and Ander, P. (1969). *Macromolecules*, **2,** 432
200. Smidsrød, O. and Haug, A. (1968). *Acta Chem. Scand.*, **22,** 1989
201. Haug, A. Unpublished results
202. Bettelheim, F. A. (1970). In: *Biological Polyelectrolytes* (A. Veis, editor), 166 (New York: Marcel Dekker
203. Payens, T. A. J. and Snoeren, Th. (1972). *J. Electroanal. Chem.*, **37,** 291
204. Anderson, N. S., Campbell, J. W., Harding, M. M., Rees, D. A. and Samuel, J. W. B. (1969). *J. Mol. Biol.*, **45,** 85
205. Rees, D. A., Steele, I. W. and Williamson, F. B. (1969). *J. Polymer. Sci. C*, **28,** 261
206. McKinnon, A. A., Rees, D. A. and Williamson, F. B. (1969). *Chem. Commun.*, 701
207. Rees, D. A., Scott, W. E. and Williamson, F. B. (1970). *Nature (London)*, **227,** 390
208. Rees, D. A. (1972). *Biochem. J.*, **126,** 257
210. Atkins, E. D. T. and Sheehan, J. K. (1971). *Biochem. J.*, **125,** 92 *P*
211. Smidsrød, O. (1970). *Carbohydr. Res.*, **13,** 359
212. Smidsrød, O. and Haug, A. (1971). *Biopolymers*, **10,** 1213
213. Smidsrød, O. and Painter, T. (1973). *Carbohydr. Res.*, **26,** 125

214. Brucker, R. F., Wormington III, C. M. and Nakada, H. I. (1971). *J. Macromol. Sci. Chem.*, **A5,** 1169
215. Smidsrød, O., Glover, R. M. and Whittington, S. (1973). *Carbohydr. Res.*, **27,** 107
216. Whittington, S. (1971). *Biopolymers*, **10,** 1481
217. Whittington, S. (1971). *Biopolymers*, **10,** 1617
218. Kohn, R. and Larsen, B. (1972). *Acta Chem. Scand.*, **26,** 2455
219. Smidsrød, O. and Haug, A. (1972). *Acta Chem. Scand.*, **26,** 2063
220. Smidsrød, O., Haug, A. and Whittington, S. G. (1972). *Acta Chem. Scand.*, **26,** 2563
221. Haug, A. and Smidsrød, O. (1970). *Acta Chem. Scand.*, **24,** 843
222. Anthonsen, T., Larsen, B. and Smidsrød, O. (1972). *Acta Chem. Scand.*, **26,** 2988
223. Angyal, S. J. and Davies, K. P. (1971). *Chem. Commun.*, 500
224. Smidsrød, O., Haug, A. and Lian, B. (1972). *Acta Chem. Scand.*, **26,** 71
225. Smidsrød, O. and Haug, A. (1972). *Acta Chem. Scand.*, **26,** 79
226. Smidsrød, O. and Skipnes, O. (1973) In: *Some Physical Properties of Alginates in Solution and in the Gel State.* Report No. 34. (Trondheim: Norwegian Institute of Seawood Research)
227. Haug, A. and Smidsrød, O. (1967). *Nature* (*London*), **215,** 1167
228. Su, J. C. and Hassid, W. Z. (1962). *Biochemistry*, **1,** 474
229. Barber, G. A. (1971). *Arch. Biochem. Biophys.*, **147,** 619
230. Barber, G. A. and Chang, M. T. Y. (1967). *Arch. Biochem. Biophys.*, **118,** 659
231. Lin, T. and Hassid, W. Z. (1966). *J. Biol. Chem.*, **241,** 3282
232. Lin, T. and Hassid, W. Z. (1966). *J. Biol. Chem.*, **241,** 5284
233. Loewus, F., Wagner, G., Schiff, J. H. and Weistrop, J. (1971). *Plant Physiol.*, **48,** 373
234. Ramus, J. and Groves, S. T. (1972). *J. Cell. Biol.*, **54,** 399
235. Lawson, C. J. and Rees, D. A. (1970). *Nature* (*London*), **227,** 392
236. Linker, A. and Jones, R. S. (1966). *J. Biol. Chem.*, **241,** 3845
237. Gorin, P. A. J. and Spencer, J. F. T. (1966). *Can. J. Chem.*, **44,** 993
238. Larsen, B. and Haug, A. (1971). *Carbohydr. Res.*, **17,** 287
239. Haug, A. and Larsen, B. (1971). *Carbohydr. Res.*, **17,** 297
240. Larsen, B. and Haug, A. (1971). *Carbohydr. Res.*, **20,** 225
241. Larsen, B. and Haug, A. (1973). *8th International Seaweed Symposium*, **12,** 491 (Tokyo: University of Tokyo Press)
242. Hellebust, J. and Haug, A. (1972). *Can. J. Bot.*, **50,** 177
243. Lindahl, U., Bäckström, G., Malmström, A. and Fransson, L.-Å. (1972). *Biochem. Biophys. Res. Commun.*, **46,** 985
244. Percival, E. and Smestad, B. (1972). *Carbohyd. Res.*, **25,** 299
245. Mian, A. J. and Percival, E. (1973). *Carbohyd. Res.*, **26,** 133
246. Mian, A. J. and Percival, E. (1973). *Carbohyd. Res.*, **26,** 147
247. Usov, A. I., Adamyants, K. S., Yarotsky, S. V., Anoshina, A. A. and Kochetkov, N. K. (1973). *Carbohyd. Res.*, **26,** 282
248. Chen, L. C-M., McLachlan, J., Neish, A. C. and Shacklock, P. F. (1973). *J. Mar. Biol. Ass. U.K.*, **53,** 11
249. McCandless, E. L., Craigie, J. S. and Walter, J. A. (1973). *Planta*, **112,** 201

3
Pathways of Carbohydrate Breakdown in Higher Plants

T. AP REES
University of Cambridge

3.1 INTRODUCTION

In this review, I aim to consider the extent to which the facts available at present can be used to establish a precise sequence of reactions for the breakdown of carbohydrates in higher plants. The emphasis is on the path of carbon from the two commonest storage carbohydrates, starch and sucrose, to CO_2. Well established reactions are not dealt with in detail but particular attention is paid to aspects, such as the breakdown of starch and sucrose to hexose, where our understanding is still fragmentary. Within this context the following limitations are applied. First, carbohydrate oxidation during photosynthesis is not dealt with because this subject has been well reviewed recently[1,2]. Secondly, control of hexose oxidation is not considered in detail. This is because I believe that it is necessary to establish the reaction sequences before speaking of control and that the addition of this major topic to the present review would make it unwieldy. Thirdly, the metabolism of fructans, sugar alcohols, and oligosaccharides related to sucrose, is not discussed in depth. This is not an implication that these compounds are unimportant, but a reflection of the fact that our understanding of their metabolism in plants is so slight that their inclusion in the review would lead to fragmentation rather than to synthesis. The review is not meant to be encyclopaedic and references are used only where they are required to substantiate statements. Even here the number is restricted as it is assumed that reference to a particular paper includes those references in that paper.

3.2 METHODS

Two particular methods of investigating carbohydrate oxidation warrant discussion because they are so often used without due appreciation of their attendant pitfalls. These methods are those used to assess the amounts of substrates and of enzymes in plant cells. The usefulness of such measurements is often questionable because inadequate care has been taken to ensure their reliability.

3.2.1 Measurement of intermediates of carbohydrate breakdown in plants

It is often important to know the tissue content of the intermediates of carbohydrate oxidation and of compounds like ATP, NAD and NADP that are closely involved in this process. Such measurements have been made successfully for animal and microbial cells. However, particular care must be taken in adapting techniques, shown to be successful with other types of cells, to plants. In comparison with animal and microbial cells, plant cells generally contain 1–10% of the amounts of intermediates involved in carbohydrate breakdown. In contrast, the content of substances, like pigments, carbohydrates and cations, that may interfere with the assay of such intermediates is appreciably higher in plants. Three points are specifically relevant.

3.2.1.1 Artefacts arising during killing of tissues

The technique used for killing and extracting plant tissues may cause changes in the amounts of metabolic intermediates present. This is particularly true of phosphorylated compounds. The use of hot acids or alkalis will hydrolyse some phosphate esters. Probably the most dangerous source of error is the ability of plant phosphatases to resist many of the commonly used killing agents for long enough to cause significant alteration in the amounts of substrates recovered in the extracts. Bieleski[3,4] demonstrated the persistence of phosphatase activity in a range of plant tissues after killing them with a variety of methods. This persistence was associated with marked changes in the amounts of some compounds found in the extracts. For example, the ATP/ADP ratio in extracts of potato was changed from 8.1 to 0.75 by killing with boiling methanol rather than with a cold mixture. Bieleski's work shows that the conventional killing techniques are not necessarily reliable and that the extent of their unreliability varies for different compounds and for different tissues.

Thus in any series of experiments it is imperative to provide evidence that the killing technique is reliable. Such evidence can be provided in two ways. First, a variety of techniques can be compared. It is not possible to designate any one technique as the best as the choice will be dictated by the compound and the tissue involved. From Bieleski's work it seems likely that cold-killing in organic solvents at an acid pH is the most satisfactory general approach. Possibly the best technique is to freeze the sample rapidly in liquid air as described by Williamson and Corkey[5] and then transfer the sample to a mixture of methanol–chloroform–7 M formic acid (12:5:3)[4] at −25 °C for about 4 h.

The second check that should be made on the reliability of the killing technique is the determination of the recovery of known amounts of compounds that have been added to the samples to be analysed. Perhaps the best procedure is to prepare duplicate samples of tissue, freeze them in liquid air and then homogenise them in stainless steel or Teflon mortars previously cooled in liquid air. One homogenate is then added to the killing solution and extracted and analysed. The other homogenate is added to the killing solution together with known amounts of the compounds to be analysed. The complete mixture is then extracted and analysed. The efficiency of the complete process of killing, extraction and assay is indicated by the extent to which the added compounds are recovered. It is important to distinguish between the above procedure and recovery experiments in which the exogenous compounds and the intact tissue are added to the killing solution together. In the latter case complete recovery of the added compounds is not entirely convincing since they may be much less accessible to the tissue phosphatases than are their endogenous counterparts. Even less convincing are experiments that show complete recovery of compounds added to plant extracts. These experiments only test the efficiency of the analysis of the extracts and ignore the possibility of losses during the preparation of the extracts.

3.2.1.2 Artefacts arising during extraction and analysis

Loss of metabolic intermediates can occur during extraction and analysis. Methods that are known to be satisfactory for animal tissues should not be applied uncritically to plant tissues. The relatively small losses that accompany standard techniques for animal tissues may become quite significant in work with plant cells where the content of metabolic intermediates is low. For example Bieleski and Young[6] found that extraction of tissue of potato and avocado pear with hot 70 % ethanol failed to remove 15 % of the acid soluble phosphates. Better extraction was achieved with perchloric acid but then 11 % of the phosphates were lost through co-precipitation with perchlorate later in the procedure. The efficiency of the extraction and the reliability of the assay should be checked for each tissue. The recovery experiments mentioned in the last section will act as an overall check.

Two main methods have been used to assay intermediates of carbohydrate metabolism in plant extracts. The most popular has been enzymic analysis of unfractionated extracts. Accurate results generally depend upon passage of the extract over charcoal to remove interfering substances. This method has been applied satisfactorily to extracts of a number of plants[7,8]. The second method involves the isolation of individual intermediates, by chromatography or electrophoresis, followed by assay by chemical or enzymic procedures[9]. This method finds little favour at present but it is worth developing because it involves the isolation of the compounds concerned. This would permit measurements of the specific activity and labelling pattern of the different intermediates of carbohydrate breakdown. Such data is badly needed before we can estimate the flux through the different pathways of carbohydrate breakdown.

3.2.1.3 *Relationship between content and concentration of substrate* in vivo

Even if the amount of a particular intermediate present in a sample of plant tissue has been measured accurately, the extensive compartmentation of plant tissue makes it very difficult to assess the relationship between content and concentration *in vivo*. This problem is particularly severe in plant tissues as so little of the total volume is cytoplasm. Pitman[10] has calculated that the cytoplasm occupies no more than 5% of the volume of the storage tissue of red beet. Figures such as this can be used to obtain some estimate of the concentration *in vivo* provided that the compound is uniformly distributed throughout the cytoplasm. A uniform distribution is extremely unlikely for many of the substances involved in carbohydrate breakdown. For example, in liver there is good evidence that the ratios $NAD^+/NADH$[11] and $ATP/ADP \times P_i$[12] in mitochondria are very much less than those in the cytoplasm. Thus knowledge of the total content of a compound in a sample of tissue may be no guide at all to the concentration at a particular catalytic site *in vivo*.

To some extent this problem can be attacked by the centrifugation of freeze-dried material in organic solvents[13]. In general this technique has been used mainly for the larger organelles but has yielded little information about substrate levels in the cytoplasm and the smaller compartments of the cell. A more promising approach has been developed for studies of animal cells. This is the redox metabolite indicator method that has recently been very well reviewed[14]. This method is particularly applicable to NAD and NADP but has been extended to studies of adenine nucleotides and intermediates of the tricarboxylic acid cycle. The approach is exemplified by its application to determination of the ratio $NAD^+/NADH$ in the cytoplasm of liver cells. The ratio is calculated from the ratio of the concentrations of oxidized and reduced substrates of an NAD specific dehydrogenase located in the cytoplasm. For liver, lactate dehydrogenase may be regarded as an exclusively cytoplasmic enzyme. Thus

$$\frac{[NAD^+]}{[NADH]}\text{ cytoplasm} = \frac{[\text{Pyruvate}]}{[\text{Lactate}]} \times \frac{1}{K_{\text{Lactate dehydrogenase}}}$$

where the concentrations of pyruvate and lactate are µmol g^{-1} fresh weight of tissue. By the appropriate choice of enzyme the method can be extended to other compartments and to other compounds. It is clear that the application of this method to plants will encounter more difficulties than are found with animal tissues. None the less this approach is likely to be more fruitful for NAD and NADP and the adenine nucleotides than the present fashion of measuring the total amounts of these compounds in plant tissues. The evidence that these compounds are distributed unequally throughout an animal cell is now strong enough to cast doubt on the usefulness of further measurements of the total amounts present in any eukaryotic cell.

3.2.2 Measurement of enzymes

Measurement of the maximum catalytic activities of enzymes in plant tissues can make important contributions to the elucidation of metabolic pathways and the mechanisms that control these pathways. Care must be taken to measure the maximum activity in a tissue, particularly when comparisons are to be made between different tissues or differently treated samples of the same tissue. Recent experience indicates that the following points need careful attention.

3.2.2.1 Extraction of enzymes from plant cells

The extraction must be complete and two precautions are worth noting. First, homogenates should be examined under a microscope to check that all the cells have been broken, The dangers of not doing this are illustrated by the fact that failure to break many of the bundle sheath cells of maize leaves contributed significantly to the view that ribulosediphosphate carboxylase was not present in amounts sufficient to mediate photosynthesis[15]. Secondly, a proportion of some enzymes may be associated with the cell-wall fraction of the homogenates. In extracts of carrot storage tissue significant but variable amounts of acid invertase were found in the cell-wall fraction[16].

Homogenisation of plant cells may lead to rapid inactivation of enzymes. This problem is particularly acute in the more mature cells that may contain large amounts of secondary products, and in cells that are rich in phenol oxidase activity. This question and possible answers have been reviewed by Anderson[17]. Great care must be taken in developmental studies to ensure that changes in enzyme activity in extracts are not due to changes in the extent to which the enzyme is inhibited during the preparation of the extract. This point is emphasised by Young[18] who showed that an apparent increase in aldolase activity during the ripening of bananas was due to changes in the ability of leucoanthocyanins to inactivate the enzyme in the extracts. The extent to which enzyme activity is lost during the preparation of homogenates can be investigated as follows. First, a sample of purified enzyme can be added to the extraction medium before the tissue is homogenised and its recovery in the extract measured subsequently. Secondly, where two different samples of tissue are to be compared, the activity recovered from a 1 : 1 mixture of the two samples can be contrasted with that predicted from measurements made on separate samples of tissue[19]. Neither of the above techniques is completely conclusive because the endogenous enzyme is probably more accessible to any inhibitors than is the added enzyme.

3.2.2.2 Assay of enzymes in plant extracts

The reliability of the assay must be established. Assays developed for pure enzymes are not always suitable for use with unfractionated extracts. Pure glucose 6-phosphate dehydrogenase (EC 1.1.1.49) can be assayed by following the reduction of $NADP^+$ in the presence of glucose 6-phosphate. This procedure may not be applied automatically to an unfractionated extract because some reduction of $NADP^+$ could be catalysed by 6-phosphogluconate dehydrogenase (EC 1.1.1.44) using as a substrate 6-phosphogluconate produced by glucose 6-phosphate dehydrogenase. In extracts of pea roots about 20% of the $NADP^+$ reduced in the presence of glucose 6-phosphate is due to 6-phosphogluconate dehydrogenase. The extent of this contribution from 6-phosphogluconate dehydrogenase has been shown to vary with the type of tissue and its state of differentiation (M. W. Fowler, unpublished results). Thus the practices of either ignoring the contribution of 6-phosphogluconate dehydrogenase or assuming that 50% of the $NADP^+$ reduction is due to this dehydrogenase would both give unreliable results. A similar situation has been demonstrated in extracts of rat liver by Glock and McLean[20] who also describe two ways of coping with the problem.

In addition to the above points, it is important to establish that the enzyme is being assayed under optimum conditions. Thus the pH and the composition of the reaction mixture should be varied to give optimum rates. Care should be taken to avoid extrapolation between different types of sample or tissue. This caution is emphasised by the initial attempts to assay ribulosediphosphate carboxylase in maize leaves[15] and even more strongly by the fact that a very thorough study[21] failed to reveal the aldolase activity now known to be present in blue-green algae[22].

3.2.2.3 *Interpretation of measurements of enzyme activity*

Measurements of enzyme activity should be reported for a sufficiently large number of samples for us to be able to assess the statistical significance of any differences that are claimed. Even if all the above conditions are met, we may not equate changes in the maximum catalytic activity of an enzyme in a tissue with changes in the total amount of enzyme present. First, the checks described above cannot be regarded as completely conclusive. Secondly, changes in maximum catalytic activity could be caused by factors other than variation in the total amount of enzyme. For example there is good evidence for the existence of a specific inhibitor of acid invertase in a number of plants[23] and it appears that the amount of this inhibitor present can vary considerably[24]. Conversely, conversion of a pre-existing enzyme to an active form occurs in respect of β-amylase during the germination of barley[25]. In view of the above arguments and our extremely limited knowledge of the mechanisms responsible for regulating the amounts of individual proteins in plant cells, it can be argued forcibly that it is not permissible to speak of enzyme induction and repression in plants solely on the basis of measurements of enzyme activities.

The question of the relationship between changes in maximum catalytic activity and the amount of enzyme is a particularly pressing problem. The sensitivity of changes in activity to inhibitors of protein and nucleic acid synthesis can provide data that is consistent with the view that increased activity is due to enzyme synthesis. Such experiments are not conclusive because they do not show that the effect is due primarily to inhibition of the synthesis of the enzyme under investigation. A general inhibition of protein synthesis could affect metabolism by altering the amount of substrate available for various reactions, or by causing critical depletion of rapidly turning-over enzymes. Both of these effects could alter enzyme activity by interfering with long-term mechanisms of enzyme activation or inhibition. More informative data can be obtained from labelling experiments[26]. In interpreting such experiments it is important to distinguish between isotope incorporation due to turnover and that due to net synthesis. Thus such data may be enhanced by pulse and chase experiments and by measurements of the total amount of enzyme present.

3.3 BREAKDOWN OF STARCH

The α-(1→4) bonds of starch may be hydrolysed by amylases and maltase or broken by starch phosphorylase. The α-(1→6) bonds appear to be broken by hydrolytic debranching enzymes. The roles of these enzymes in starch breakdown in plants must be assessed from their properties *in vitro*, and the relationship between their activities *in vivo* and changes in the starch content of tissues.

3.3.1 Enzymes that catalyse starch breakdown

Greenwood and Milne[27] have reviewed the properties of enzymes that react with starch, and Thoma, Spradlin and Dygert[28] have also reviewed aspects of amylases. Both reviews pay particular attention to mechanisms of enzyme action and this aspect is not discussed in this article.

3.3.1.1 α-Amylase

α-Amylase (EC 3.2.1.1) appears to be almost ubiquitous in living cells but its properties vary with its origin. The enzyme has been purified from a range of plants and a number of preparations have been studied in detail. α-Amylase from plants contains 1 g atom of calcium per mole of enzyme although this is less tightly bound than in the enzyme from animals[27]. The molecular weight of the enzyme from plants is about 45 000 but its precise structure has yet to be reported[29]. The enzyme from pig pancreas has two binding sites for maltotriose per molecule of enzyme and these are involved in the formation of a stable multimolecular complex between the enzyme and dextrins[30]. Multiple forms of α-amylase have been reported to be present in barley[31] and in wheat[32]. Manners and Marshall[31] have stressed the ease with which apparent isozymes of α-amylase can be created during extraction and fractionation. Whilst some of the isozymes of α-amylase reported from plants almost certainly fall into this category of artefacts, those in the above papers appear to be genuine. The significance of the multiple forms of α-amylase in plants is not apparent.

α-Amylase from plants catalyses the hydrolysis of the glycosidic bonds in α-(1→4)-D-glucan. The linkage in maltose is not attacked. There is evidence that plant α-amylases do not readily attack either the five bonds nearest the non-reducing end of an α-(1→4)-glucan or the bond next to the reducing group. Relatively small oligosaccharides are hydrolysed more slowly than larger polymers. Studies of the action of plant α-amylases on amylose indicate that initially the α-(1→4)-bonds are cleaved at random but non-random action of the enzyme becomes important in the later stages of hydrolysis[27]. Thus there is an initial stage of amylolysis, during which there is a rapid decrease in the size of amylose, and a final stage characterised by the slow hydrolysis of the products of the first stage. These stages are not due to different reactions but to differences in the enzyme's affinity for large and small molecules[33]. The final products are glucose and maltose.

The action of α-amylase on amylopectin is more complicated. The presence of α-(1→6)-bonds makes nearby α-(1→4)-bonds resistant to attack. Initial hydrolysis is believed to be random except for bonds near chain ends, branch points and in inaccessible parts of the molecule[29]. The initial products of amylopectin hydrolysis by barley α-amylase are compounds bigger than pentaose[34]. Recently the final products for α-amylase from rye have been shown to be glucose, maltose, maltotriose, and a series of branched α-limit dextrins with a degree of polymerisation of four or more[35].

3.3.1.2 β-Amylase

β-Amylase (EC 3.2.1.1) has only been reported from cells of higher plants. Pure preparations have been obtained from a number of plants and all such preparations that have been examined appear to be similar[27, 28]. There are reports of multiple forms of β-amylase in plants but there is insufficient evidence to rule out the possibility that these are artefacts of extraction[28]. β-Amylase from sweet potato (*Ipomoea batatas*) has been shown to be a tetramer with a molecular weight of 206 000 and with molecular symmetry which includes, at least to low resolution, a diad axis[36]. The enzyme is readily inactivated by sulphydryl reagents. Spradlin and Thoma[37] have provided evidence that there are three exposed sulphydryl groups per monomer and that the thiol modifications that cause marked inhibition are accompanied by a small change in conformation that does not greatly alter the enzyme's affinity for its substrate. The sulphydryl groups do not appear to be directly involved in binding the substrate or in catalysis but could be involved in regulation of the enzyme. This view is strengthened by the fact that β-amylase can be reversibly inactivated by disulphide interchange and by the fact that a range of plants has been shown to contain protein disulphide reductase activity[38].

Further support for the above view is provided by studies of β-amylase in cereal seeds. A significant proportion of the β-amylase in these seeds is present in a latent or inactive form that appears to be converted to an active form during germination[25, 39]. The latent enzyme may be associated with protein bodies[40]. The latent and active forms are almost certainly the same protein[41, 42]. The data of Shinke and Mugibayashi[43] suggest that the latent enzyme is present in two forms. One may be a heteropolymer between β-amylase and another protein, possibly glutenin[44]. This form seems to require the cleavage of both peptide and disulphide bonds for complete activation. The other form of latent β-amylase may be an inactive homopolymer of the enzyme that can be almost completely activated by breakage of disulphide bonds alone. During ripening of barley the amount of latent enzyme increases[45]. It is likely that the oxidation of the sulphydryl groups of β-amylase contributes to the formation of the latent forms of the enzyme during ripening and that the reverse process, possibly catalysed by disulphide reductase, is involved in the formation of active enzyme during germination.

Studies of the mechanism of action of β-amylase have revealed no requirement for any co-factor. The enzyme catalyses the successive removal of maltose units from the non-reducing end of α-(1→4)-D-glucan. Modification of the glucan prevents further hydrolysis by the enzyme. Thus β-amylase can catalyse the complete conversion of amylose to maltose. Its action on amylopectin is complicated by the α-(1→6)-bonds. The enzyme catalyses the removal of maltose units from the non-reducing ends of the external chains until it is stopped by an α-(1→6)-bond. The number of glucose units left as stubs near the branching points is not known but is probably two or three. In general, the action of β-amylase results in the formation of maltose, and of a β-limit dextrin that constitutes about 43% of the original amylopectin[27].

3.3.1.3 *Maltase*

Hutson and Manners[46] demonstrated maltase activity in extracts of a wide range of plants. The preparations also hydrolysed negarose and isomaltose at rates that were 70–90% and 10–20%, respectively, of those found with maltose. Work with purified preparations failed to separate the maltase and negarase activities but indicated that the two sugars were hydrolysed at different sites. More recently two types of α-glucosidase activity have been demonstrated in extracts of rice seeds. These preparations showed optimum activity at pH 4.0 and hydrolysed maltose and a range of α-(1→4)-linked gluco-oligosaccharides[47]. Maltase activity has also been demonstrated in pea seeds but no detailed studies have been reported[48]. The role of maltase in starch breakdown in seeds is important and the enzyme merits much more detailed investigation.

3.3.1.4 *Starch phosphorylase*

Plants contain starch phosphorylase that catalyses the reaction

$$\alpha\text{-}(1\rightarrow4)\text{-glucan}(_n) + P_i \rightleftharpoons \alpha\text{-}(1\rightarrow4)\text{-glucan}(_n - 1) + \text{glucose 1-phosphate}$$

$$K = \frac{[\alpha\text{-}(1\rightarrow4)\text{-glucan}_{(n)}]\quad[P_i]}{[\alpha\text{-}(1\rightarrow4)\text{-glucan}_{(n}-1_{)}]\ [\text{glucose 1-phosphate}]} = \begin{matrix}10.8 \text{ at pH } 5.0\\ 3.1 \text{ at pH } 7.0\end{matrix}$$

This enzyme is classified with glycogen phosphorylase as α-glucan phosphorylase (EC 2.4.1.1). The properties of the enzyme from animals have been discussed recently very clearly[49]. Compared with glycogen phosphorylase, investigations of starch phosphorylase have been few and suffer from the disadvantage of being almost all confined to potato phosphorylase. Thus we are not in a position to make firm generalisations about starch phosphorylase.

Starch phosphorylase can catalyse the successive phosphorylytic removal of glucose units from the non-reducing end of amylose. Unless the amylose contains anomalous linkages degradation can be almost complete. The enzyme attacks amylopectin readily to give 33–45% as glucose 1-phosphate and the rest as a limit dextrin. α-(1→6)-Linkages are a considerable barrier to the enzyme and activity stops rather further from α-(1→6)-linkages than is the case with β-amylase[50]. Potato phosphorylase has been purified[51-53]. The enzyme has a molecular weight of 200 000[53] and contains firmly bound pyridoxal phosphate[54]. Potato phosphorylase is similar to muscle phosphorylase in its amino acid composition, its reaction with glyoxal, its circular dichroism[55], and its kinetic properties and mechanism[52]. There are, however, very important differences between the potato phosphorylase and that from muscle. When potato phosphorylase is treated with iodoacetamide or *p*-chloromercuric benzoic acid it does not dissociate into sub-units in the way muscle phosphorylase does[56]. Potato phosphorylase cannot be phosphorylated to give tetramers, is not stimulated by AMP, and in general lacks the regulatory and allosteric properties characteristic of muscle phosphorylase[52,54,57].

There is an urgent need for the study of starch phosphorylase from a wide range of plants so that we can judge whether potato phosphorylase is typical. The apparent lack of regulatory properties of the potato phosphorylase, as compared with muscle phosphorylase, is perhaps not surprising if we compare potato metabolism with the need for a rapid and sensitive control of sugar level in mammals. Although data from plants other than potato is sparse, some of it suggests that some starch phosphorylases from plants are not as devoid of regulatory properties as the enzyme from potatoes seems to be. Tsai and Nelson[58,59] have described four forms of phosphorylase from maize endosperm. To varying degrees, these were found to be inhibited by purine and pyrimidine nucleotides. Frederick[60] found two electrophoretically distinct starch phosphorylases in *Oscillatoria* and *Spirogyra* and provided evidence that one of the forms from *Oscillatoria* needed AMP for activity.

3.3.1.5 Debranching enzymes

The enzymic cleavage of α-(1→6)-bonds in starch and glycogen has been reviewed recently[61]. Our understanding of this process in plants stems from the observation that extracts of potato and of broad bean (*Vicia faba*) catalysed the hydrolysis of α-(1→6)-bonds in amylopectin, amylopectin β-limit dextrin, and oligosaccharides. This activity was called 'R-enzyme'. Subsequent studies of 'R-enzyme' led to the view that the preparations contained two debranching enzymes; one that acted on amylopectin and its β-limit dextrin but not on oligosaccharide α-limit dextrins; and one with the reverse specificity. More recently purer preparations of 'R-enzyme' from potatoes have been shown to hydrolyse α-(1→6)-bonds in amylopectin and in both its α- and β-limit dextrins. Dilution of the enzyme caused loss of ability to attack amylopectin. Bacterial pullulanase, known to be a single protein, behaved in the same way[62]. Lee and Whelan[61] argue that the original 'R-enzyme' is not two enzymes of differing specificity but a single enzyme capable of debranching both large and small substrates. They argue that the enzyme is so similar to bacterial pullulanase that it should be called plant pullulanase. Manners and Yellowlees[63] remain unconvinced as they have purified an enzyme from germinating barley that attacked the α-(1→6)-bonds in oligosaccharides and in amylopectin β-limit dextrins but not in amylopectin itself, even at high concentrations of enzyme. Whichever view finally prevails, it is clear that plants possess appreciable ability to hydrolyse the α-(1→6)-bonds in starch.

3.3.2 Starch breakdown *in vivo*

The above enzymes may not be the only ones present in plants that can catalyse starch breakdown, but collectively they are capable of catalysing considerable breakdown of both amylose and amylopectin *in vivo*. Plants do not appear to have any means of conserving the energy of the α-(1→6)-bonds in starch but considerable conservation of the energy of the α-(1→4)-bonds could be achieved if starch breakdown were predominantly phosphorylytic. The general roles of the above enzymes in starch metabolism have not yet been established but considerable progress has been made in understanding their roles in a few specialised examples. These are the germinating seeds of barley (*Hordeum vulgare*), rice (*Oryza sativa*) and peas (*Pisum sativum*). The main method of investigation has been comparison of changes in the rates of starch breakdown with changes in the activities of enzymes in plant extracts. The difficulties of measuring enzyme activity in plant tissues must be borne in mind in interpreting these results. This is especially true for starch phosphorylase as this is not easy to array in crude extracts[64]. It is known to be readily inhibited by naturally-occurring phenols[65], and Tsai and Nelson[59] have reported that there are natural inhibitors of phosphorylase in extracts of maize. Further, appreciable and variable amounts of tannins have been demonstrated in extracts of cereal seeds[66].

3.3.2.1 Starch breakdown in cereal seeds

Most of the significant observations have been made with barley or rice. Starch breakdown is slow at the start of germination, but after an initial lag proceeds rapidly and linearly (Table 3.1). α-Amylase activity in extracts of barley[67] and rice[68] seeds is very low, rises strikingly during starch breakdown

Table 3.1 Activities of enzymes that can breakdown starch in germinating seeds. The rates were estimated for the period of rapid starch breakdown from data in the papers quoted. The values represent mg of starch broken down per hour by single grains of barley and rice or by two cotyledons of pea.

Seed	*Barley*	*Rice*	*Pea*
Starch breakdown	0.03[67]	0.1[68]	0.59[81]
α-Amylase	34.4[67]	31.8[68]	19.0[82]
β-Amylase	11.4[25]	120[70]	Low activity reported[48]
Starch phosphorylase	—	0.09[68]	14.6[81]

and then falls when the starch has disappeared. There is conclusive and exemplary evidence that the increased activity in barley is due to synthesis of the enzyme[69]. This is probably so in rice as well because the changes in activity are accompanied by changes in the patterns on zymograms and are prevented by cycloheximide[70]. The maximum activities of α-amylase found during the germination of barley and rice are very high and are much greater than the observed rates of starch breakdown (Table 3.1). In both barley[67] and rice[68] the peak of α-amylase activity coincides with a peak in the content of malto-oligosaccharides and glucose. In rice this latter peak also coincides with a dramatic increase in maltase activity[71]. There is some evidence that maltase activity increases during the germination of barley[72] and *Avena fatua*[73].

The production of α-amylase during the germination of barley has been studied intensively. The enzyme is synthesised in and secreted by the aleurone layer and the overall process is dependent upon gibberellin[74]. There are two reports that the secretion can be enhanced by cyclic AMP but neither establishes that the enhancement was due specifically to the cyclic AMP[75,76]. Two recent studies of the location of the enzyme have given contrasting results. Jones[77] has argued that all of the α-amylase in homogenates of aleurone layers of barley is in the soluble fraction and that the enzyme is released from the cytoplasm without the involvement of a discrete organelle. Gibson and Paleg[78] found that at least half of the α-amylase in extracts of wheat aleurone layers was readily sedimentable and concluded that the enzyme was within a membrane-bound vesicle, the lysosome, *in vivo*. Failure to sediment an enzyme is not proof that it is soluble. In this connexion it is important to note that the technique used by Jones to prepare homogenates gave the lowest yield of particulate enzyme when compared with other methods by Gibson and Paleg. On the other hand acceptance of the view that α-amylase is located in the lysosomes of aleurone cells must await more definitive biochemical and structural characterisation of the sediments obtained by Gibson and Paleg.

The activity of free β-amylase in extracts of barley[25] and rice[70] rises during germination. The increases coincide with starch breakdown. The relative increase in activity found during germination is much smaller than that found with α-amylase. For rice the evidence indicates a tenfold rise in β-amylase activity and up to a 200-fold rise in α-amylase activity[70]. β-Amylase activity during germination is generally lower than that of α-amylase but still appreciably higher than the observed rates of starch breakdown (Table 3.1). The increase in β-amylase activity that occurs during the germination of barley is almost entirely due to the release of latent activity present in the ungerminated seed. There is evidence that this process is accelerated by gibberellin but we do not know whether this is a direct effect or an indirect effect resulting from some action of gibberellin that is far removed from the release of β-amylase[25]. Evidence that the increased activity of β-amylase is not due to protein synthesis is provided by the observation that germinating seeds of wheat incorporated [^{14}C]lysine into α-amylase but not into β-amylase[41].

Very much less data about the activity of phosphorylase during cereal germination is available. Data from rice conflict as to whether any increase in phosphorylase activity occurs during germination[68,70]. Perhaps the most significant feature of these results is that the measured activities of starch phosphorylase during germination are all very much lower than the observed activities of either α- or β-amylase (Table 3.1). There appear to be even fewer studies of the role of 'R-enzyme' during normal germination but there is evidence that the enzyme functions in the production of fermentable sugars in malt[79]. In addition there is evidence that a substantial increase in the activity of 'R-enzyme' occurs during the germination of rice[70].

There is evidence that α-amylase, but not β-amylase, can attack intact starch grains[80]. This observation, the dominance of α-amylase activity in germinating cereals, and the correlation between the fall in starch and the rise in α-amylase and in the content of glucose and malto-oligosaccharides, make it almost certain that α-amylase initiates and mediates a considerable proportion of starch breakdown in cereal grains. β-Amylase is also likely to be involved and its main role may be hydrolysis of the shorter α-(1→4)-glucans produced by the action of α-amylase. It is probable that the α-(1→6)-bonds are broken by the debranching enzyme. In addition, the behaviour of maltase during germination indicates that the maltose and malto-oligosaccharides formed by amylase and the debranching enzyme are next hydrolysed to glucose by maltase. Finally, even if we make a generous allowance for incomplete recovery of starch phosphorylase, the available data strongly indicate that, quantitatively, its role in starch breakdown in cereal seeds is not very significant. Since such starch breakdown is essentially an extracellular process, the predominance of hydrolysis, yielding readily absorbed glucose, over phosphorylysis, yielding the less easily absorbed phosphate ester, is perhaps expected.

3.3.2.2 Starch breakdown in pea seeds

Comparison of starch breakdown in pea seeds with that in cereals is important because the process is intracellular in peas. During the germination of peas there is an initial slow phase of starch breakdown that is succeeded by a very rapid phase[81]. Swain and Dekker[82, 83] showed that α-amylase activity in pea seeds was low, that it increased on germination and that the phase of rapid starch breakdown coincided with a dramatic increase in α-amylase activity. They present good evidence that their measurements represent the maximum catalytic activities of the enzyme, and additional evidence that the increase in activity depended upon protein synthesis. This latter conclusion is supported by the work of Juliano and Varner[81]. The activity of α-amylase in germinating peas is well in excess of that needed to support the observed rates of starch breakdown (Table 3.1). β-Amylase is present in pea cotyledons. The available evidence indicates that during germination β-amylase activity does not alter and is low compared to α-amylase activity in the cotyledons and to β-amylase activity in other parts of the seedling[48]. The activity of starch phosphorylase in pea cotyledons rises during germination to a value that is comparable to that achieved by α-amylase[48, 81] (Table 3.1). Changes in the viscosity of amylopectin during the rapid decline in starch indicate that α-amylase is mainly responsible for the initial breakdown of starch in pea seeds[81]. Thus for peas, the available data indicate that α-amylase plays a dominant role in, at least, the initial steps of starch breakdown during germination. The high activities of phosphorylase and low activities of β-amylase suggest that phosphorylase may make significant contributions to the breakdown of the products of α-amylase activity.

There is a clear need to extend studies of starch breakdown to all types of situation in which it occurs in plants. We lack information about starch breakdown in leaves and in cells that are not specialised for starch storage. From the present data it is perhaps worthwhile making the following tentative generalisations as a basis for further study. α-Amylase is implicated in all examples of starch breakdown that have been studied in detail. The enzyme is extremely widely distributed and its presence is closely correlated with the presence of starch[84]. In addition it appears to be the only enzyme that has been conclusively shown to attack the α-(1→4)-bonds in intact starch granules. Thus it is possible that α-amylase is always involved in the initial stages of starch breakdown. The initial products of α-amylase activity may be broken down by hydrolysis by means of α- and β-amylases and maltase, or by phosphorylysis, or by some combination of hydrolysis and phosphorylysis. The hydrolytic route may predominate where breakdown is extracellular and the phosphorylytic mechanism where breakdown is intracellular.

3.3.2.3 Conversion of starch to sucrose

The products of starch breakdown may be used *in situ* or translocated. The latter usually involves conversion to sucrose and we might expect there to be a close relationship between starch breakdown and sucrose synthesis. This question has been studied successfully in seeds of cereals. It has been shown that scutella contain considerable amounts of sucrose and can readily convert glucose to sucrose[85]. Sucrose is the main sugar present in rice scutellum at that point in germination when glucose, maltose and malto-oligosaccharides predominate in the endosperm. Also, rice scutella at this stage have been shown to contain sucrose phosphate synthetase (EC 2.4.1.14) activity of the order needed to cope with the products of starch breakdown[71]. Finally, Chen and Varner[86] have demonstrated that the breakage of dormancy in seeds of *Avena fatua* is closely associated with the development of the ability to metabolise maltose to sucrose. They also show that the distribution of label from [^{14}C]maltose, injected into the endosperm during germination, was consistent with the conversion of maltose to sucrose in the scutellum followed by export of the sucrose to the axis.

Thus it is almost certain that during the germination of cereals starch is mainly broken down to glucose that is converted to sucrose in the scutellum and then translocated to the rest of the seedling. The events that occur where starch is stored intracellularly have not been thoroughly investigated, and the immediate fate of the products of starch breakdown is not known. It is interesting to note that Swain and Dekker[48] report that most of the β-amylase activity was in the root and axis of pea seedlings and that they considered the possibility that malto-oligosaccharides were exported from the cotyledons to the root and axis.

3.4 SUCROSE BREAKDOWN

It is important to understand the mechanism of sucrose breakdown in plants and the extent to which regulation of such breakdown contributes to the determination of the sucrose content of plant tissues. Sucrose is the major soluble storage carbohydrate of higher plants and the major form in which carbon is translocated[87]. Some aspects of the relationship between the properties of sucrose and its specific roles in plant metabolism have been discussed by Arnold[88]. In addition to Arnold's points it is worth noting that sugar alcohols[89] and oligosaccharides[90] like raffinose and stachyose sometimes fulfil the role of sucrose in both storage and translocation in some plants. In fungi the available evidence indicates that trehalose and sugar alcohols are the main soluble storage carbohydrates[89]. In insects trehalose is the major sugar[91]. Thus it appears that one of the important properties of soluble carbohydrates that are accumulated to any great extent in cells is that they should be non-reducing.

3.4.1 Enzymes that break down sucrose

Higher plants are known to contain two types of enzyme, invertase and sucrose synthetase, that can catalyse the breakdown of sucrose. The invertases may be divided into acid invertases, and alkaline or neutral invertases. There are claims that sucrose phosphorylase (EC 2.4.1.7) is present in higher plants[92,93]. These claims are not convincing, as evidence for the sucrose synthesis *in vitro* is limited to that obtained after incubations of 8–24 h, and the likelihood of microbial contamination is considerable. Careful attempts to confirm these claims were unsuccessful[94]. At the moment it may be argued that sucrose phosphorylase has not been demonstrated in any higher plant and it seems likely that it will prove to be an enzyme characteristic of prokaryotic cells only.

3.4.1.1 Acid invertase

Acid invertase activity is widespread in plants. The enzyme has not been completely purified but there have been a number of studies of partially purified preparations[95,96]. The available evidence indicates that the plant enzyme is a β-fructofuranosidase. The pH optimum varies with the source of enzyme but is in the range pH 5.3–4.0. The lack of pure preparations means that we do not know whether any of the enzyme is associated with carbohydrate in the manner of the external invertase of yeast[97].

One of the most investigated aspects of acid invertase in plants is its location in the cell. Exhaustively washed preparations of plant cell walls frequently contain a very high proportion of the tissue's acid invertase[98]. Initial, but determined, attempts to free the enzyme from the cell-wall fraction were unsuccessful[99] and at least some of the enzyme was regarded as being attached to the cell wall *in vivo*. Subsequent work has cast doubt on the validity of conclusions based on cell fractionation alone. Most, but not all, of the invertase in cell-wall preparations of grapes (*Vitis vinifera*) was released by treatment with borate and there is convincing evidence that the presence of acid invertase in these preparations was due to the formation of protein–tannin or protein–tannin–cell wall complexes during extraction[100]. Extraction of the storage tissue of carrot (*Daucus carota*) with buffers of acid pH led to the inclusion of most of the acid invertase in the cell-wall fractions. Extraction with neutral or alkaline buffers gave most of the activity in the soluble fraction. This effect was readily reversible[16]. Recently this phenomenon has been confirmed by Little and Edelman[98] who have shown that the major factor involved in freeing acid invertase from cell-wall preparations of storage tissue of Jerusalem artichoke (*Helianthus tuberosus*) is the ionic strength of the extraction medium rather than the pH. Their results indicate that acid invertase can bind to the cell-wall fraction by salt linkages.

In respect of the location of acid invertase *in vivo*, the essential feature of the above results is that much, but not all, of the acid invertase, previously held to be indissolubly bound to the cell wall, can be freed by relatively simple techniques. Thus cell fractionation is not a reliable guide to the location of acid invertase *in vivo*. The most that can be said of these studies is that in nearly all instances some of the acid invertase was found to be readily soluble and some successfully resisted all attempts to free it from the cell-wall preparation. The data are consistent with, but do not prove, a dual location of acid invertase in plant cells.

For sugar cane (*Saccharum officinarum*) there is good supplementary evidence for a dual location of acid invertase. The pH optima and K_m of the activities in cell-wall preparations of immature[94] and mature[101] storage tissue differ from those of the activities in the soluble fractions. Although association of an enzyme with the cell wall may change its properties, the differences in the mature tissue, at least, are so great that they are unlikely to be artefacts. In addition there is evidence that sucrose uptake depends upon hydrolysis in the free space (discussed in Section 3.4.1.1) and there is a close relationship between sugar content and soluble acid invertase activity in sugar cane. Taken as a whole the available data point convincingly to the presence of intracellular and free-space acid invertase in sugar cane storage tissue.

Some evidence for a dual location of acid invertase in other plants is provided by measurements of sucrose hydrolysis by intact tissues. A comparison is made between sucrose hydrolysis by pieces of untreated tissues and by replicate pieces that have been treated with ethyl acetate[102]. It is argued that the first measurement represents free-space invertase and the second represents total invertase. This method is likely to overestimate free-space activity because sucrose could enter the cell, be hydrolysed within the plasmalemma, and then the products of hydrolysis could leak out into the free space. Ethyl acetate treatment has been shown to increase sucrose hydrolysis by storage tissues of carrot, potato and red beet[103], and by different regions of the root of peas[104]. The qualitative agreement between these results and data from cell fractionation indicates that acid invertase may be present both in the free space and within the plasmalemma in these tissues. The precise distribution cannot be determined as none of the available methods for measuring how much activity is present in the free space are satisfactory. In carrot tissue cultures some of the enzyme, at least, is likely to be within the plasmalemma because the activity of acid invertase in these cultures is high[105] and yet there is conclusive evidence that sucrose can escape hydrolysis during uptake[106].

3.4.1.2 *Alkaline invertase*

Invertase with optimum activity in the range pH 7.0–7.8 has been demonstrated in enough plants to suggest that it is generally distributed[16, 94, 104, 107]. The evidence that alkaline invertase is distinct from acid invertase is that the two activities have been separated and shown to have different properties and to vary independently during development. The alkaline invertase from broad bean appears to be a β-fructofuranosidase[108]. Alkaline invertase from plants has not been purified. During the differentiation of the cells in pea roots, the ratio of alkaline invertase activity to readily extractable protein remains constant[104]. This observation, the pH optimum and the fact that the activity is always recovered exclusively in the soluble fraction of homogenates, suggest that alkaline invertase is located in the cytoplasm.

3.4.1.3 *Sucrose synthetase*

Sucrose synthetase (EC 2.4.1.13) catalyses the reaction:

$$\text{Sucrose} + \text{Nucleoside diphosphate} \rightleftharpoons \text{Nucleoside diphosphoglucose} + \text{Fructose}$$

The enzyme is widely distributed in plants and has been purified from *Phaseolus aureus*[109, 110]. Although the equilibrium favours sucrose synthesis, the enzyme is reversible and could catalyse the synthesis of nucleoside diphosphoglucose from sucrose. The enzyme from *Phaseolus aureus* has a broad pH optimum with a maximum at pH 7.8. The nucleoside in the above equation may be uridine, adenine, thymidine, cytosine or guanidine. The Michaelis constants for all five possible nucleoside diphosphates are said to be similar but the V_{max} of the forward reaction is markedly higher when UDP is the substrate[110]. In the reverse direction the Michaelis constants for the nucleoside diphosphate glucoses are similar except that the K_m for UDP–glucose is ten times smaller than that for the others. In addition UDP–glucose has been shown to inhibit sucrose synthesis from each of the other nucleoside diphosphoglucoses[109]. A number of compounds of physiological importance can alter the activity of sucrose synthetase but, as yet, there is no evidence that any of these effects are important *in vivo*[110]. The location of the enzyme in the cell is not known, but it is of interest that the pure enzyme appears as a particle of molecular weight 1×10^6 and a density that suggests a lipid content as high as 36%[109].

3.4.2 Sucrose breakdown *in vivo*

At the moment the investigation of sucrose breakdown in plants is dominated by the results of work with sugar cane[111]. It is important to bear in mind that cultivated varieties of sugar cane are selected and distinguished from other plants by their ability to store sucrose. Thus sucrose metabolism in sugar cane may differ, in some respects, from that in other plants. Similarly we should realise that the fact that sucrose metabolism in a particular plant differs from that in sugar cane does not invalidate schemes proposed for sugar cane. Acid invertase, inside and outside the plasmalemma, alkaline invertase, and sucrose synthetase could all contribute to sucrose breakdown *in vitro*. Possible roles for each enzyme are discussed below.

3.4.2.1 Acid invertase in the free space

In immature storage tissue of sugar cane the labelling of intracellular sucrose shows that accumulation from exogenous sucrose involves hydrolysis[112]. The effects of inhibitors, of varying the pH[112] and of anti-invertase antiserum[113] collectively show that this accumulation depends upon hydrolysis in the free space. Studies with mature storage tissue of sugar cane show that movement of exogenous sucrose into the cells is at least partially dependent upon sucrose hydrolysis and there is evidence that some of this hydrolysis occurs in the free space[101]. In sugar cane the products of photosynthesis are translocated almost exclusively as sucrose[114] and there appears to be a considerable level of sucrose in the free space of storage tissue[115]. Taken together these experiments provide strong support for the view that acid invertase in the free space of sugar cane storage tissue plays an important role in sucrose uptake. The quantitative importance of this role is likely to depend upon the extent to which the movement of sucrose through the free space is the main means of transfer of carbon from the phloem to the storage tissue.

In considering possible roles for acid invertase in the free space of tissues other than sugar cane, we should distinguish between whether hydrolysis of exogenous sucrose occurs during uptake, and whether such hydrolysis is a prerequisite for uptake. Studies similar to those of Sacher, Hatch and Glasziou[112] on sugar cane have been reported for tissues of bean[116] (*Phaseolus vulgaris*), potato tuber[117], castor bean (*Ricinus communis*) cotyledons[118] and tissue cultures of carrot[106]. The results for each tissue show that significant uptake of sucrose can occur without prior hydrolysis in the free space. Thus hydrolysis in the free space is not a general prerequisite for sucrose uptake by plant cells.

The function of free-space acid invertase in the tissues considered in the last paragraph is not obvious. One possibility is that free-space invertase contributes to the regulation of the intercellular concentration of sucrose. This could be important in differentiation as there is evidence that provision of sucrose can affect differentiation in plants[119]. In this field, perhaps the most important results are those of Jeffs and Northcote[120, 121] who showed that the differentiation of phloem in cultures of *Phaseolus vulgaris* was dependent upon a supply of sucrose or another α-glucosyl disaccharide. Glucose or fructose would not substitute for sucrose. More recently Wright and Northcote[122] have shown that phloem formation in cultures of *Acer pseudoplatanus* can be induced by glucose as readily as by sucrose. They suggest that differentiation of phloem will occur on any sugar that supports growth well enough.

The difference between *Phaseolus* and *Acer* cultures is explained by suggesting that sucrose is a superior carbon source to hexose for *Phaseolus* but not for *Acer*. Irrespective of whether sucrose exerts its effects as a carbon source or in a manner comparable to a hormone, the results of Jeffs and Northcote show that under some circumstances regulation of the sucrose content of the free-space by acid invertase located there could be important in differentiation. Concentration of sucrose in one type of cell, for example the phloem, and the localisation of free-space acid invertase in a distant region of the surrounding tissue could create a gradient of the type envisaged as being important in morphogenesis[123,124]. It is interesting to note that sucrose is concentrated in the stele in pea roots and that there is evidence that the free-space acid invertase activity is lower in the stele than in the cortex[104]. In addition it is important to note that the ability of exogenous sucrose to suppress chlorophyll synthesis in carrot tissue cultures is confined to cultures with very low free-space acid invertase activity[106,125].

3.4.2.2 *Intracellular acid invertase*

It is not possible to decide upon the function of intracellular acid invertase activity until we can measure how much of the total acid invertase activity is intracellular. High activity of acid invertase correlates quite closely with rapid expansion growth in internodes of sugar cane[126], in epicotyls of lentils[127] and peas[128], in petals of *Ipomoea*[129], and in developing roots of carrots[16] and peas[104]. The marked increase in metabolism that occurs when thin slices of storage tissue are incubated under physiological conditions is accompanied by striking rises in acid invertase activity[16]. The activity of the enzyme also rises as hexose accumulates during the ripening of grapes[130]. Only in sugar cane, and less certainly in grapes and pea roots, can we argue that the above measurements refer to intracellular acid invertase. None the less, the above data show that high acid invertase activity, some of which may well be intracellular, is characteristic of plant tissues in which there is a marked need for hexose production from stored or from recently translocated sucrose. In nearly all of the papers quoted the activity of acid invertase can be related to the sucrose content of the tissue. High activity of acid invertase correlates well with a low content of sucrose. This is particularly well shown by the developmental studies. The fall in sucrose in incubated slices of storage tissue coincides with the rise in acid invertase activity[16]. In sugar cane[126] and carrot roots[16] accumulation of large amounts of sucrose occurs only when the high acid invertase activity, characteristic of young rapidly growing tissue, falls. This point is emphasised by comparing different species and varieties of sugar cane. Those types in which little sucrose is stored do not show the fall in acid invertase activity that occurs during the maturation of the varieties that accumulate large quantities of sucrose[126].

Measurements of alkaline invertase and sucrose synthetase are available for only a few of the tissues that have been shown to have high acid invertase activity. Such data as there is shows that when acid invertase activity is high, the activities of the other two enzymes are generally comparatively low (Table 3.2). In the specific instances mentioned in the last paragraph the peak activities of acid invertase are very high and could support considerable rates of sucrose breakdown. Thus it seems likely that acid invertase makes a major, if not dominant, contribution to sucrose breakdown in the above instances. The general role of the enzyme may be the catalysis of sucrose breakdown where there is a marked need for hexose. This hypothesis accounts for the high activities of acid invertase in rapidly growing cells, in slices of storage tissue that are undergoing a sudden stimulation of metabolism and in ripening grapes. The pH optimum of the enzyme, and the inverse relationship between its activity and sucrose content, prompt the speculation that intracellular acid invertase is located in the storage compartment. If this is so then it is easy to see why cells with high acid invertase activity contain little sucrose. Indeed high intracellular acid invertase activity may be a mechanism that prevents a cell from storing sucrose by diverting endogenous and absorbed sucrose to satisfy pressing demands for hexose.

Table 3.2 Activities of enzymes that can breakdown sucrose in plant tissues. The values were calculated from data in the papers quoted.

	Enzyme activity (nmol sucrose metabolised h^{-1} g^{-1} fresh wt)		
Tissue	*Acid invertase*	*Alkaline invertase*	*Sucrose synthetase*
Immature stem of sugar cane	1300[114]	<2[114]	26[94]
Mature stem of sugar cane	<2[114]	90[114]	50[101]
Developing cotyledons of *Vicia faba*	3[134]	7[134]	260[134]
Cortex from tip of pea root	455[104]	96[104]	86[133]
Stele from tip of pea root	136[104]	343[104]	440[133]

Present views on the role of acid invertase in sucrose metabolism have led to the study of the mechanism whereby plants vary the maximum catalytic activity of this enzyme. Almost all the useful data have been obtained from experiments with sugar cane. This work has been reviewed[131] and a comprehensive hypothesis has been put forward to explain the regulation of the amount of intracellular acid invertase in sugar cane. The central feature of this hypothesis is that glucose present in the metabolic compartment of the cell is held to be able to repress the synthesis of intracellular acid invertase. The evidence has been obtained mainly from measurements of enzyme activity in extracts of tissues that have been subjected to treatment with combinations of sugars, growth substances, and inhibitors of protein and RNA synthesis. The results are consistent with the hypothesis but conclusive proof must await satisfaction of the points made in Section 3.2.2. We require proof of the specificity of the inhibitors, and definitive evidence that the changes in enzyme activity always represent synthesis or breakdown of the enzyme. Acid invertase in tissue cultures and storage tissue of carrots[105] and in lentil (*Lens culinaris*) epicotyls[127] was not affected by incubation in glucose. This may indicate a different control mechanism from that in sugar cane. Alternatively, the latter results could be explained by arguing that variation in exogenous hexose does not readily alter the concentration of glucose in the metabolic compartments of carrot and lentil tissue.

3.4.2.3 Alkaline invertase

Variation of alkaline invertase during development has been investigated in sugar cane storage tissue[126] and in the roots of carrots[16] and peas[104]. The results are not sufficiently definitive to reveal the role of this enzyme. In the above instances alkaline invertase activity was most marked in tissues that had low activity of acid invertase, an appreciable content of sucrose, and a definite, but not enormous, demand for hexose. Alkaline invertase has not been shown to attain the high values often found for acid invertase (Table 3.2). In respect of sugar cane, Hawker and Hatch[101] suggested that the alkaline invertase characteristic of mature storage tissue fulfilled the role played by acid invertase in immature storage tissue. In general terms of hexose production this is very likely. However, this explanation does not really explain the differences between alkaline and acid invertases and the elaborate variation in their relative activities that has been observed during the development of sugar cane, carrot and pea tissues.

The data available at present for alkaline invertase can be accommodated within the hypothesis put forward for acid invertase. This hypothesis holds that intracellular acid invertase activity is low in cells that are storing appreciable amounts of sucrose. These are often the cells with the highest activities of alkaline invertase. If, as seems likely, alkaline invertase is located in the cytoplasm, then its role could be to catalyse sucrose breakdown in the cytoplasm of cells that store sucrose. The separation of the stored sucrose from the cytoplasmic alkaline invertase would permit considerable sucrose storage despite the presence of an irreversible invertase. At the same time the cell would still possess the ability to hydrolyse sucrose in order to meet the demands for hexose. Thus the ability to synthesise two different invertases, each conceivably confined to a particular compartment, may permit the cell to regulate sucrose storage independently from sucrose breakdown.

3.4.2.4 Sucrose synthetase

The properties of sucrose synthetase suggest that it could be important in catalysing the formation of sugar nucleotides from sucrose. Structural and storage polysaccharides form a considerable proportion of the plant cell. Thus a direct conversion of sucrose to sugar nucleotides could account for a significant fraction of sucrose breakdown. Sucrose synthetase appears to be generally distributed and there are no convincing reports of its absence from tissues in which appreciable polysaccharide synthesis occurs. There is evidence that sucrose synthetase activity is high in tissues in which there are heavy demands for sugar nucleotides for the synthesis of structural or storage polysaccharides. These measurements should be treated with caution because the enzyme is not easy to assay and appears to be very sensitive to inhibition by substances formed during the oxidation of phenolic compounds in plant extracts. There is evidence that most of the enzyme in the internodes of sugar cane is confined to the vascular tissue[132]. The activity of sucrose synthetase in the stele of young roots of peas is substantial, greater than that in the surrounding cortex, and comparable to the activities of the two invertases[133]. These results may reflect an association of high activity of sucrose synthetase and cell wall synthesis.

Hawker[134] measured the activity of sucrose synthetase in a range of tissues and found the highest activities in the developing cotyledons of broad bean and the developing endosperm of maize. These activities were high in comparison to those of the invertases and were capable of supporting considerable rates of starch synthesis. In another study[135] of the developing endosperm of maize it was shown that the onset of starch accumulation coincides with a fall in invertase activity and a substantial rise in sucrose synthetase activity. The activity of sucrose synthetase was well in excess of that required to support the highest rate of starch synthesis observed. There is evidence that the activity of sucrose synthetase in potato tubers declines as the sucrose content falls and the starch content rises[136]. Finally the activity of sucrose synthetase is much higher in those parts of the seedling of *Phaseolus aureus* that metabolise translocated sucrose than in the photosynthetic cells[137].

All the above results indicate that sucrose synthetase plays an important part in converting sucrose to sugar nucleotides. It is tempting to suggest that translocated sucrose is converted to sugar nucleotides in this way. Before we accept this view a number of questions must be answered. First, the relationship between sucrose synthetase activity and polysaccharide synthesis should be examined in a wider range of tissues to see if the correlation is general. Secondly, we need to know the extent to which sucrose from the phloem reaches the cytoplasm of non-photosynthetic cells as sucrose. At present we have very little knowledge of the form in which carbon moves from the phloem to the surrounding cells nor do we have any general understanding of either the mechanism or the pathway involved. Thirdly, we need more information about the relative roles of sucrose synthetase and alkaline invertase. Both of these enzymes may be present in appreciable amounts in the same tissue[133]. It is conceivable that the two enzymes are separated in the cell. It is likely that both structural[138] and storage[139] polysaccharides are formed within or on membrane systems. The high lipid content of purified sucrose synthetase suggests that the enzyme may be associated with such membrane systems *in vivo*. Separation of sucrose synthetase from invertase in this way might provide a means for the independent regulation of sucrose consumption in polysaccharide synthesis and respiration. A final point on compartmentation is that schemes for the overall conversion of sucrose to starch involve sucrose synthetase and the use of pyrophosphate, generated from UDPG, in the synthesis of ADPG[140]. This mechanism is easier to imagine if the whole process occurs within a compartment that would separate the pyrophosphate from pyrophosphatase.

3.5 HEXOSE OXIDATION

In higher plants only two pathways are known to catalyse the oxidation of the hexose produced by the breakdown of sucrose and starch. These are glycolysis and the pentose phosphate pathway. Additional pathways cannot be excluded yet but there is no convincing evidence for such pathways. The general features of the known pathways and the evidence for their operation in plants have been discussed[141, 142]. Thus I shall concentrate upon the relationship between the two pathways and their function.

3.5.1 Relationship between glycolysis and the pentose phosphate pathway

The two pathways are considered separately and then their relationship is discussed.

3.5.1.1 Glycolysis

There is enough evidence to support the view that glycolysis is universal in higher plants. The basic pathway is similar to that described for animal and microbial cells. The only aspect of glycolysis that has been shown to vary amongst plants is the mechanism of disposal of pyruvate under anaerobic conditions. It is generally held that glycolysis in plants under anaerobic conditions produces ethanol. This is true for many plants as alcohol dehydrogenase (EC 1.1.1.1) and the accumulation of ethanol under anaerobic conditions have been demonstrated in a wide range of species[143, 144]. Alcohol dehydrogenase has been partially purified from plants and some of its properties have been determined[145, 146]. The activity of this enzyme varies with the plant but is often comparable to that of the other glycolytic enzymes[144]. In some plants periods of anaerobiosis lead to marked increases in the activity found in extracts but we do not know whether these increases represent synthesis of the enzyme[147]. Lactate dehydrogenase and lactic acid accumulation have been demonstrated in a range of higher plants and in some instances must contribute to the metabolism of pyruvate under anaerobic conditions. Both lactate and alcohol dehydrogenases may be present in the same tissue although the activity of the latter generally predominates[148-150]. Recently the properties of lactate dehydrogenase from potato tubers have been described[151]. In addition to the above work, there is evidence that anaerobiosis in plants may lead to the formation of oxaloacetate from phosphoenolpyruvate and that the NADH formed in glycolysis can be oxidised by the reduction of this oxaloacetate to malate[149].

Despite the considerable capacity for fermentation shown by higher plants, it is sometimes argued that they only encounter anaerobiosis in the laboratory. The presence of so much alcohol dehydrogenase in plants indicates that this view is mistaken. Specific evidence that it is mistaken is provided by proof that fermentation, presumably caused by poor penetration of the seed coat by oxygen, occurs during germination[150, 152]. There is also proof of fermentation in plants growing under waterlogged conditions[153]. The studies with peas show that seeds may survive brief periods of anaerobiosis even when ethanol is produced and that the ethanol is metabolised via the tricarboxylic acid cycle when oxygen becomes available[152]. Crawford's[153] study of flood tolerance in plants suggests that prolonged production of ethanol is lethal. His work also provides strong support for the view that at least part of the mechanism of flood tolerance is an ability of the plant to form compounds other than ethanol when placed under anaerobic conditions.

3.5.1.2 Pentose phosphate pathway

Glucose 6-phosphate dehydrogenase (EC 1.1.1.49) and 6-phosphogluconate dehydrogenase (EC 1.1.1.44) have been demonstrated in many different plants. The patterns of $^{14}CO_2$ production from specifically labelled glucose supplied to a wide range of plants strongly indicate that a proportion of hexose oxidation proceeds via these two dehydrogenases. There is little doubt that the pentose phosphate pathway is a normal route of carbohydrate oxidation in plants. Despite this, we still do not know the precise reactions of this pathway. The essential problem is the discovery of the detailed fate of the ribulose 5-phosphate formed by the two dehydrogenases of the pathway.

Figure 3.1 is a common formulation of the pentose phosphate pathway. Recently this type of formulation has been challenged vigorously and an alternative scheme has been put forward on the basis of results obtained with liver cells[154, 155]. Perhaps the most important of these results is the evidence that the early labelling of the individual carbons of hexose 6-phosphates by [1-^{14}C]ribose and [2-^{14}C]glucose, supplied to liver cells for brief periods, is different from that predicted in Figure 3.1. At present the evidence that is

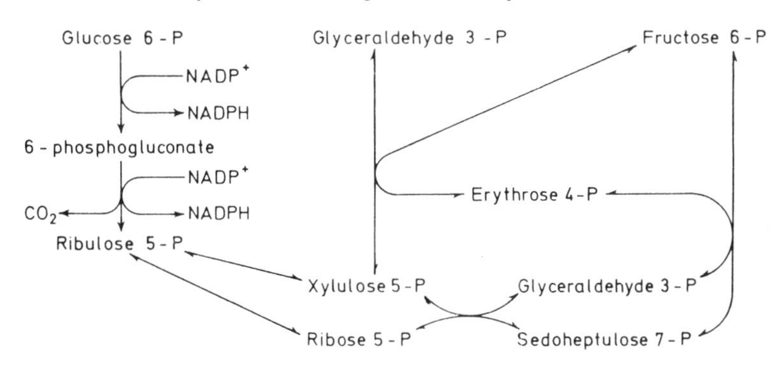

Figure 3.1 The pentose phosphate pathway

available for higher plants favours a scheme similar to that in Figure 3.1 rather than the new proposals.

The results of feeding experiments carried out with plants are more readily explained by Figure 3.1 than by the new hypothesis. The following specific instances of agreement between the labelling predicted by the scheme in Figure 3.1 and that found experimentally are stressed. First, extracts of peas metabolised labelled pentose phosphate to hexose phosphate with the expected labelling[156]. Secondly, and of greater significance, there are the results of experiments carried out with intact tissues. Specifically labelled pentose has been shown to give rise to the hexose units of sucrose[157] and of cell-wall polymers[158]. The labelling of these hexose units showed the pattern predicted by Figure 3.1. The labelling of ethanol and CO_2 by specifically labelled pentose supplied to plant tissues under anaerobic conditions indicates that the pentose was converted to hexose phosphate via the pathway in Figure 3.1[159]. In addition the labelling of hexose in tomato fruits supplied with [2-^{14}C]-glucose and [^{14}C]gluconate accords with Figure 3.1[160]. Finally, it is important to bear in mind that studies with one particular and specialised mammalian tissue do not form an adequate basis for generalisations about metabolic pathways in plants. This is especially true of a tissue like liver in which the results of short-term labelling experiments may be complicated by the occurrence of gluconeogenesis.

Overall, the evidence that plants can convert pentose phosphate to hexose phosphate and triose phosphate is overwhelming. Although the data available can be explained by the scheme in Figure 3.1 it must be borne in mind that the broad specificity and the ready reversibility of the enzymes involved in the interconversion of pentose and hexose phosphates will permit a variety of pathways that are consistent with the experimental results. Thus we cannot specify completely the reactions involved in the metabolism of pentose phosphate. At present it is convenient to distinguish between the oxidative reactions of the pentose phosphate pathway that lead from glucose 6-phosphate to ribulose 5-phosphate, and the non-oxidative reactions that catalyse the interconversion of pentose, hexose and triose phosphates. Until data to the contrary are obtained we should follow the advice of Davies[161] and regard the non-oxidative part of the pathway as a pool of substrates in dynamic equilibrium. Thus these reactions may be viewed as producing fructose 6-phosphate and glyceraldehyde 3-phosphate from ribulose 5-phosphate with the precise yield and stoichiometry depending upon the extent to which intermediates are removed for biosynthetic reactions such as phenylpropanoid synthesis.

3.5.1.3 Metabolism of the products of the pentose phosphate pathway

The fate of the glyceraldehyde 3-phosphate and fructose 6-phosphate formed in the pentose phosphate pathway is the crux of the relationship between the pathway and glycolysis. The pentose phosphate pathway is sometimes drawn as a cycle that catalyses the complete oxidation of glucose 6-phosphate independently of glycolysis and the tricarboxylic acid cycle. This requires the synthesis of fructose 6-phosphate from glyceraldehyde 3-phosphate and the complete recycling of fructose 6-phosphate through the pentose phosphate pathway. The available evidence indicates that this view of the pathway is incorrect, at least in respect of higher plants.

The patterns of $^{14}CO_2$ production from specifically labelled substrates suggest that there is not much recycling through the pentose phosphate pathway. In general, tissues that have an initial C_6/C_1 ratio well below unity are not characterised by a later phase in which the ratio rises above unity[162, 163]. Such a rise might be expected if there was extensive recycling of the glyceraldehyde 3-phosphate. Comparison of $^{14}CO_2$ production from [^{14}C]glucose with that from [^{14}C]pyruvate suggests that most of the pentose phosphate formed in the pathway is eventually metabolised to pyruvate via glycolysis[164]. This view is very strongly supported by the detailed distribution of label from [1-^{14}C]- and [6-^{14}C]-glucose supplied to carrot storage tissue[162, 164] and to different regions of the root of pea[165]. Finally, the distribution of label from [1-^{14}C]ribose, and [2-^{14}C]- and [6-^{14}C]-gluconate fed to tomato fruits also supports the view that the bulk of the pentose phosphate formed in that pathway is metabolised eventually to pyruvate by glycolysis[160].

It is important to note that schemes for recycling glyceraldehyde 3-phosphate through the pentose phosphate pathway assume the presence of fructose 1,6-diphosphatase (EC 3.1.3.11). The occurrence of this enzyme in plant cells that are neither photosynthetic nor gluconeogenic has received little attention. Two such tissues have been examined and the activities found were very low[166, 167]. An additional point is that provision of a fructose 1,6-diphosphatase for complete recycling in the pentose phosphate pathway could establish the possibility of a futile cycle between fructose 1,6-diphosphate and fructose 6-phosphate. In summary, all the available data indicate that the glyceraldehyde 3-phosphate formed in the pentose phosphate pathway is metabolised along with that formed in glycolysis.

The extent to which the fructose 6-phosphate formed in the pentose phosphate pathway undergoes recycling cannot be judged yet. Such fructose 6-phosphate could be metabolised by either phosphofructokinase (EC 2.7.1.11) or glucosephosphate isomerase (EC 5.3.1.9). In the latter instance the glucose 6-phosphate so formed could re-enter the pentose phosphate pathway or be converted to glucose 1-phosphate and thence to sugar nucleotides. Thus even where the hexose 6-phosphates are in complete equilibrium recycling is unlikely to be complete. In plant tissues in which there is a particularly active pentose phosphate pathway, the metabolism of specifically labelled glucose and fructose to CO_2 shows that the corresponding hexose 6-phosphates are not in complete equilibrium. The results strongly indicate that glucose 6-phosphate enters the pentose phosphate pathway more readily than does fructose 6-phosphate[168]. Similar results have been reported for animal tissues[169]. Thus it appears that recycling of fructose 6-phosphate through the pentose phosphate pathway is partially restricted in tissues where the pathway is particularly active. This conclusion has an important bearing on methods used to calculate the relative activities of the two pathways of carbohydrate metabolism. Some methods assume no recycling and others assume complete recycling. It appears that neither type of method can be applied to plants unless the degree of recycling is determined independently. The restriction on recycling could be due to the partial inhibition of glucosephosphate isomerase by intermediates of the pentose phosphate pathway. The enzyme from peas is inhibited by phosphogluconate[170], and the mammalian enzyme is inhibited by erythrose 4-phosphate[171] and by sedoheptulose 7-phosphate[172].

3.5.1.4 Location of pathways of carbohydrate oxidation

The intracellular location of the enzymes of the two pathways of carbohydrate oxidation is important in determining their relationship. A claim that the enzymes of the pentose phosphate pathway are within a glucose 6-phosphate oxidising particle has been made[173]. A more thorough investigation failed to substantiate this claim and showed that the enzymes were recovered in the soluble fraction of the cell even after careful fractionation[174].

Barker[175, 176] and his colleagues put forward carefully considered arguments in favour of the view that the glycolytic enzymes are located in a granule or a glycolytic structure. Barker's suggestion was offered as an explanation of the Pasteur Effect and was based, in part, on the effect of anaerobiosis on the levels of glycolytic intermediates *in vivo*. Two issues are involved here. The first is whether it is necessary to propose a glycolytic structure to explain Barker's results and the Pasteur Effect. The essential feature of the results that led Barker and his colleagues to reject the conventional explanation of the Pasteur Effect was the failure to detect a cross-over point between hexose 6-phosphate and fructose 1,6-diphosphate. The difficulties of measuring the concentration of glycolytic intermediates, discussed earlier in this review, were not all overcome in this work, and we cannot be sure that anaerobiosis did not lead to a fall in the concentration of fructose 6-phosphate in the vicinity of phosphofructokinase. There are substantial reasons for believing that negative results of the type obtained by Barker and his colleagues are not conclusive[177]. These arguments, the properties of phosphofructokinase from plants[178] and the changes in glycolytic intermediates in some plants[179, 180] suggest that allosteric regulation of phosphofructokinase is likely to play an important role in regulating glycolysis in plants. It does not yet seem necessary to propose a glycolytic structure specifically to explain the Pasteur Effect in plants.

Regardless of the result of the above argument, the question of the location and organisation of both the glycolytic enzymes and those of the pentose phosphate pathway remains as one of the most important gaps in our understanding of carbohydrate oxidation. As yet there is no direct evidence for any kind of structural organisation of the enzymes of either pathway in any plant. Conventional fractionation techniques leave the enzymes in the soluble fraction. It can be argued that it is unlikely that the enzymes and their substrates are randomly distributed throughout the cytoplasm and that some form of organisation, too fragile to resist current techniques of fractionation, exists. This need not be location on or within a membrane system but may merely take the form of a multi-enzyme complex. The question is of sufficient importance to warrant investigation with recently developed techniques for the gentle rupture and analysis of plant cells.

In conclusion the available data all point to there being a very close relationship between the two pathways of carbohydrate oxidation and they may be regarded as two different routes to triose phosphate as shown in Figure 3.2.

3.5.2 Roles of glycolysis and the pentose phosphate pathway

The significance of the presence in the same cell of two different routes from glucose 6-phosphate to triose phosphate has been discussed at length. The dominant idea, put forward initially by Kaplan and his colleagues[181], is that glycolysis followed by the tricarboxylic acid cycle forms NADH that is used predominantly in respiratory chain phosphorylation. In contrast the pentose phosphate pathway is seen as producing NADPH, which, because it is not readily oxidised via the respiratory chain, can supply the reducing equivalents needed for biosynthesis. Thus the two pathways are regarded as performing

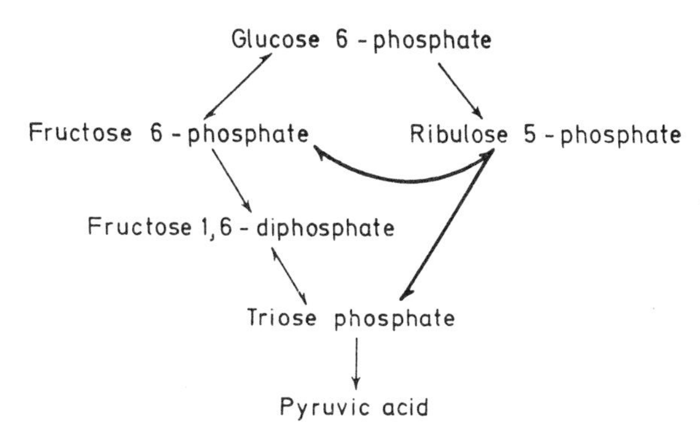

Figure 3.2 Relationship between glycolysis and the pentose phosphate pathway. The non-oxidative reactions of the pentose phosphate pathway are shown by the heavy lines

quite different functions that are largely determined by the properties of their characteristic co-enzymes. There is adequate evidence for this view in respect of animal and microbial cells[182, 183]. As yet we do not have enough data for us to decide whether this view is applicable to higher plants. The data that is available is discussed below in relation to the two major functions of carbohydrate oxidation, the provision of carbon compounds for biosynthesis, and the formation of ATP and reduced co-enzymes.

3.5.2.1 Provision of intermediates for biosynthesis

From Figure 3.2 it is clear that both pathways can provide carbon for all the biosynthetic routes that originate from triose phosphate or from compounds derived from triose phosphate. Thus any unique contribution from either pathway must come from the steps between glucose 6-phosphate and triose phosphate. For glycolysis this leaves only fructose 1,6-diphosphate and this is not known to be sequestered, as such, for biosynthesis. The pentose phosphate pathway could contribute pentose for the synthesis of pentan and nucleic acids and erythrose 4-phosphate for the synthesis of phenylpropanoid compounds. The possibility that the pentose phosphate pathway is required for the production of the pentose used in pentan synthesis is eliminated by the properties of the enzymes involved in pentan synthesis and the results of the feeding experiments[184]. The synthesis of the pentose in nucleic acids in plants has received very little attention. Work with animal and microbial cells, reviewed by Sable[185], shows that in cells, in which there is an appreciable flux through the oxidative steps of the pentose phosphate pathway, the pentose of the nucleic acids is formed from the pentose made in these oxidative steps[186]. However, in cells in which there is relatively little flow through the oxidative steps, the pentose for nucleic acid biosynthesis is formed from glycolytic intermediates via a reversal of the non-oxidative steps of the pentose phosphate pathway. Thus it appears that, whilst the oxidative steps of the pentose phosphate pathway can provide pentose for nucleic acid synthesis, they are not an absolute requirement for such synthesis.

Plants require erythrose 4-phosphate for the synthesis of shikhimic acid and the wide range of phenylpropanoid compounds derived therefrom[187]. The labelling of lignin in spruce by [^{14}C]glucose indicates that in this instance, at least, the erythrose 4-phosphate used in phenylpropanoid synthesis was derived in part from the product of the oxidative reactions of the pentose phosphate pathway[188]. There is some circumstantial evidence from other plant tissues that lignification is associated with the pentose phosphate pathway[189, 190]. All the above evidence of an association between lignification and the pentose phosphate pathway could merely be a reflection of the use of NADPH in lignin biosynthesis rather than an absolute requirement for the oxidative steps of the pathway as the sole source of erythrose 4-phosphate. Thus there is no proof, at present, that the complete pentose phosphate pathway is required for the provision of the erythrose 4-phosphate that is used in phenylpropanoid synthesis in plants. This compound could equally well be made from glycolytic intermediates via the non-oxidative steps of the pathway.

There is no convincing evidence that the complete pentose phosphate pathway in plants is essential for the provision of any intermediate that is used in biosynthesis. The fact that some compounds used in biosynthesis are formed in the oxidative pathway is probably incidental and due to a concomitant requirement for NADPH. The above considerations and comparative biochemistry suggest that this view will not be proved wrong when more data become available for plants. Overall, the significance of the co-existence of the two pathways of carbohydrate oxidation does not appear to be related to the provision of intermediates for biosynthesis.

3.5.2.2 Fate of NADH and NADPH formed by carbohydrate oxidation

This section considers the relative roles of glycolysis and the pentose phosphate pathway in providing reducing equivalents for biosynthesis and for ATP synthesis. The reactions of the pentose phosphate pathway do not generate ATP directly and the significance of this pathway is likely to be found in the type and fate of reduced co-enzyme that it produces.

The co-enzyme specificity of the two pathways is considered first. The two dehydrogenases of the pentose phosphate pathway from a wide range of plants have been shown to react readily with $NADP^+$[191]. However, there have been very few detailed studies of the co-enzyme specificity of these enzymes from plants. Both enzymes have been purified from sweet potatoes. The enzymes reduced $NADP^+$ but not NAD^+[192, 193]. Crude preparations of both dehydrogenases from bamboo (*Phyllostachys pubescens*) and of glucose 6-phosphate dehydrogenase from mung beans (*Phaseolus aureus*)[194] also showed the above specificity. There is only one claim that glucose 6-phosphate dehydrogenase from a plant can react with NAD^+[195]. This claim is based on the observation that the addition of glucose 6-phosphate to a crude extract of lettuce (*Lactuca sativa*) seeds led to the reduction of NAD^+. Acceptance of the view that this was due to reduction of NAD^+ by glucose 6-phosphate dehydrogenase must await studies with the purified enzyme. The available evidence strongly supports the view that the two dehydrogenases of the pentose phosphate pathway in plants are specific for NADP.

The co-enzyme specificity of glyceraldehyde 3-phosphate dehydrogenase in plant tissues has been studied in some detail. The enzyme from non-photosynthetic cells has been found to be specific for NAD[196, 197]. Studies with photosynthetic cells yielded preparations that reacted with NAD but this activity has not been separated from that with NADP[198]. The situation in photosynthetic cells remains unknown but there seems little doubt that the glycolytic enzyme is specific for NAD in non-photosynthetic cells. Studies of the co-enzyme specificity of the mitochondrial dehydrogenases involved in the tricarboxylic acid cycle in plants indicate that these are specific for NAD[197]. The available evidence strongly suggests that in plants the dehydrogenases of the pentose phosphate pathway differ in their co-enzyme specificity from those of glycolysis and the tricarboxylic acid cycle in the manner required by Kaplan's hypothesis. Since it is clear that plant mitochondria can couple the oxidation of NADH to ATP synthesis, it can be argued that the significance of the two pathways of carbohydrate oxidation lies in the manner in which the NADPH of the pentose phosphate pathway is oxidised.

A variety of mechanisms for the oxidation of NADPH in plants has been suggested. It is sometimes inferred that NADPH is oxidised via the respiratory chain[199]. There is hardly any evidence for this view and quite a lot against it. Mitochondria isolated from plants contain very little $NADP^+$ or NADPH[200]. Specific attempts to demonstrate NADPH oxidation by plant mitochondria have been unsuccessful[174, 201] although there is one exception[202]. The evidence available at present does not support the view that NADPH formed in the pentose phosphate pathway is primarily oxidised directly via the respiratory chain *in vivo*. A second possible route for NADPH oxidation is via a transhydrogenase to give NADH that is then oxidised by the respiratory chain. There is no evidence for this suggestion. The activities of such transhydrogenases in plant extracts are very low[197, 203, 228] and this route is probably not a major means of NADPH oxidation in plants. A third possibility is that NADPH oxidation in plants proceeds via ascorbic acid oxidase (EC 1.10.3.3) or polyphenolase (EC 1.10.3.2). Plants contain enzymes that can be arranged *in vitro* into sequences that could catalyse NADPH oxidation via the above oxidases[142]. None of these sequences has been shown to operate *in vivo* or to be capable of being coupled to ATP synthesis. The above routes of NADPH oxidation would not give the pentose phosphate pathway a role that was specific and distinct from that of glycolysis. The first two proposals imply the co-existence of a specific pathway of carbohydrate oxidation that is characterised by its ability to reduce $NADP^+$, and a mechanism that promptly equates NADPH with NADH. The third scheme implies that much of the reducing power generated in the pentose phosphate pathway is lost.

Comparative biochemistry suggests that the NADPH from the pentose phosphate pathway in plants is most likely to be oxidised in biosynthetic reactions that require reducing equivalents. Three lines of evidence suggest that the NADPH formed in the pentose phosphate pathway in plants supplies some, but not all, of the reducing equivalents needed for biosynthesis in plants. Firstly, a number of the enzymes that catalyse biosynthetic reactions in plants require NADPH[191, 199] rather than NADH. However, it appears that by no means all of the enzymes involved in reductive biosynthesis in plants show this co-enzyme specificity. A number of such enzymes will function with NADH as well as with NADPH or in preference to NADPH. This seems to be particularly true of the enzymes involved in the assimilation of inorganic nitrogen[204-206]. Although fatty acid synthesis from acetyl-CoA or malonyl-CoA by cell-free systems from plants requires NADPH, some such systems also need NADH[207, 208]. In addition there is fairly strong evidence that the reductive step in gluconeogenesis in marrow cotyledons requires NADH not NADPH[167].

The second type of evidence that NADPH from the pentose phosphate pathway is used in reductive biosynthesis comes from correlations between increased activity of the pathway and an increased need for reducing equivalents. This is well shown during lipogenesis in mammals[14] and during the assimilation of nitrate by yeast[209]. There is relatively little data of this type from higher plants. There is a general correlation between lipid synthesis and the pentose phosphate pathway in developing castor beans[203]. The general stimulation of biosynthesis that occurs when thin slices of carrot storage tissue are incubated under physiological conditions is accompanied by an increase in the activity of the pentose phosphate pathway relative to that of glycolysis[19]. Changes of the sort demonstrated in carrot almost certainly occur in other tissues[19]. A similar correlation between growth and the relative activity of the pentose phosphate pathway has been shown in tissue cultures of sycamore[210]. On the other hand there is data that strongly suggests that the relative activity of the pentose phosphate pathway increases as plant tissues mature[141, 190]. In these instances there is no obvious correlation between the activity of the pentose phosphate pathway and the total requirement for reducing equivalents. However, it is conceivable that only some of the reductive biosyntheses in a plant are dependent upon the pentose phosphate pathway and that these reactions are characteristic of maturation. The production of phenylpropanoid compounds in general and lignin in particular could fall into this category of reactions.

Neither of the above types of evidence proves that NADPH formed in the pentose phosphate pathway is used in reductive biosynthesis. More definitive conclusions might be drawn from experiments in which specifically labelled substrates have been used to generate NADP^{3}H and NAD^{3}H intracellularly, and in which the ability of the two labelled co-enzymes to transfer tritium to compounds formed in reductive biosyntheses has been compared. For example, we might expect [1-^{3}H]glucose to label preferentially compounds that derive their reducing equivalents from the pentose phosphate pathway. In contrast, compounds that obtain their reducing equivalents from NADH might be labelled preferentially by [1-^{3}H]ethanol or [2-^{3}H]glycerol. This seems a powerful technique, but the more it has been used the more pitfalls have been recognised. Two are of particular importance.

The bond energies of carbon–hydrogen and carbon–tritium differ markedly. Thus the reaction rates of the hydrogen isotopes may differ so that appreciable isotopic discrimination may occur with tritiated substrates. In assessing the role of the pentose phosphate pathway, it is important to remember that significant discrimination against [1-^{3}H]glucose has already been demonstrated in plants[207] and animals[211]. No discrimination against [3-^{3}H]glucose was found. The second pitfall in working with tritiated substrates is the danger that the tritium in the labelled compounds may exchange with protons. Considerable exchange from [2-^{3}H]glucose has been found in experiments with animal cells and it is clear that the extent of this exchange varies widely and in a complicated way[212]. Further, there is now convincing evidence that the hydrogen of cytoplasmic NADH can exchange extensively with protons[213]. In this last paper the authors present evidence that, of the sugars, only [3-^{3}H]glucose can give an accurate estimate of NADPH formation, and conclude justifiably that the use of tritium to evaluate the contribution of different pathways to the production of reducing equivalents is greatly restricted.

Tritiated substrates have been used to investigate the source of reducing equivalents in the hypocotyls of etiolated peas[214] and in the developing seed of castor bean[207]. In both tissues the results provide strong evidence that NADPH formed in the pentose phosphate pathway is used in lipid synthesis. The results also indicate that some of the reducing equivalents for lipid synthesis are provided by NADH. Agrawal and Canvin[207] used the detailed distribution of ^{14}C and ^{3}H from specifically labelled glucose to calculate that the pentose phosphate pathway accounted for only 20–27% of the reducing equivalents needed for fat synthesis in castor beans. They suggested that the remaining 75% is supplied by NADH. It is quite clear that both NADPH and NADH are needed for fat synthesis in the developing castor bean. The conclusion that 75% of the reducing equivalents needed by the castor bean are provided by NADH should be treated with reserve until our understanding of carbohydrate metabolism is sufficient to allow quantitative estimates of fluxes of carbon and hydrogen to be made with confidence. Agrawal and Canvin's estimates of the contribution of the pentose phosphate pathway are likely to be minimal. These estimates, and the observations that cell-free systems from castor beans need NADH for the conversion of oleic to ricinoleic acid and require NADH at three times the concentration of NADPH, do not establish that 75% of the reducing equivalents come from NADH.

All of the above lines of evidence agree in that they indicate that the pentose phosphate pathway in plants provides NADPH for reductive biosyntheses. As yet no other unique function for this pathway has been demonstrated in any plant. Therefore it is likely that the significance of the co-existence of glycolysis and the pentose phosphate pathway in plants lies in the ability of the latter to produce NADPH for biosynthesis. This conclusion does not mean that all the reducing equivalents required by plants are derived from the pentose phosphate pathway. Firstly, there may be alternative sources of NADPH. Secondly, the available data shows that some reductive biosyntheses need NADH. The relative importance of the different sources of reducing equivalents cannot be assessed at present. We need a fuller understanding of the relationship between biosynthesis and carbohydrate oxidation. This must be obtained for a wide range of compounds in a variety of different plants.

3.5.3 Metabolism of pyruvate

The major fate of the pyruvate produced by the two pathways of carbohydrate oxidation in plants is metabolism via the tricarboxylic cycle. The evidence for this view has been documented in detail[141, 142, 215, 216]. The above conclusion is based partly on the evidence for the widespread operation of the cycle in plants, partly on the fact that during normal respiration there is no accumulation of pyruvate or the products of its anaerobic metabolism, and partly on the detailed distribution of label from [^{14}C]glucose and [^{14}C]pyruvate. It is emphasised that some of the last type of evidence is sufficiently detailed to provide very strong evidence that the products of both glycolysis and the pentose phosphate pathway are converted to pyruvate that enters the tricarboxylic acid cycle[162, 164, 165].

Studies with thin slices of potato tubers led to the view that there might be instances in which plant respiration did not involve the tricarboxylic acid cycle[217]. When thin slices of potato are incubated in a moist atmosphere, a gradual increase in the rate of respiration occurs until, after 12–24 h, the rate reaches a value two–four times that of the freshly cut slice. This development of an increased rate of respiration is accompanied by marked physiological and biochemical changes that include the synthesis of nucleic acid and protein[218]. Laties has presented a great deal of evidence that the tricarboxylic acid cycle is virtually inactive in freshly cut slices but becomes very active during the development of the increased respiration[217, 219, 220]. This led Laties to suggest that the changes associated with the development of the increased rate of respiration stemmed from the increased activity of the tricarboxylic acid cycle. Freshly cut slices of potato yield mitochondria capable of oxidising intermediates of the tricarboxylic acid[221] and the lack of activity of the cycle in fresh slices was attributed to an inhibition of the cycle between the steps involving citrate and α-ketoglutarate[219]. Such inhibition was envisaged as a mechanism of respiratory control[217].

Studies of thin slices of other plant tissues have shown that increases in the rate of respiration, in the ability to metabolise exogenous substrates, and in protein synthesis, comparable to those found in potato, occur so widely that they are likely to be general[222-224]. These observations do not mean that the tricarboxylic cycle is inoperative in these tissues as it is now clear that the behaviour of freshly cut slices, particularly those of potato, is anomalous and does not represent the metabolism of the intact tissue. First, the development of the increased rate of respiration is not necessarily correlated with an absence of tricarboxylic cycle activity in freshly cut slices. The cycle has been shown to be active in freshly prepared slices of carrot storage tissue[224]. Secondly, there is convincing evidence that the respiration of intact potato tubers does involve the oxidation of carbohydrate[220] and the operation of the tricarboxylic acid cycle[225, 226]. It has been suggested that the low activity of the cycle in freshly cut slices of potato represents a temporary and anomalous condition resulting from cellular disorganisation caused by wounding and manipulation during the cutting of the slices[224]. Further evidence for this view has been provided lately[227]. There seems no reason to doubt the generally accepted view that under natural and aerobic conditions the tricarboxylic acid cycle is the normal means of pyruvate metabolism in plants.

References

1. Raven, J. A. (1972). *New Phytologist*, **71,** 227
2. Jackson, W. A. and Volk, R. J. (1970). *Annu. Rev. Plant Physiol.*, **21,** 385
3. Bieleski, R. L. (1963). *Biochim. Biophys. Acta*, **74,** 135
4. Bieleski, R. L. (1964). *Anal. Biochem.*, **9,** 431
5. Williamson, J. R. and Corkey, B. E. (1969). *Methods in Enzymology*, Vol. 13, 434 (J. M. Lowenstein, editor) (New York and London: Academic Press)
6. Bieleski, R. L. and Young, R. E. (1963). *Anal. Biochem.*, **6,** 54
7. Barker, J., Jakes, R., Solomos, T., Younis, M. E. and Isherwood, F. A. (1964). *J. Exp. Botany*, **15,** 284
8. Adams, P. B. and Rowan, K. S. (1970). *Plant Physiol.*, **45,** 490
9. Rowan, K. S. (1966). *Int. Rev. Cytol.*, **19,** 301
10. Pitman, M. G. (1963). *Aust. J. Biol. Sci.*, **16,** 647
11. Williamson, D. H., Lund, P. and Krebs, H. A. (1967). *Biochem. J.*, **103,** 514
12. Krebs, H. A. and Veech, R. L. (1970). *Pyridine Nucleotide-Dependent Dehydrogenases*, 413 (H. Sund, editor) (Berlin, Heidelberg and New York: Springer-Verlag)
13. Dounce, A. L., Tishkoff, G. H., Barnett, S. R. and Freer, R. H. (1950). *J. Gen. Physiol.*, **33,** 629
14. Gumaa, K. A., McLean, P. and Greenbaum, A. L. (1971). *Essays in Biochemistry*, Vol. 7, 39 (P. N. Campbell and F. Dickens, editors) (London and New York: Academic Press)
15. Andrews, T. J. and Hatch, M. D. (1971). *Phytochemistry*, **10,** 9
16. Ricardo, C. P. P. and ap Rees, T. (1970). *Phytochemistry*, **9,** 239
17. Anderson, J. W. (1968). *Phytochemistry*, **7,** 1973
18. Young, R. E. (1965). *Arch. Biochem. Biophys.*, **111,** 174
19. Ricardo, C. P. P. and ap Rees, T. (1972). *Phytochemistry*, **11,** 623
20. Glock, G. E. and McLean, P. (1953). *Biochem. J.*, **55,** 400
21. Fewson, C. A., Al-Hafidh, M. and Gibbs, M. (1962). *Plant Physiol.*, **37,** 402
22. Willard, J. M., Schulman, M. and Gibbs, M. (1965). *Nature* (*London*), **206,** 195
23. Pressey. R. (1968). *Plant Physiol.*, **43,** 1430
24. Pressey, R. and Shaw, R. (1966). *Plant Physiol.*, **41,** 1657
25. Shinke, R. and Mugibayashi, N. (1972). *Agr. Biol. Chem.*, **36,** 378
26. Sacher, J. A., Towers, G. H. N. and Davies, D. D. (1972). *Phytochemistry*, **11,** 2383
27. Greenwood, C. T. and Milne, E. A. (1968). *Advan. Carbohyd. Chem.*, **23,** 281
28. Thoma, J. A., Spradlin, J. E. and Dygert, S. (1971). *The Enzymes*, Vol. 5, 115 (P. D. Boyer, editor) (New York and London: Academic Press)
29. Greenwood, C. T. and Milne, E. A. (1968). *Staerke*, **20,** 139
30. Loyter, A. and Schramm, M. (1966). *J. Biol. Chem.*, **241,** 2611
31. Manners, D. J. and Marshall, J. J. (1972). *Staerke*, **24,** 3
32. Kruger, J. E. (1972). *Cereal Chem.*, **49,** 379
33. Greenwood, C. T., MacGregor, A. W. and Milne, E. A. (1965). *Arch. Biochem. Biophys.*, **112,** 466
34. Bird, R. and Hopkins, R. H. (1954). *Biochem. J.*, **56,** 86
35. Manners, D. J. and Marshall, J. J. (1971). *Carbohyd. Res.*, **18,** 203
36. Colman, P. M. and Matthews, B. W. (1971). *J. Mol. Biol.*, **60,** 163
37. Spradlin, J. and Thoma, J. A. (1970). *J. Biol. Chem.*, **245,** 117
38. Hatch, M. D. and Turner, J. F. (1960). *Biochem. J.*, **76,** 556
39. Pollock, J. R. A. and Pool, A. A. (1958). *J. Inst. Brewing*, **64,** 151
40. Tronier, B. and Ory, R. L. (1970). *Cereal Chem.*, **47,** 464
41. Daussant, J. and Corvazier, P. (1970). *FEBS Lett.*, **7,** 191
42. Kruger, J. E. (1970). *Cereal Chem.*, **47,** 79
43. Shinke, R. and Mugibayashi, N. (1971). *Agr. Biol. Chem.*, **35,** 1381
44. Rowsell, E. V. and Goad, L. J. (1962). *Biochem. J.*, **84,** 73P
45. Mugibayashi, N., Shinke, R. and Nichitai, Y. (1965). *Proc. Symp. Amylase*, Osaka, 1956, 80
46. Hutson, D. H. and Manners, D. J. (1965). *Biochem. J.*, **94,** 783
47. Takahashi, N., Shimomura, T. and Chiba, S. (1971). *Agr. Biol. Chem.*, **35,** 2015
48. Swain, R. R. and Dekker, E. E. (1966). *Biochim. Biophys. Acta*, **122,** 87
49. Fischer, E. H., Pocker, A. and Saari, J. C. (1970). *Essays in Biochemistry*, Vol. 6,

23 (P. N. Campbell and G. D. Greville, editors) (London and New York: Academic Press)

50. Liddle, A. M., Manners, D. J. and Wright, A. (1961). *Biochem. J.*, **80**, 304
51. Kamogawa, A., Fukui, T. and Nikuni, Z. (1968). *J. Biochem.* (*Tokyo*), **63**, 361
52. Gold, A. M., Johnson, R. M. and Sánchez, G. R. (1971). *J. Biol. Chem.*, **246**, 3444
53. Franken, K-D., Keilich, G. and Husemann, E. (1972). *Staerke*, **24**, 37
54. Lee, Y-P. (1960). *Biochim. Biophys. Acta*, **43**, 25
55. Fukui, T. and Kamogawa, A. (1969). *J. Jap. Soc. Starch Sci.*, **17**, 117
56. Kamogawa, A., Fukui, T. and Nikuni, Z. (1971). *Agr. Biol. Chem.*, **35**, 248
57. Lee, Y-P. (1960). *Biochim. Biophys. Acta*, **43**, 18
58. Tsai, C. Y. and Nelson, O. E. (1968). *Plant Physiol.*, **43**, 103
59. Tsai, C. Y. and Nelson, O. E. (1969). *Plant Physiol.*, **44**, 159
60. Frederick, J. F. (1967). *Phytochemistry*, **6**, 1041
61. Lee, E. Y. C. and Whelan, W. J. (1971). *The Enzymes*, Vol. 5, 191 (P. D. Boyer, editor) (New York and London: Academic Press)
62. Drummond, G. S., Smith, E. E. and Whelan, W. J. (1970). *FEBS Lett.*, **9**, 136
63. Manners, D. J. and Yellowlees, D. (1971). *Staerke*, **23**, 228
64. Turner, D. H. and Turner, J. F. (1957). *Aust. J. Biol. Sci.*, **10**, 302
65. Blank, G. E. and Sondheimer, E. (1969). *Phytochemistry*, **8**, 823
66. Arora, S. K. and Luthra, Y. P. (1972). *Staerke*, **24**, 51
67. Briggs, D. E. (1968). *Phytochemistry*, **7**, 513
68. Murata, T., Akazawa, T. and Fukuchi, S. (1968). *Plant Physiol.*, **43**, 1899
69. Filner, P. and Varner, J. E. (1967). *Proc. Nat. Acad. Sci. U.S.A.*, **58**, 1520
70. Palmiano, E. P. and Juliano, B. O. (1972). *Plant Physiol.*, **49**, 751
71. Nomura, T., Kono, Y. and Akazawa, T. (1969). *Plant Physiol.*, **44**, 765
72. Briggs, D. E. (1963). *J. Inst. Brewing*, **69**, 13
73. Simpson, G. M. and Naylor, J. M. (1962). *Can. J. Bot.*, **40**, 1659
74. Chrispeels, M. J. and Varner, J. E. (1967). *Plant Physiol.*, **42**, 398
75. Duffus, C. M. and Duffus, J. H. (1969). *Experientia*, **25**, 581
76. Galsky, A. G. and Lippincott, J. A. (1969). *Plant Cell Physiol.* (*Tokyo*), **10**, 607
77. Jones, R. L. (1972). *Planta*, **103**, 95
78. Gibson, R. A. and Paleg, L. G. (1972). *Biochem. J.*, **128**, 367
79. Hopkins, R. H. and Wiener, S. (1955). *J. Inst. Brewing*, **61**, 488
80. Knight, R. A. and Wade, P. (1971). *Chem. Ind.* (*London*), 568
81. Juliano, B. O. and Varner, J. E. (1969). *Plant Physiol.*, **44**, 886
82. Swain, R. R. and Dekker, E. E. (1969). *Plant Physiol.*, **44**, 319
83. Swain, R. R. and Dekker, E. E. (1966). *Biochim. Biophys. Acta*, **122**, 75
84. Gates, J. W. and Simpson, G. M. (1968). *Can. J. Bot.*, **46**, 1459
85. Edelman, J., Shibko, S. I. and Keys, A. J. (1969). *J. Exp. Botany*, **10**, 178
86. Chen, S. S. C. and Varner, J. E. (1969). *Plant Physiol.*, **44**, 770
87. Edelman, J. (1971). *Sugar*, 95 (J. Yudkin, J. Edelman and L. Hough, editors) (London: Butterworths)
88. Arnold, W. N. (1968). *J. Theoret. Biol.*, **21**, 13
89. Lewis, D. H. and Smith, D. C. (1967). *New Phytologist*, **66**, 143
90. Trip, P., Nelson, C. D. and Krotkov, G. (1965). *Plant Physiol.*, **40**, 740
91. Sacktor, B. (1970). *Advances in Insect Physiology*, Vol. 7, 267 (J. W. L. Beament, J. E. Treherne and V. B. Wigglesworth, editors) (London and New York: Academic Press)
92. Pandya, K. P. and Ramakrishnan, C. V. (1956). *Naturwissenschaften*, **43**, 85
93. Shukla, J. P. and Prabhu, K. A. (1959). *Naturwissenschaften*, **46**, 325
94. Hatch, M. D., Sacher, J. A. and Glasziou, K. T. (1963). *Plant Physiol.*, **38**, 338
95. Arnold, W. N. (1965). *Biochim. Biophys. Acta*, **110**, 134
96. Frost, G. H., Greenshields, R. N. and Teale, F. W. J. (1968). *Biochem. J.*, **107**, 625
97. Gascón, S., Neumann, N. P. and Lampen, J. O. (1968). *J. Biol. Chem.*, **243**, 1573
98. Little, G. and Edelman, J. (1973). *Phytochemistry*, **12**, 67
99. Edelman, J. and Hall, M. A. (1965). *Biochem. J.*, **95**, 403
100. Hawker, J. S. (1969). *Phytochemistry*, **8**, 337
101. Hawker, J. S. and Hatch, M. D. (1965). *Physiol. Plantarum*, **18**, 444
102. Burger, M., Bacon, E. E. and Bacon, J. S. D. (1961). *Biochem. J.*, **78**, 504
103. Vaughan, D. and MacDonald, I. R. (1967). *Plant Physiol.*, **42**, 456
104. Lyne, R. L. and ap Rees, T. (1971). *Phytochemistry*, **10**, 2593

105. Ricardo, C. P. P., ap Rees, T. and Fuller, W. A. (1972). *Phytochemistry*, **11,** 2435
106. Edelman, J. and Hanson, A. D. (1971). *Planta*, **101,** 122
107. Tupy, J. (1969). *Planta*, **88,** 144
108. Pridham, J. B. and Walter, M. W. (1964). *Biochem. J.*, **92,** 20P
109. Grimes, W. J., Jones, B. L. and Albersheim, P. (1970). *J. Biol. Chem.*, **245,** 188
110. Delmer, D. P. (1972). *Plant Physiol.*, **50,** 469
111. Glasziou, K. T. and Gayler, K. R. (1972). *Botan. Rev.*, **38,** 471
112. Sacher, J. A., Hatch, M. D. and Glasziou, K. T. (1963). *Plant Physiol.*, **38,** 348
113. Bowen, J. E. and Hunter, J. E. (1972). *Plant Physiol.*, **49,** 789
114. Hatch, M. D. and Glasziou, K. T. (1964). *Plant Physiol.*, **39,** 180
115. Glasziou, K. T. and Gayler, K. R. (1972). *Plant Physiol.*, **49,** 912
116. Sacher, J. A. (1966). *Plant Physiol.*, **41,** 181
117. Hardy, P. J. and Norton, G. (1968). *New Phytologist*, **67,** 139
118. Kriedemann, P. and Beevers, H. (1967). *Plant. Physiol.*, **42,** 174
119. Torrey, J. G., Fosket, D. E. and Helper, P. K. (1971). *Amer. Scientist*, **59,** 338
120. Jeffs, R. A. and Northcote, D. H. (1966). *Biochem. J.*, **101,** 146
121. Jeffs, R. A. and Northcote, D. H. (1967). *J. Cell Sci.*, **2,** 77
122. Wright, K. and Northcote, D. H. (1972). *J. Cell Sci.*, **11,** 319
123. Northcote, D. H. (1969). *Essays in Biochemistry*, Vol. 5, 90 (P. N. Campbell and G. D. Greville, editors) (London and New York: Academic Press)
124. Crick, F. (1970). *Nature (London)*, **225,** 420
125. Edelman, J. and Hanson, A. D. (1972). *J. Exp. Botany*, **23,** 469
126. Hatch, M. D. and Glasziou, K. T. (1963). *Plant Physiol.*, **38,** 344
127. Seitz, K. and Lang, A. (1968). *Plant Physiol.*, **43,** 1075
128. Maclachlan, G. A., Datko, A. H., Rollit, J. and Stokes, E. (1970). *Phytochemistry*, **9,** 1023
129. Winkenbach, F. and Matile, Ph. (1970). *Z. Pflanzenphysiol.*, **63,** 292
130. Hawker, J. S. (1969). *Phytochemistry*, **8,** 9
131. Glasziou, K. T. (1969). *Annu. Rev. Plant. Physiol.*, **20,** 63
132. Slack, C. R. (1966). *Phytochemistry*, **5,** 397
133. Lyne, R. L. and ap Rees, T. (1972). *Phytochemistry*, **11,** 2171
134. Hawker, J. S. (1971). *Phytochemistry*, **10,** 2313
135. Tsai, C. Y., Salamini, F. and Nelson, O. E. (1970). *Plant Physiol.*, **46,** 299
136. Pressey, R. (1969). *Plant Physiol.*, **44,** 759
137. Delmer, D. P. and Albersheim, P. (1970). *Plant Physiol.*, **45,** 782
138. Bowles, D. J. and Northcote, D. H. (1972). *Biochem. J.*, **130,** 1133
139. Akazawa, T., Minamikawa, T. and Murata, T. (1964). *Plant Physiol.*, **39,** 371
140. Turner, J. F. (1969). *Aust. J. Biol. Sci.*, **22,** 1321
141. Beevers, H. (1960). *Respiratory Metabolism in Plants*, 13 (Evanston: Row, Peterson and Company)
142. Davies, D. D., Giovanelli, J. and ap Rees, T. (1964). *Plant Biochemistry*, 101 (Oxford: Blackwell)
143. James, W. O. (1953). *Plant Respiration*, 118 (Oxford: Oxford University Press)
144. Crawford, R. M. M. (1967). *J. Exp. Botany*, **18,** 458
145. Cossins, E. A., Kopala, L. C., Blawacky, B. and Spronk, A. M. (1968). *Phytochemistry*, **7,** 1125
146. Leblová, S. and Ehlichová, D. (1972). *Phytochemistry*, **11,** 1345
147. Crawford, R. M. M. and McManmon, M. (1968). *J. Exp. Botany*, **19,** 435
148. Hanson-Porath, E. and Poljakoff-Mayber, A. (1970). *Plant Cell Physiol. (Tokyo)*, **11,** 891
149. McManmon, M. and Crawford, R. M. M. (1971). *New Phytologist*, **70,** 299
150. Ovcharov, K. E. and Akhmedov, A. (1972). *Fiziol. Rast.*, **19,** 360
151. Davies, D. D. and Davies, S. (1972). *Biochem. J.*, **129,** 831
152. Cameron, D. S. and Cossins, E. A. (1967). *Biochem. J.*, **105,** 323
153. Crawford, R. M. M. (1969). *Ber. Deut. Botan. Ges.*, **82,** 111
154. Williams, J. F. and Clark, M. G. (1971). *Search*, **2,** 80
155. Williams, J. F., Rienits, K. G., Schofield, P. J. and Clark, M. G. (1971). *Biochem. J.*, **123,** 923
156. Gibbs, M. and Horecker, B. L. (1954). *J. Biol. Chem.*, **208,** 813
157. Ginsburg, V. and Hassid, W. Z. (1956). *J. Biol. Chem.*, **223,** 277

158. Altermatt, H. A. and Neish, A. C. (1956). *Can. J. Biochem., Physiol.*, **34,** 405
159. Beevers, H. (1956). *Plant Physiol.*, **31,** 339
160. Wang, C. H., Doyle, W. P. and Ramsey, J. C. (1962). *Plant Physiol.*, **37,** 1
161. Davies, D. D. (1961). *Intermediary Metabolism in Plants*, 21 (Cambridge: Cambridge University Press)
162. ap Rees, T. and Beevers, H. (1960). *Plant Physiol.*, **35,** 830
163. ap Rees, T., Blanch, E. and Davies, D. D. (1965). *Plant Physiol.*, **40,** 748
164. ap Rees, T. and Beevers, H. (1960). *Plant Physiol.*, **35,** 839
165. Fowler, M. W. and ap Rees, T. (1970). *Biochim. Biophys. Acta*, **201,** 33
166. Scala, J. and Semersky, F. E. (1971). *Phytochemistry*, **10,** 567
167. Thomas, S. M. and ap Rees, T. (1972). *Phytochemistry*, **11,** 2177
168. ap Rees, T., Blanch, E., Graham, D. and Davies, D. D. (1965). *Plant Physiol.*, **40,** 910
169. Landau, B. R. and Katz, J. (1964). *J. Biol. Chem.*, **239,** 697
170. Takeda, Y., Hizukuri, S. and Nikumi, Z. (1967). *Biochim. Biophys. Acta*, **146,** 568
171. Grazi, E., De Flora, A. and Pontremoli, S. (1960). *Biochem. Biophys. Res. Commun.*, **2,** 121
172. Venkataraman, R. and Racker, E. (1961). *J. Biol. Chem.*, **236,** 1876
173. Forti, G., Tua, C. and Tognoli, L. (1959). *Biochim. Biophys. Acta*, **36,** 19
174. Ragland, T. E. and Hackett, D. P. (1961). *Biochim. Biophys. Acta*, **54,** 577
175. Barker, J., Khan, M. A. A. and Solomos, T. (1964). *Nature (London)*, **201,** 1126
176. Barker, J., Khan, M. A. A. and Solomos, T. (1967). *New Phytologist*, **66,** 577
177. Newsholme, E. A. and Gevers, W. (1967). *Vitamins Hormones*, **25,** 1
178. Kelly, G. J. and Turner, J. F. (1969). *Biochem. J.*, **115,** 481
179. Givan, C. V. (1968). *Plant Physiol.*, **43,** 948
180. Kobr, M. J. and Beevers, H. (1971). *Plant Physiol.*, **47,** 48
181. Kaplan, N. O., Swartz, M. N., Freck, M. E. and Ciotti, M. M. (1956). *Proc. Nat. Acad. Sci. U.S.A.*, **42,** 481
182. Horecker, B. L. (1962). *The Harvey Lectures*, Series 57, 35 (New York and London: Academic Press)
183. Lowenstein, J. M. (1961). *J. Theoret. Biol.*, **1,** 98
184. Hassid, W. Z. (1967). *Annu. Rev. Plant Physiol.*, **18,** 253
185. Sable, H. Z. (1966). *Advan. Enzymol.*, **28,** 391
186. Katz, J. and Rognstad, R. (1967). *Biochemistry*, **6,** 2227
187. Yoshida, S. (1969). *Annu. Rev. Plant Physiol.*, **20,** 41
188. Acerbo, S. N., Schubert, W. J. and Nord, F. F. (1960). *J. Amer. Chem. Soc.*, **82,** 735
189. Higuchi, T. and Shimada, M. (1967). *Plant Cell Physiol. (Tokyo)*, **8,** 71
190. Wong, W. J. L. and ap Rees, T. (1971). *Biochim. Biophys. Acta*, **252,** 296
191. Davies, D. D., Teixeira, A. and Kenworthy, P. (1972). *Biochem. J.*, **127,** 335
192. Muto, S., Asahi, T. and Uritani, I. (1969). *Agr. Biol. Chem.*, **33,** 176
193. Muto, S. and Uritani, I. (1972). *Plant Cell Physiol. (Tokyo)*, **13,** 931
194. Chakravorty, M. and Burma, D. P. (1959). *Biochem. J.*, **73,** 48
195. Mayer, A. M., Poljakoff-Mayber, A. and Krishmaro, N. (1966). *Plant Cell Physiol. (Tokyo)*, **7,** 25
196. Fuller, R. C. and Gibbs, M. (1959). *Plant Physiol.*, **34,** 324
197. Ragland, T. E. and Hackett, D. P. (1964). *Arch. Biochem. Biophys.*, **108,** 479
198. Schulman, M. D. and Gibbs, M. (1968). *Plant Physiol.*, **43,** 1805
199. Goodwin, T. W. and Mercer, E. I. (1972). *Introduction to Plant Biochemistry*, 139 (Oxford: Pergamon)
200. Harmey, M. A., Ikuma, H. and Bonner, W. D. (1966). *Nature (London)*, **209,** 174
201. Wiskich, J. T., Young, R. E. and Biale, J. B. (1964). *Plant Physiol.*, **39,** 312
202. Koeppe, D. E. and Miller, R. J. (1972). *Plant Physiol.*, **49,** 353
203. Agrawal, P. K. and Canvin, D. T. (1971). *Can. J. Bot.*, **49,** 267
204. Beevers, L. and Hageman, R. H. (1969). *Annu. Rev. Plant Physiol.*, **20,** 495
205. Yue, S. B. (1969). *Plant Physiol.*, **44,** 453
206. Pahlich, E. and Joy, K. W. (1971). *Can. J. Biochem.*, **49,** 127
207. Agrawal, P. K. and Canvin, D. T. (1971). *Plant Physiol.*, **47,** 672
208. Drennan, C. H. and Canvin, D. T. (1969). *Biochim. Biophys. Acta*, **187,** 193
209. Osmond, C. B. and ap Rees, T. (1969). *Biochim. Biophys. Acta*, **184,** 35
210. Fowler, M. W. (1971). *J. Exp. Botany*, **22,** 715
211. Katz, J., Rognstad, R. and Kemp, R. G. (1965). *J. Biol. Chem.*, **240,** PC1484

212. Katz, J. and Rognstad, R. (1969). *J. Biol. Chem.*, **244,** 99
213. Katz, J., Wals, P. A. and Schmidt, K. (1971). *Biochim. Biophys. Acta*, **239,** 16
214. Ragland, T. E. and Hackett, D. P. (1965). *Plant Physiol.*, **40,** 1191
215. Harley, J. L. and Beevers, H. (1963). *Plant Physiol.*, **38,** 117
216. MacLennan, D. H., Beevers, H. and Harley, J. L. (1963). *Biochem. J.*, **89,** 316
217. Laties, G. G. (1963). *Control Mechanisms in Respiration and Fermentation*, 129 (B. Wright, editor) (New York: Ronald Press)
218. Sampson, M. J. and Laties, G. G. (1968). *Plant Physiol.*, **43,** 1011
219. Laties, G. G. (1964). *Plant Physiol.*, **39,** 654
220. Jacobson, B. S., Smith, B. N., Epstein, S. and Laties, G. G. (1970). *J. Gen. Physiol.*, **55,** 1
221. Hackett, D. P., Haas, D. W., Griffiths, S. K. and Niederpruem, D. J. (1960). *Plant Physiol.*, **35,** 8
222. ap Rees, T. (1966). *Aust. J. Biol. Sci.*, **19,** 981
223. Bryant, J. A. and ap Rees, T. (1971). *Phytochemistry*, **10,** 1191
224. ap Rees, T. and Royston, B. J. (1971). *Phytochemistry*, **10,** 1199
225. Barker, J. and Mapson, L. W. (1953). *Proc. Roy. Soc. (London) B*, **141,** 338
226. Barker, J. and Mapson, L. W. (1955). *Proc. Roy. Soc. (London), B*, **143,** 523
227. Laties, G. G., Hoelle, C. and Jacobson, B. S. (1972). *Phytochemistry*, **11,** 3403
228. Tanner, W. and Beevers, H. (1965). *Z. Pflanzenphysiol.*, **53,** 72

4
Plant Growth Substances

D. G. MORGAN and CLARE B. MORGAN
University of Cambridge

4.1 INTRODUCTION

Over the last 5 years a vast number of publications on the biochemistry and physiology of plant growth substances have appeared, and several detailed reviews have been published to report progress in research on auxins[1-3], gibberellins[4-6], cytokinins[7-9], ethylene[10-12], abscisic acid[13,14], and various other chemicals[15,16]. The present review surveys selected topics and concentrates in greatest detail on those aspects in which there has been considerable progress in recent years and which have not been reviewed elsewhere; in particular the biosynthesis and metabolism of abscisic acid and xanthoxin, as well as the mode of action of gibberellic acid in increasing the mobilisation of food reserves in cereal grain and of auxins in promoting cell elongation. An attempt is made to consider critically research on growth substances from the standpoints of the methods used, the results obtained and their significance in interpreting the physiological and biochemical roles of plant growth substances.

Results on the distribution of plant growth substances in plant tissues and on the effects of these compounds when applied to plants are variable and in some cases apparently conflicting. From data presented later is appears likely that these variations owe much to relative differences in the genotype, stage of growth and development, organ, process and concentration of applied growth substances being studied, as well as upon the environmental conditions. It is therefore unfortunate that insufficient attention is often paid to these factors in the design and description of experiments and in the analysis of the results. Failure to do this often makes it difficult, if not impossible, to make a critical comparison of the results of different workers. It is also regrettable that statistical analyses of results are often conspicuous by their absence.

4.2 OCCURRENCE, BIOSYNTHESIS AND METABOLISM OF PLANT GROWTH SUBSTANCES

4.2.1 Auxins

Research on the distribution, biosynthesis and metabolism of auxins has been reviewed by Audus[1] and Thimann[2]. Of particular interest in recent years has been the confirmation by Erdmann and Schwiewer[17] that indolylacetic acid (IAA) is solely derived from tryptophan in pea species. They supplied tritium-labelled serine and [^{14}C] labelled indole to sterile stem apices, extracted tryptophan and IAA subsequently, and found that the [^{3}H] [^{14}C] ratios were the same in both compounds. A major advance in determining how and where the above conversion take place in intact plants has been made by Sheldrake and Northcote[18-22]. They showed that autolysing tissues are rich sources of tryptophan and IAA *in vitro*, and suggested that dying cells are an important source of IAA, probably produced via tryptophan. In some elegant experiments using tobacco internode sections cultured on a basic medium, they were able to establish that the production of auxin by the sections was dependent on continued cambial activity and vascular differentiation. They suggest a self-perpetuating system in which auxin induces xylem differentiation and as a result further auxin is produced in the differentiating xylem, which is therefore a major source of IAA in plants. This discovery makes understandable a large amount of indirect evidence that shoot and root apices are sites of auxin production[1].

Libbert and co-workers[23-27] have found that epiphytic bacteria are also capable of converting tryptophan to IAA and probably contribute considerably to the production of auxin by non-sterile plant tissues. It is likely, therefore, that some of the earlier claims of IAA production from tryptophan by plants may have been based on bacterial metabolism.

4.2.2 Gibberellins

Six further gibberellins, GA_{30}–GA_{35}, have been isolated recently and characterised[28-33]. The biosynthesis of gibberellins has been described in detailed reviews by Lang[4], Cross[5] and MacMillan[33,34]. Initial studies were performed on *Fusarium moniliforme* but since then evidence that the pathways of synthesis are the same in higher plants has been obtained using cell-free enzyme systems from the endosperm of *Echinocystis macrocarpa*[35] and cell-free homogenates from the endosperm of *Cucurbita pepo*[36]. However, in the latter case mevalonic acid was only converted as far as the C_{12} aldehyde. Growth retardants have been used to unravel the biosynthetic pathways of the gibberellins, and it has been found that Phosphon D blocks the synthesis at the stage between *trans*-geranyl geraniol pyrophosphate and (−)-kaurene, whereas chlorocholine chloride (CCC) blocks a subsequent stage between (−)-kaurene and gibberellic acid itself.

4.2.3 Cytokinins

The origin and biosynthetic pathways of cytokinins are complex and little understood. However, Sheldrake and Northcote[19] suggest that, as well as auxins, cytokinins might be produced during autolysis of the contents of differentiating xylem and phloem cells as a result of breakdown of the nuclei. In this connection they note that t-RNA contains purine bases with strong kinin activity.

4.2.4 Ethylene

Ethylene has now been shown to be produced by most plant tissues and its role in regulating various processes in growth and development has become increasingly evident[37]. The biosynthesis of ethylene was largely determined before 1969 and has been described by Mapson[11] and Abeles[10].

4.2.5 Abscisic acid

The discovery of abscisic acid (ABA) as a constituent of the β-inhibitor complex of plants[38], its chemical characterisation and physiological properties were reviewed in 1969 by Milborrow[39] and Addicott and Lyon[13]. Publications on ABA up to May 1970 are catalogued comprehensively by Hoffmann La Roche[40], and aspects of the physiology and biochemistry not dealt with here are reviewed by Dörffling[41] and Addicott[42].

4.2.5.1 Isomers and their activity

ABA exists in two stereoisomeric forms, depending on a *cis*-(1) or *trans*-(2) orientation of the $\Delta^{2,3}$ double bond. The *cis*-isomer (usually referred to simply as ABA) is the form in which it is almost always found in plants[43];

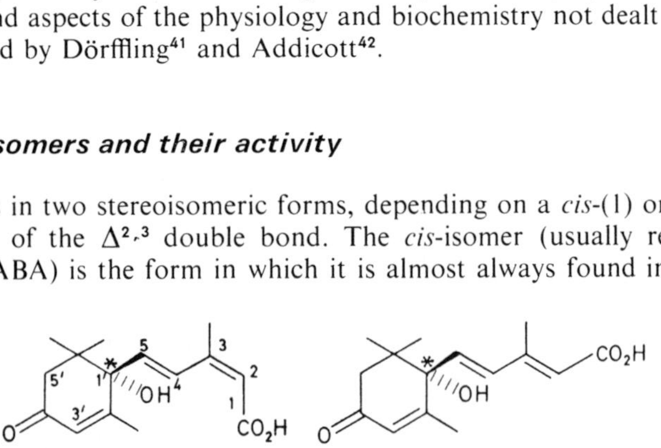

(1) (+)-*cis*-ABA

(2) (+)-*trans*-ABA

The new absolute configuration attributed to abscisic acid[193]

in only a few cases[44-46] has the *trans*-isomer been isolated in small amounts in the presence of predominantly high concentrations of the *cis*-form. These two isomers are interconvertible in light to give a 1:1 equilibrium mixture[47] and since the *trans*-isomer is inactive in bioassays carried out in the dark, any activity it possesses in tests carried out in the light is attributed to photolytic isomerisation *in vivo* to *cis*-ABA[39,44].

Milborrow found that [^{14}C] labelled *trans*-ABA was not isomerised enzymically to ABA in tomato shoots, and suggested that the small proportion of *trans*-isomer proved to be present in rose leaves might arise by light isomerisation of the relatively large amount of ABA within the pale green leaves[44]. Since ABA possesses one centre of assymetry*, both of the stereoisomers exist in optically-active forms, of which only the (+) is naturally occurring[43,44]. However the (+)- and (−)-enantiomers have been reported to be equally active in inhibiting coleoptile growth of dissected wheat embryos[47,48], and to differ in only a few test systems[194] (see Section 4.2.5.4) (p. 138).

4.2.5.2 Estimation of abscisic acid

Methods based on spectropolarimetry and gas-liquid chromatography have been developed which enable the low concentrations of ABA found in plants to be determined accurately. These methods are more specific than bioassays (see Section 4.3.1) but, being less sensitive, necessitate the extraction of larger quantities of plant material. Irrespective of the method of estimation, extensive fractionation and purification procedures are necessary beforehand and these result in unavoidable losses of the order of 60–70 %[43,44]. Correction for these losses can be made by inclusion in the analysis of an internal standard, enabling the absolute concentration of ABA in the plant to be accurately assessed. The criteria for such a standard are that it must have the same chemical and physical properties as ABA, and therefore suffer identical losses during the purification, and that concentrations of it and ABA in the final mixture can be estimated separately.

The first method is Milborrow's racemate dilution method[43], which takes advantage of the fact that only the (+)-enantiomer of ABA is naturally occurring and exhibits a strong Cotton effect in its optical rotatory dispersion (o.r.d.) curve. Synthetic racemic ABA is added to the alcohol extract as an internal standard, and after purification by solvent partition and column- or thin layer- chromatography (t.l.c.), the total (±)- and (+)-ABA recovered is measured by its u.v. absorption; the (+)-ABA is estimated by o.r.d., and by comparison with the (±)-ABA obtained by difference, the concentration of (+)-ABA in the extract can be calculated.

Milborrow[44,49] has also applied isotopic dilution analysis by addition of either [2-^{14}C]ABA or hexadeuterio-ABA as diluent to determine the absolute recovery of ABA, but unless it can be combined with spectropolarimetric measurements this method entails exceptionally rigorous purification of the ultimate mixture since the amount present is too small for isolation in a crystalline form.

ABA can also be estimated after similar extraction and purification techniques by gas–liquid chromatography (g.l.c.) of its trimethylsilyl derivative[13,45] or methyl ester[50], and this can be combined with mass spectrometry[46] for more positive identification. Lenton, Perry and Saunders[51] have corrected for losses by adding pure *trans*-ABA as internal standard. This method has the advantage that the acids recovered are separated and estimated simultaneously by g.l.c. of their methyl esters, eliminating any errors incurred by measuring relative quantities by different methods[44]. This technique cannot of course be used for the analysis of ABA in tissues containing any endogenous *trans*-ABA and also demands the rigorous exclusion of light to prevent photo-induced isomerisation. The authors have proved that no significant inter-conversion of the isomers occurs during their treatment, and this has been confirmed in our laboratories using slightly different purification procedures. In the absence of added standard, confirmation of the identity and purity of the methyl-ABA peak can also be achieved by irradiation of the methylated mixture by ultraviolet light; if the previous peak was due entirely to *cis*-methyl-ABA then g.l.c. of the irradiated mixture should show *cis*- and *trans*-methyl-ABA peaks in a 1 : 1 ratio.

4.2.5.3 Biosynthesis of abscisic acid

It has been established[39,52] that ABA is synthesised from three isoprene units derived from mevalonic acid (MVA) (3), via a C_{15} precursor, probably farnesyl pyrophosphate (4), but it was suggested that the subsequent transformations could be effected by two pathways: (a) a 'direct-synthesis' pathway involving the formation of a C_{15} monocyclic precursor, or (b) a photolytic 'carotenoid pathway' involving oxidative cleavage of a C_{40} carotenoid to an intermediate C_{15} precursor with the same carbon skeleton as ABA; this was based on the observed similarity in structure of ABA and certain carotenoids,

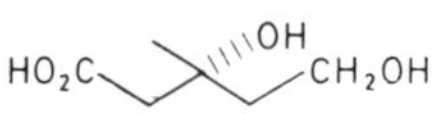

HO_2C OH CH_2OH

(3)

Mevalonic acid

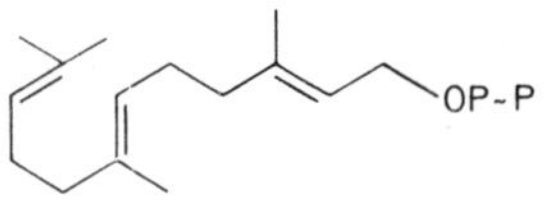

OP-P

(4)

Farnesyl pyrophosphate

OH O O HO

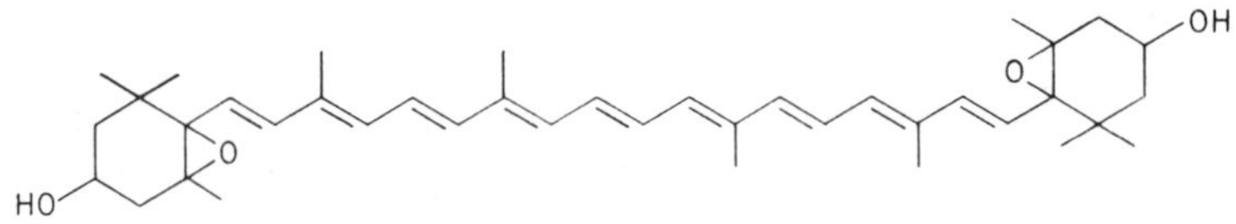

(5)

Violaxanthin

such as violaxanthin (5) and the fact that these gave rise to inhibitors on illumination[53] (see also Section 4.2.6.1)

In the past few years intensive investigations have been carried out to clarify this situation, with the result that (a) is now regarded as the main pathway, although it is still not impossible that (b) could occur in some tissues.

Many of the biosynthetic studies have been carried out in fruits, which are rich sources of ABA, and in which ABA is probably synthesised during ripening[54,55]. In four fruits, including avocado and tomato, [^{14}C]MVA was converted to [^{14}C]ABA[56]. Robinson and Ryback[57] supplied stereospecifically-tritiated MVA to avocado fruits and studied the distribution of the tritium atoms in the resulting ABA molecule. Their results showed that the $\Delta^{2,3}$ double bond of ABA is first formed in the *trans*-configuration and isomerised to the *cis*-form at a later stage in the biosynthesis, but they failed to differentiate between the two routes.

Subsequent work has favoured the 'direct synthesis' pathway in avocado pears, the main evidence being that (a) conversion of MVA to ABA occurs in the fruits in darkness, showing a photolytic step to be unnecessary, and (b) when Dr. D. R. Robinson[49] supplied a [^{14}C] labelled phytoene (considered to be a carotenoid precursor) and [2-^{3}H]MVA simultaneously to avocados the [^{14}C] label was subsequently found in the carotenoids but not in the ABA, which was, however, heavily labelled with tritium. This indicated that ABA was synthesised from MVA by a route which did not involve a carotenoid.

As well as in fruits, there is also evidence for the 'direct synthesis' pathway in leaves and other tissues. In 1969 it was observed by Wright[58] and Wright and Hiron[59] that the ABA content of detached wheat leaves increased 40-fold on wilting. Furthermore, Wright found that this increase was the same whether the plants were wilted in the light or dark, and he pointed out that some precursor other than violaxanthin was probably involved. Milborrow and Noddle[60] have taken advantage of this finding in a novel way to investigate the biosynthesis of ABA in wheat leaves. They found that when [^{3}H]-MVA was supplied to leaves just prior to wilting, these plants incorporated nine times more into ABA than did turgid plants. This meant that the ABA had been produced by new synthesis rather than by release from a bound form or from a large pool of precursor. Milborrow and Robinson[54] have now also demonstrated wilt-induced increases in ABA concentration, in parallel with increased incorporation of [2-^{14}C]MVA, in avocado leaves and stems; they have also found incorporation of labelled MVA into ABA in the cotyledons of mature avocado seeds and embryos and endosperms of developing wheat seeds.

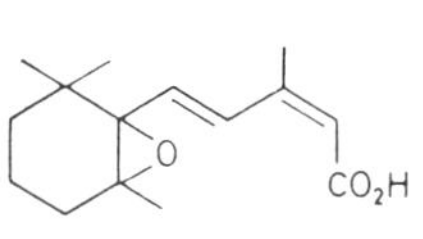

CO_2H (6) Synthetic epoxide

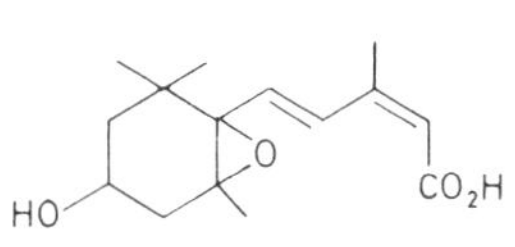

HO CO_2H (7) Xanthoxin acid

Further corroborative evidence for the 'direct-synthesis' pathway, as well as indications of the possible nature of intermediates in this pathway, has been obtained using as a tool a synthetic epoxy compound (6), very similar to ABA in structure and inhibitory activity[61]. Milborrow and Noddle[60] found that the [^{14}C]labelled epoxide could be converted to ABA in the dark in avocado and tomato fruits. They also supplied this labelled epoxide, alone or with [^{3}H]MVA, to wheat leaves which were subsequently allowed to wilt or kept turgid, and not only was the label incorporated into ABA but there was a greater conversion in the wilting than in the turgid leaves. This suggested that the epoxide or a metabolite of it could be incorporated into the natural biosynthetic pathway leading to ABA, and that either the epoxide or a closely-related compound might be a precursor of ABA. However, in an experiment carried out by Robinson, cited by Milborrow[62], [^{3}H]MVA was not incorporated into added unlabelled epoxide but only into ABA, indicating that the epoxide is not a naturally-occurring intermediate. Thus it seemed likely that not the epoxide but a compound very similar to it, which we might call 'Y' is a precursor of ABA (Figure 4.1).

MVA - - - - - - - - - - - - - → 'Y' - - - - - - - - - - - → ABA
unnatural epoxide - - - - - - - - - →ABA
↓
xanthoxin acid
xanthoxin - - - - - - - - - - - →ABA

Figure 4.1

The stage at which the synthetic epoxide joins the natural pathway between 'Y' and ABA is unknown, but a labelled metabolite of the [^{14}C]epoxide has been isolated[62] which is probably identical with xanthoxin acid (7*), this may therefore be an intermediate between the epoxide and ABA and could possibly be a natural precursor of ABA. The fact that xanthoxin itself has been shown to be converted to ABA when supplied to tomato shoots is also relevant (see Section 4.2.6.5) but whether it is a natural precursor of ABA in the direct pathway remains to be investigated. Although the direct pathway is now firmly established as the main route for ABA biosynthesis it is still an open question whether ABA can also be produced from carotenoids via xanthoxin in some tissues. Obviously our knowledge in this sphere is still fragmentary and will be the subject of further research.

4.2.5.4 Metabolism of abscisic acid

In previous reviews[39,48] it was reported that synthetic (±)-[2-^{14}C]ABA was rapidly metabolised in tomato plants to three radioactive products named 'metabolites A, B, and C', and these have now been identified by Milborrow.

'Metabolite A' has been shown[62] to be the methyl ester of ABA (8) and is regarded probably to be an artefact formed from ABA by a *trans*-esterification reaction if the methanolic plant extract is allowed to become slightly acidic.

'Metabolite B', the major radioactive product, has been identified[44] as (+)-abscisyl-β-D-glucopyranoside (ABA glucose ester) (9), characterised previously by Koshimizu *et al.*[63].

'Metabolite C' has been identified[65] as the hydroxylated derivative of ABA (10), which on methylation undergoes molecular rearrangement to give a product identical with the methyl ester of phaseic acid, this acid having been

* Latest evidence dictates against this[196].

isolated previously from seeds of *Phaseolus multiflorus*[66]. A new structure (11) was ascribed to phaseic acid[65], which is the only compound Milborrow has been able to obtain in further attempts to isolate 'metabolite C'[62]. He expresses some doubts as to whether it is a naturally-occurring degradation product of ABA or is merely an artefact produced during extraction[62, 65].

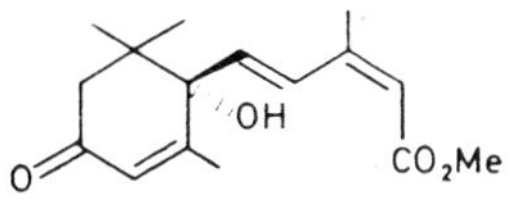

(8)

ABA methyl ester
'Metabolite A'

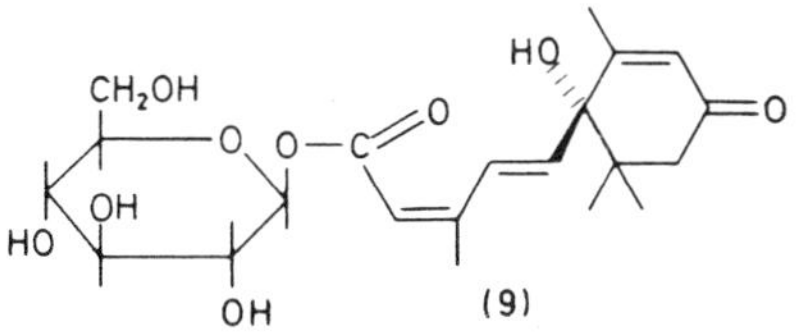

(9)

(+)-abscisyl-β-D-glucopyranoside
'Metabolite B'

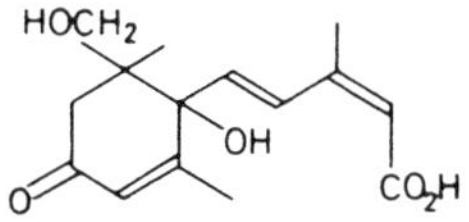

(10)

'Metabolite C'

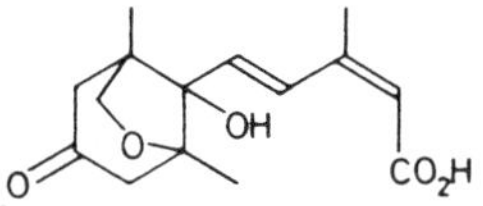

(11)

Phaseic acid

It is interesting to note that phaseic acid has now been detected by g.l.c. in extracts of cotton fruits[67]; it had *ca.* 1/10 of the activity of ABA in a cotton explant abscission bioassay, compared with 1/200 of its inhibitory activity in the wheat embryo germination assay[65].

The above metabolites of ABA were detected in tomato shoots, but the pattern of metabolism may not necessarily be the same in all species. That there are quantitative differences is obvious from the different concentrations of endogenous ABA glucose ester relative to ABA in different organs of different species[43,54], and this is obviously an important metabolite of ABA. Being an ester, it is not affected by β-glucosidase but is hydrolysed rapidly by tomato cell sap[44]. How stable it is *in vivo* and whether it is transported in the plant or functions as a storage form of ABA are uncertain.

As well as possible variations in the metabolism of ABA between species, there is evidence for differences even between different organs of the same species. When Milborrow[48] supplied [2-^{14}C]ABA to petiole sections of *Phaseolus vulgaris* the major product was the glucose ester. This was also found with young seedlings of *Phaseolus vulgaris* by Walton and Sondheimer[68,69], but when these workers incubated [2-^{14}C]ABA with excised embryonic axes of *Phaseolus vulgaris* it was metabolised, not to the glucose ester or 'metabolite C', but to two other unidentified compounds, one of which appeared to be the precursor of the other, which accumulated*. The physiological effects of these various metabolites will differ, and it is possible that the way in which ABA is metabolised in any particular organ may be significant in elucidating its effect therein.

* Now identified as phaseic acid and 4′-dihydro phaseic acid respectively[195].

In the above studies synthetic (±)-ABA was supplied to plants and various metabolites were detected, but the individual metabolic fates of the (+)-ABA and (—)-ABA were not investigated. However, Milborrow[44] has found that when racemic ABA is supplied to tomato shoots, the two enantiomers are metabolised differently, which is not surprising since only the (+)-enantiomer is naturally-occurring. A few hours after applying (±)-[2-^{14}C]ABA a large proportion of the (+)-enantiomer was converted to 'metabolite C' and some to its glucose ester. Of the [2-^{14}C]ABA remaining, there was a preponderance of the (—)-enantiomer, this not being converted to 'metabolite C'. However, a large proportion of the (—)-enantiomer had been metabolised to its glucose ester, in fact to a greater extent than had the (+)-enantiomer. There is thus a rapid accumulation of (—)-enantiomers resulting from (a) removal of the (+)-enantiomer by conversion to its glucose ester, 'metabolite C', phaseic acid, or other less inhibitory compounds, and (b) the more rapid conversion of the (—)-enantiomer to its glucose ester. In this situation the inhibitory activity of the (+)-ABA glucose ester becomes important, as also does that of the accumulating (—)-ABA and (—)-ABA glucose ester. The glucose ester was found by Koshimizu *et al.*[63,64] to have half the inhibitory activity of ABA applied to rice seedlings. Milborrow[44] reported (—)-ABA to have equal activity to the (+)-enantiomer in inhibiting growth of dissected wheat embryos. Sondheimer *et al.*[194] have also reported equal activity for the two enantiomers in bioassays involving effects of ABA on petiole abscission, stomatal closure and α-amylase production is barley endosperm; however they found that (—)-ABA was considerably *less* active than (+)-ABA in inhibiting (1) the germination of excised embryos of ash, and (2) root growth in germinating barley seeds, where its effect on shoot growth, however, was almost as great as that of (+)-ABA. The observation by these authors that in excised bean axes (+)-[^{14}C]ABA penetrated and was metabolised faster than the corresponding (—)-enantiomer gives an indication as to how differences in activity may arise in some biosystems.

Obviously the metabolism of (±)-ABA is complex, not only as regards the metabolites produced, but also as regards the relative quantities produced from the (+)- and (—)-enantiomers. This must be borne in mind in comparing the activity of ABA in various tests and in interpreting the effects of its exogenous application.

4.2.5.5 Biological activity of analogues of abscisic acid

Results of structure–activity studies using synthetic analogues of ABA are conflicting, probably reflecting differences of penetration and metabolism in different tissues of the assay systems used. Numerous workers claim the ring double bond to be generally necessary for activity in several bioassays[70-73]. It is of interest that Tamura and Nagao[61] found that the epoxide (6) used in Milborrow and Noddle's biosynthetic studies was comparable to ABA in suppressing the growth of rice seedlings, while related analogues without the epoxy group had much lower activity. Popoff *et al.*[74] suggest that the pentadienoic side chain of ABA is unnecessary, a skeleton of citrylideneacetic acid being sufficient for inhibition in their assay, and make speculations on the degradation of the side chain of ABA as part of its mode of action.

Relative importance of other structural groups has been found to be very dependent on the assay system[61,72,73], and McWha *et al.*[73], testing analogues in two bioassay systems and comparing their results with those of other workers, reached the conclusion that it was impossible to ascribe an absolute order of activity for ABA and the analogues tested.

4.2.6 Xanthoxin

Concurrently with the above researches on the biosynthesis of ABA, another approach was being followed at Wye College and this resulted in the discovery of a new naturally occurring inhibitor, xanthoxin, with a structure closely related to that of ABA.

4.2.6.1 Isolation and characterisation

Following the speculation of Taylor and Smith[53] that carotenoids might be precursors of ABA (see Section 4.2.5.3), Taylor[75] separated nettle leaf pigments and showed that illumination of violaxanthin (5) and neoxanthin yielded inhibitors of seed germination. However, contrary to expectations, the inhibitory activity from violaxanthin was present in the neutral fraction and was therefore not ABA. Violaxanthin was extracted on a large scale from orange peel and on illumination it yielded several compounds, one of which was highly active in inhibiting wheat coleoptile growth and cress seed germination[76]. After extensive fractionation and purification of the photo-oxidation products, Taylor and Burden isolated this compound, named xanthoxin, and characterised it by chemical and spectroscopic means[77,78]. It is an aldehyde existing in two stereoisomeric forms, namely the 2-*cis*,4-*trans*- and 2-*trans*,4-*trans*-isomers of 5-(1′,2′-epoxy-4′-hydroxy-2′,6′,6′-trimethyl-1′-cyclohexyl)-3-methyl-pentadienal ((12) and (13) respectively). Although Taylor and Burden refer to the stereoisomers as *cis–trans* and *trans–trans*-xanthoxin, in this text they are referred to simply as *cis*-xanthoxin (12) and *trans*-xanthoxin (13) respectively, depending on the configuration of the $\Delta^{2,3}$ double bond.

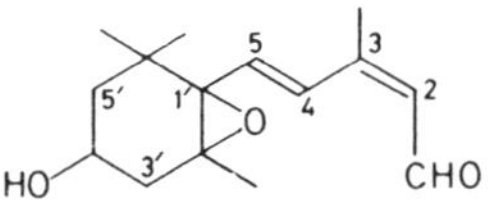

5 3 5′ 1′ O 4 2 HO 3′ CHO CHO O HO

(12) (13)

cis-Xanthoxin *trans*-Xanthoxin

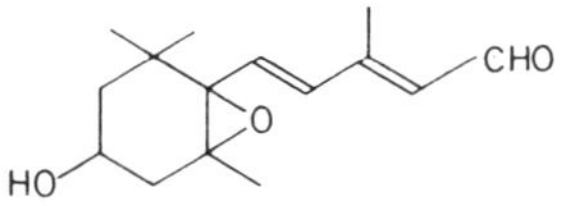

Like ABA, *cis*-xanthoxin was found to be more active than the *trans*-isomer in inhibition tests, and the isomers were also interconvertible in sunlight to a 1:1 equilibrium mixture.

Taylor and Burden[79] showed xanthoxin to be endogenous in plants when they identified it by g.l.c. of its acetate in dwarf bean and wheat seedlings, isolating it under conditions which precluded its formation by photo-oxidation of xanthophylls during extraction; this result stimulated a careful study of the natural occurrence and biological properties of the inhibitor[78,80].

4.2.6.2 *Estimation of xanthoxin*

Xanthoxin can be estimated by the wheat coleoptile straight growth or cress seed germination bioassays. Firn, Burden and Taylor[80] have also developed a method for estimation of xanthoxin in plants by which the acetylated derivatives of the *cis*- and *trans*-isomers are separated and estimated by g.l.c. In spite of extensive fractionation and purification by solvent partition and t.l.c. the gas–liquid chromatograms indicate a complex mixture which often necessitates the use of different columns and conditions, especially in the case of extracts of low xanthoxin content. In the absence of a suitable compound to use as an internal standard it has not been feasible to correct for losses during isolation and equate results to absolute amounts present in the plant as is possible for ABA.

4.2.6.3 *Occurrence in plants*

In all cases where it has so far been detected in plants both isomers of xanthoxin have been present, with a preponderance of the *trans*-isomer[80]; this is in contrast to ABA where in all but a few cases only the *cis*-isomer is naturally occurring[44]. It was found in the young shoots of some higher plants, namely dwarf and tall peas, dwarf beans, buttercup and wheat, where the isomers were estimated separately but their combined concentrations were in the region of 30–200 $\mu g\ kg^{-1}$ fresh tissue—of approximately the same order as ABA in these tissues[43]. In first leaves of beans the concentration of xanthoxin declined with age; it was also present in the bean stems and petioles. It was not detected in tomato shoots, maple seeds, rose hips (a rich source of ABA), pea and bean roots and potato peelings; neither was it present in a liverwort nor a brown seaweed. The most primitive plants in which it was detected being two species of ferns.

4.2.6.4 *Physiological activity of xanthoxin and related compounds*

Taylor and Burden[78] have oxidised chemically violaxanthin from orange peel to produce *cis*- and *trans*- xanthoxin ((14) (15); $R^1 = CHO$, $R^2 = H$)), prepared the *O*-acetyl derivatives ((14), (15); $R^1 = CHO$, $R^2 = MeCO$) and also by chemical conversions prepared the mixed *cis*- and *trans*-isomers of the corresponding xanthoxin alcohols ((14) (15); $R^1 = CH_2OH$, $R^2 = H$) xanthoxin acids ((14), (15); $R^1 = CO_2H$, $R^2 = H$) and acid esters ((14), (15); $R^1 = CO_2Me$, $R^2 = H$). Xanthoxin was also chemically oxidised to abscisic aldehydes ((16), (17); $R = CHO$) which could then be further oxidised to produce *cis*- and *trans*-(+)-ABA((16), (17); $R = CO_2H$).

The biological activities of xanthoxin and these related compounds have been compared with that of ABA in various tests[78]. Where both isomers were tested separately it was always found that the *cis*- was much more active than the *trans*-isomer, as is the case with ABA. Comparison of *cis*-xanthoxin with (±)-*cis*-ABA showed similar activities in the wheat coleoptile section test (where both produced non-toxic inhibition of growth, reversible by subsequent treatment with IAA) in the lettuce hypocotyl test and in the bean petiole abscission test, but in the cress seed germination test *cis*-xanthoxin

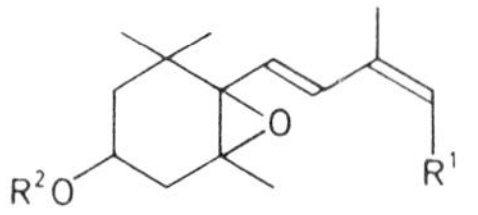

(14) 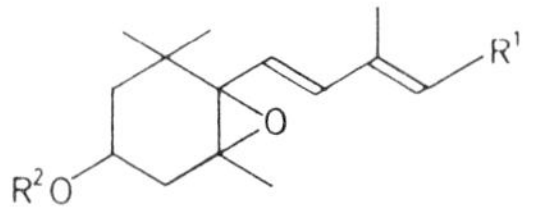 (15)

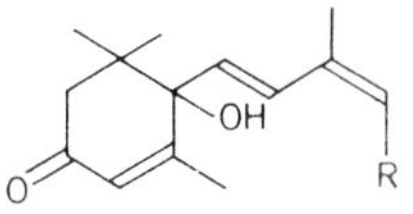

(16) 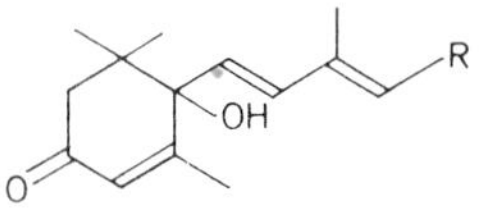 (17)

was at least ten times more inhibitory than ABA. In general, the alcohols of ABA and xanthoxin had comparable activities, as did the respective aldehydes; however, xanthoxin acid was an exception, being a much poorer inhibitor of cress seed germination than ABA. The order of activity of the analogues was not similar for all the tests and the results are difficult to interpret on account of possible differences of penetration and subsequent metabolism within the tissues. It is unknown whether any of these compounds are themselves inhibitory or have to be converted to a more active derivative to exert their effect*.

Interaction studies of xanthoxin with other growth substances indicated that it could antagonise the promoting effect of IAA in the wheat coleoptile section test, of GA_3 in a 'young wheat coleoptile' test and of kinetin in the growth of tobacco pith tissue.

4.2.6.5 Biosynthesis and metabolism of xanthoxin

Taylor and Burden[78] have shown that photolysis or mild chemical oxidation of isolated plant xanthophylls results in the formation of xanthoxin of the same stereochemical configuration as the parent pigment. It seems possible that xanthoxin might be produced endogenously in plant tissues containing these pigments, but this is not yet established. Plants are known to contain enzymes capable of oxidising carotenoids[82,83] and it has recently been shown by Firn and Friend[84] that xanthoxin can be produced enzymatically by oxidation of violaxanthin coupled to oxidation of linoleic acid by soyabean lipoxygenase. However, some plants which are known to contain xanthophylls

* The properties of *O*-methyl derivatives of xanthoxin have now also been examined[197].

e.g. tomato, have not yet been reported to contain detectable amounts of xanthoxin, and therefore the presence of xanthoxin may not necessarily be associated with xanthophylls.

The metabolism of xanthoxin has been little studied as yet, but Taylor and Burden[78] have shown that it can be converted to ABA in cut tomato shoots. When xanthoxin was supplied to the shoots, there was a 70-fold increase in their ABA content; that this was due to transformation of the xanthoxin to ABA was proved by conversion of [2-^{14}C] xanthoxin to [2-^{14}C]ABA.

The natural conversion of xanthoxin to ABA is a significant finding linking these two similar inhibitors. Whether xanthoxin is a true growth inhibitor in its own right, or owes its activity to conversion to ABA is still uncertain and must be the subject of further work. There is as yet little evidence for its having any physiological effects distinct from those of ABA. However, it has been reported[81] that illumination of etiolated pea seedlings with red light resulted in a five fold increase of xanthoxin in the dry weight of the tissue together with a marked increase in xanthophylls, whereas the low levels of ABA were unaffected. It seemed possible therefore that the xanthoxin, rather than ABA, might have been implicated in the 'dwarfing effect' induced by the illumination.

It is clear from all the above evidence, as well as that presented in Section 4.2.5.3, that considerable work is still needed to assess in physiological and biochemical terms any inter-relationship between xanthoxin and abscisic acid.

4.2.7 Lunularic acid

Lunularic acid (18), of similar structure and inhibitory activity to abscisic acid[85-87], has been suggested by Pryce[88] to be its biological equivalent in the more primitive green plants, liverworts and algae.

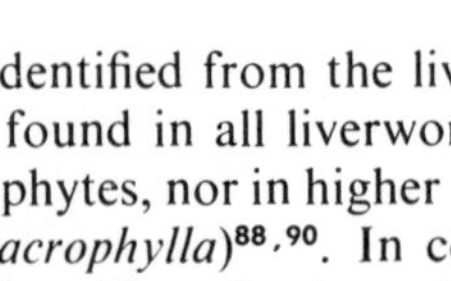

HO_2C OH

HO

Lunularic acid

It was first isolated and identified from the liverwort *Lunularia cruciata*[89], and has subsequently been found in all liverworts and algae examined, but not in any mosses or pteridophytes, nor in higher plants (with one exception—the leaves of *Hydrangea macrophylla*)[88,90]. In contrast, ABA is found universally in higher plants[43,52], and has also been detected in pteridophytes and mosses[90]. The almost universal difference in the distribution of the two substances, shown in Table 4.1 seems to be of possible phylogenetic significance.

Pryce[88] has also suggested that the presence of either ABA or lunularic acid might act as a chemical marker in taxonomic identification of mosses and liverworts within the bryophytes.

Table 4.1

	ABA	*Lunularic acid*
Higher plants	+	○ (+ in 1 exception)
Pteridophytes	+	○
Mosses	+	○
Liverworts	—	+
Algae	—	+

+ = present
○ = absent

4.2.8 Senescence factor

Evidence has been obtained by Osborne for the presence of an abscission-accelerating substance in diffusates from senescent but not young leaves of *Phaseolus vulgaris*[91], *Coleus blumei*[93] and certain other species[91,92]. It has been called Senescence Factor and its properties have been described recently by Osborne, Jackson and Milborrow[94]. The substance, which is acidic, is closely associated with ABA during its purification from plant extracts by the usual fractionation procedures, but it is not ABA. It is more active than ABA in promoting abscission of petioles in explants of *Phaseolus vulgaris*, and it has been found to stimulate ethylene production in bean petiole sections, which ABA does not. Osborne *et al.* believe that it may be of general occurrence in plants and that it functions as a regulator of ethylene production *in vivo*, thus accelerating abscission in a way distinct from ABA. They also suggest that it may be membrane-bound in young tissues but is released into the cytoplasm in damaged or senescent leaves.

Because the Senescence Factor and ABA are difficult to separate and possess similar abscission-promoting activity it might now be necessary to reappraise the results of previous work in which endogenous concentrations of ABA have been measured by abscission bioassays. For instance, it would seem possible that a substance assumed by Böttger[95] to be ABA, and found to be present in greater amounts in diffusates from senescent than from young leaves of *Coleus rehneltianus*, might not have consisted wholly of ABA but have been a mixture of ABA and the Senescence Factor.

4.3 QUANTITATIVE CHANGES IN THE CONCENTRATIONS OF PLANT GROWTH HORMONES IN PLANTS AND THEIR PHYSIOLOGICAL SIGNIFICANCE

4.3.1 Methods

A major obstacle in the accurate estimation of growth substances is inevitably their low concentrations in plant tissues, necessitating the analysis of large amounts of material. This imposes a practical limitation both on the degree of replication and the extent to which individual plant organs can be analysed, as well as making it virtually impossible to achieve total recoveries of the hormones. The variability of the recovery of hormones after purification can severely limit the significance of the results of comparative analyses unless the differences are large, whether they are determined by biological or physico-chemical methods. The accuracy can be improved by use of an internal standard in some cases (see Section 4.2.5.2), but it becomes increasingly apparent that, in general, if accuracy and sensitivity are to be increased, still better fractionation techniques must be found. Adsorption chromatography, including preparative t.l.c., attractive for its speed and ease of location, has been widely used in recent years, but it is accepted that extensive losses can be incurred on such adsorbents (in our laboratory we find we can lose up to 30% of the ABA applied to a silica gel plate), and perhaps it would be profitable to investigate alternative means of fractionation. It seems surprising, in the face of the tremendous advances which have been made in fractionation techniques, that this is still the area where further improvements need to be sought if we are to attain more precise estimates of hormones in smaller amounts of plant material.

Bioassays are advantageous in that they are more sensitive than physical or chemical methods of estimation, but with increasing reports of unidentified inhibitory and promotory substances which are difficult to separate with certainty from established hormones it has become apparent that the lack of specificity of bioassays restricts their reliability unless used in conjunction with a more definitive method.

Improvements in the techniques of *g.l.c.* have led to the growing application of this method for the separation and estimation of hormones, while *mass spectrometry* (MS) has become a valuable tool for chemical identification of compounds which can only be isolated in micro quantities, e.g. auxin in *Zea* coleoptile tips[96]. The combination of MS with g.l.c. by MacMillan and Pryce[97] has introduced a particular advantage in providing confirmatory evidence for the identity and purity of peaks. This technique has been used increasingly in the past few years and has yielded much valuable information, especially on the identification of new compounds. A further major advance has been made in MacMillan's laboratories[98,99] by the linking of g.l.c.–MS to a small computer which processes on-line the spectroscopic data and provides a library for the storage and retrieval of reference spectra. The system has been valuable for the separation and identification of new *gibberellins*[100] and has been used to identify *ABA* in extracts of carob fruit and coffee buds[99] and also in hazelnut seeds[101].

However, in spite of these advances, MacMillan[99] points out that although relatively small amounts of growth sustances can be detected by g.l.c. there is still a requirement for very extensive fractionation and purification beforehand, and reports on *g.l.c.* of auxins[102], *ABA*[45] and *cytokinins*[103] all mention the inherent difficulty of removing interfering substances which can mask the peaks contributed by the hormones. MacMillan states that a minimum of 5 μg is usually required in practice, and that this should be in a minimal concentration of 5% in the total fraction, which is a requirement difficult to meet in cases where endogenous levels are low. Thus, as with other methods, g.l.c. can be difficult to adapt for quantitative measurements and the initial purification is still one of the main limitations.

Ethylene is unique amongst known phytochormones in that it is volatile and readily estimable by *g.l.c.*[104] without the difficulties associated with extraction and fractionation. It can therefore be detected in small amounts in localised tissues.

4.3.2 Observed changes in growth substance concentrations in plants

Notwithstanding the difficulties of extraction, separation and estimation, enough reliable information has been accumulated to show that endogenous levels of various growth substances change in plant tissues as they grow and develop and in response to environmental changes. In many cases the physiological significance of the fluctuations in growth substance concentrations is not yet clear, but in other instances there is a close correlation between the endogenous level of a growth substance and a growth process. A few of the most convincing of these are described below.

4.3.2.1 Gibberellins in seeds of Phaseolus coccineus

Changes in the gibberellins of *Phaseolus coccineus* seeds during development have been studied in detail by Durley *et al.*[105] and Sembder *et al.*[106] In the early stages of seed development the concentrations of GA_1, GA_6 and GA_8 showed two distinct maxima whereas GA_5 and GA_{20}, although produced at an early stage, remained at a low concentration throughout. GA_{17} and GA_{20} were present in such low quantities that they could not be determined reliably.

Later on in development GA_8 became dominant, but as maturity approached the concentration of this gibberellin decreased and that of the GA_8 glucoside increased. In the mature seed only the GA_8 glucoside was present and from the following evidence it now seems likely that this glucoside is the storage form of gibberellin in the seeds. Thus it has been found that (a) tritiated GA_3 and GA_6 supplied to developing seeds were converted to GA_8 glucoside and (b) the amount of label in seedlings which developed from seeds containing tritiated GA_8 glucoside decreased in the water-soluble (glucoside) fraction and increased in the ethyl acetate-soluble (GA_8) fraction. The GA_8 thus released is probably important in regulating growth since it has been found[107] that GA_8 applied to seedlings of *Phaseolus coccinues* promotes elongation of the stems.

4.3.2.2 Cytokinins in pea root callus

Short and Torrey[108] have harvested pea root callus at intervals throughout a 12 week period and measured its fresh weight, the number of cells and the cytokinin activity. Cytokinin activity rose in the early period of culture growth and peak activity was established at the beginning of the phase of growth when it was associated with a high frequency of mitoses. As growth proceeded both the mitotic index and cytokinin levels fell.

4.3.2.3 Abscisic acid in wilting leaves

Wright and Hiron[109,110] first showed that a period of wilting led to an accumulation of ABA in detached wheat leaves. This has now been confirmed by these and other workers in whole plants[111,112], where leaf water deficits of varying degrees of severity have been induced in plants by exposing them to a variety of stress conditions, and in all cases there have been increases of ten times or more in the ABA content of the plants. The physiological significance of the large increases in ABA concentrations in the leaves became apparent when it was found that the uptake of ABA from solution by excised cuttings or leaves led to reduced transpiration rates[113] and to stomatal closure[114]. A correlation has now been established between increased endogenous ABA content and stomatal closure[115] and it seems likely that under stress conditions, the closure of stomata is controlled by endogenous ABA levels. In an experiment with Brussel sprout seedlings[116], it has been found that the ABA which accumulated during wilting disappeared very slowly when the plants were rewatered—the ABA concentration in the plants which had experienced a 44% leaf-water deficit was still twice that of the controls 2 days after rewatering. The results may explain why it has often been found that the opening of stomata is inhibited for several days after a serious water stress.

There have also been reports of increases in auxin[117] and decreases in cytokinin levels[118-120] in water-stressed plants and it has become clear that the greatest care is required in the maintenance of an adequate moisture supply to plants in any work involving the study of the concentrations of ABA or other hormones in plants.

4.3.2.4 Ethylene in etiolated pea epicotyls exposed to red and far-red light

Exposure of etiolated seedlings of *Pisum sativum* (var. Alaska) to a 20 s dose of red light caused a transient decrease in ethylene produced by the plumule and the plumular hook portion of the epicotyl and led to an increased elongation of the plumule. Far-red irradiation immediately following the red light treatment reversed these effects on both ethylene production and plumule elongation. Goeschl *et al.*[121] suggested therefore that the effects of light on plumule elongation are phytochrome-mediated and are regulated by changes in the levels of ethylene produced in the tissues.

Studies which relate changes in the levels of endogenous growth substances to changes in physiological processes are extremely valuable and need to be extended. The results can be difficult to interpret and ideally, for these to yield maximum information, experiments need to establish precisely the cells, tissues and organs in which the growth substances are produced and to determine how soon and in what part of the plant changes in growth and development follow changes in phytohormone concentrations. Such research also requires to be linked with investigations which analyse the effects and modes of action of the growth substances.

4.4 THE EFFECTS AND MODES OF ACTION OF PLANT-GROWTH SUBSTANCES

4.4.1 Effects

The effects of the various plant-growth substances when applied singly or in mixtures to whole plants, tissue cultures, sections or *in vitro* enzyme systems, have been studied extensively and most publications on growth substances describe such experiments. The effects of the various substances on growth and development have been discussed in some detail in a number of books[122-124] and in this connection the tabular presentation by Hill provides a useful summary.

It has become increasingly evident that the effects of any growth substance on growth and development are by no means consistent. Thus, for example, ABA when applied to growing plants usually inhibits the growth of the stem, leaf sheath and other plant parts. However, it has now been shown to promote the elongation of the mesocotyl of etiolated rice seedlings[125], the growth and fresh weight of *Citrus* bud cultures[126], and the initiation of roots on cuttings of *Phaseolus aureus*[127]; secondly, CCC has been shown to inhibit the synthesis of gibberellic acid and cause inhibition of stem elongation in a number of plants[128], but nevertheless in *Gladiolus* it promotes the elongation of stems and the production of flowers and spikes, as well as increasing the levels of giberellins in the tissues concerned[129,130]. In these and other instances it has become clear that the response to a growth substance may depend on the species and sometimes variety to which it is applied, as well as upon the physiological process being studied.

The response to a growth substance may also change with the age of the plant or organ. Thus Wright[131] found that the response of wheat coleoptile sections to optimal concentrations of IAA, GA_3 and kinetin depended on the age of the coleoptiles from which the sections were taken. GA_3 exerted maximum effect on sections cut from coleoptiles 18 h old, kinetin on those from coleoptiles 30 h old and IAA on those from coleoptiles 54 h old. There is also an increasing weight of evidence from interaction studies that the effects of any growth substance depend not only on its concentration but also on its concentration relative to that of other phytohormones and nutrients. From this it is obvious that the influence of endogenous hormones must depend on the balance of other hormones produced by or transported to the particular tissue under consideration. The following three examples have been chosen to illustrate interactions in plant systems of differing degrees of complexity.

4.4.1.1 Interactions between kinetin and auxin in lateral buds

Sorokin and Thimann[132] showed that auxin and kinetin interacted to regulate vascular differentiation in the lateral buds of *Pisum sativum*; auxin induced vascular strand formation but kinetin was needed to convert these to functional xylem units. They and Sachs[133,134] also observed that kinetin applied to a dormant bud led to the linking up of the vascular tissue with that of the main stem but auxin supplied from the tip suppressed this. In the light of these findings, as well as the fact that kinetin applications induced the growth of dormant buds, it has been suggested that the dormancy of lateral buds is the result of a failure to differentiate vascular tissue because of an unfavourable auxin/kinetin balance in the bud tissues.

However, other experiments with peas suggest that the growth of the lateral bud is induced at a much earlier stage than that of vascular differentiation. Thus Wardlow and Mortimer[135] followed the development of axillary buds which grew out after decapitation and found that, whereas growth started 4 h after decapitation, xylem and phloem differentiation began only after 24 h, and that the completion of the differentiation of the connections needed several days. Vascular development was clearly a consequence of increased bud growth initiated by previous events. Whether both of these processes require the same balance of hormones or whether vascular development proceeds under the influence of hormones produced when growth of the buds is induced is unknown.

The interpretation of the effects of auxin and kinins in regulating the growth of lateral buds is made more complicated by the results of Ali and Fletcher[136] on another leguminous plant, soyabean. In this case it was found that the cytokinin, 6-benzyl adenine, inhibited rather than promoted the growth of the cotyledonary buds of decapitated 7-day old seedlings and that auxin alone was without effect.

4.4.1.2 Interactions between kinetin, auxin and sucrose in differentiating tissue cultures

A tissue culture provides a simple system for studying the effects of growth factors and other nutrients without interference from hormones transported from other tissues. Wright and Northcote[137] describe how a fresh isolate of *Acer pseudoplatanus* was induced to differentiate xylem, phloem and roots when the culture medium contained naphthalene acetic acid (1 mg l^{-1}), kinetin (0.05–0.5 mg l^{-1}) and sucrose 3 or 5%). The relative proportions of these were important and if the concentration of sucrose was allowed to fall below 2%, no roots were differentiated even though xylem and phloem elements were formed. The behaviour of the fresh isolate was in sharp contrast to that of a 14-year old culture which had not been induced to differentiate at any stage in its history when grown on a range of growth media.

The importance of sucrose in interaction with IAA had been stressed previously[138], e.g. in determining the pattern of differentiation of young callus tissue of *Phaseolus vulgaris* and it is clear that sucrose has a specific biological role in addition to acting as a carbon source. Thus not only is the balance of different hormones important in determining the pattern of development but also the concentrations of these relative to sucrose and probably other substances in the developing tissue. That there may be variations in different species is also apparent by the fact that Jeffs and Northcote[138] found that in bean callus, sucrose could be substituted by other disaccharides but only those possessing an α-glucosidic link, whereas sycamore tissue did not impose the same limitation and disaccharides without this particular linkage were effective.

4.4.1.3 *Interactions between kinetin and auxin in enzyme synthesis*

Kaur-Sawhney and Galston[139] emphasise the difficulty involved in interpreting interactions between growth substances in other than the simplest of systems and for this reason they chose to study the interactions between auxin and kinetin in controlling the production of a single enzyme, peroxidase, in a tissue culture containing undifferentiated parenchyma (tobacco pith). They found that IAA inhibited the *de novo* synthesis of the peroxidase, increased the level of RNA and promoted the formation of a ribonuclease-sensitive macromolecular repressor of peroxidase formation. Kinetin opposed all these effects of auxin, and the authors postulated that auxin and kinetin may interact in this system by controlling the formation of a single molecular species of RNA. They suggest that an extension of their approach of trying to understand the molecular details of interactions may help to elucidate more complex analyses in which additional hormones and more highly-differentiated systems are involved.

4.4.2 Modes of action

Two effects of growth substances which have attracted much attention, and in which our understanding of mode of action is least incomplete, have been (a) the stimulation of the mobilisation of food reserves in cereal grain by the application of GA_3 and (b) the promotion of cell elongation in tissue sections by IAA. Recent research which has tried to interpret these two effects is described and analysed in some detail since it serves to illustrate the great difficulty of defining the primary effect of a hormone even in comparatively simple plant systems.

4.4.2.1 *Gibberellic acid and the mobilisation of food reserves in cereal grain*

Research before 1968 had shown clearly that GA_3 increased the rate of mobilisation of food reserves in barley grain by stimulating the activity of hydrolytic enzymes in the cells of the aleurone layer[140]. In the case of α-amylase this was shown to be the result of an increased *de novo* synthesis of the enzyme in the cells[141] and there was some evidence and considerable support for the hypothesis that GA_3 acts by activating genes which lead to the induction of synthesis of messenger RNA which in turn results in the increased synthesis of new enzymes.

Work since then has confirmed that the application of GA_3 to the barley aleurone layer stimulates the RNA-dependent new synthesis of enzymes as well as increasing the rates of synthesis of proteins[142-147]. However, it has also been shown that GA_3 brings about important biochemical and anatomical changes in the aleurone cells well within the lag phase between its application and the increased synthesis of α-amylase (8–10 h). These are (a) an increase in the concentration of soluble carbohydrates within 15 min[148], (b) an increase in the activity of enzymes involved in phospholipid synthesis—phosphoryl cytidyl-transferase and phosphorcholine glyceride-transferase—within 2 h[149], (c) an increase in the rate of formation of endoplasmic reticulum and of polysomes bound on the reticulum within 2–4h [150a,b] and (d) an increase in the levels of adenosine 3′,5′-monophosphate (cyclic AMP) within 3–4 h[151]. It is clear, therefore, that GA_3 causes important changes within minutes, and possibly seconds, of its application to the aleurone cells; it seems likely that the primary effect of GA_3 is exerted on some organelle or enzyme system already present in the cell at the time of treatment and that the increases in protein, nucleic acid and enzyme synthesis occur subsequently and are secondary effects of hormone treatment. There is now an urgent need to extend the study of the effects of GA_3 in the aleurone cells at subcellular and molecular levels as soon as possible after treatment. Of particular importance in this connection will be the effects involving cyclic AMP since there is evidence to suggest that this substance plays an important intermediary role in the promotion of enzyme activity by GA_3. Thus it has been found that cyclic AMP, when applied to aleurone cells, evokes changes in enzymic activity and synthesis comparable to those caused by GA_3 itself[152,153].

4.4.2.2 *Auxin and the promotion of cell elongation in tissue sections*

The considerable volume of past work attempting to determine the primary effect of auxin in promoting cell elongation in sections of coleoptiles and stems has been reviewed recently by Audus[1] and Thimann[2]. In the last 5 years research in this field has concentrated largely on the mechanisms by which cell walls are made more plastic by IAA and less so by ethylene. Our understanding of the primary effect of auxin in this connection is still very incomplete but there is evidence to suggest that the hormone may act through effects on the activity of enzymes, on synthesis of nucleic acids, proteins and enzymes, on cell membranes and on cyclic AMP. This is discussed later.

(a) *Effects on the activity of enzymes*—IAA has been found to increase by 60% the activity of β-1,3-glucanase in *Avena* coleoptile segments[154]. This effect is probably important for the promotion of cell elongation by auxin since β-1,3-glucanase secreted by *Sclerotinia libertiana* and applied to oat coleoptile sections increased elongation[155,156]. In contrast to the β-1,3-glucanase, β-1,4-glucanase was without effect on the elongation of *Avena* coleoptiles even though it increased the extensibility of the cell walls[157].

Osborne and co-workers[158-159] have studied closely the effects of ethylene on cell elongation and cell wall composition in the epicotyls of etiolated plants of *Pisum sativum*. Ethylene has been found to inhibit elongation and enhance lateral cell expansion. It has also been found to increase the levels of cytoplasmic and wall-bound peroxidases (ionically and covalently bound to the cell wall) and to increase the hydroxyproline content of the wall glycoproteins. Ridge and Osborne[158a,b] speculate that ethylene influences hydroxylation of the proline in peptides in the cytoplasm and the subsequent transfer of the hydroxyproline-rich protein to the wall where this may play a part in determining wall extensibility and the orientation of growth.

(b) *Effects on nucleic acid and protein synthesis*—There have been reported a large number of experiments to show that treatment of elongating cells with IAA leads to increases in RNA and protein synthesis. The results of Nooden[160] suggest effects at the transcription level in maize coleoptiles, those of Trewavas[161,162] effects on polysome numbers and r-RNA synthesis in pea internodes, and those of O'Brien[163] effects on RNA polymerase activity. The results of other workers also suggest effects on these[164]. All this information has been held to support the hypothesis that auxin exerted its effect on cell elongation by activating genes which led to the synthesis of messenger RNA, which in turn resulted in the increased synthesis of the enzymes which increased the extensibility of the cell wall to allow greater cell elongation. Convincing as are the effects of IAA on RNA synthesis, it has been ask d whether they are primary effects or consequences of events which happened earlier. The results of elegant experiments by Nissl and Zenk[165], in which the elongation of coleoptile segments was measured as soon as possible after application of the auxin, showed that growth was promoted almost immediately at 40°C at an IAA concentration of 5×10^{-3} M, whereas changes in RNA and enzyme synthesis were only detectable at a much later stage. Other workers[166-173] have confirmed the immediacy of the effects of IAA on elongation in coleoptile and stem sections and it seems likely therefore, that the effects of IAA on RNA and protein synthesis, although very important for cell wall expansion and the maintenance of cell metabolism during later phases of growth, are secondary effects.

The primary effect of auxin in promoting cell elongation may be exerted within seconds of application but there is, at the moment, no clear picture as to what this effect might be, although there are indications as follows.

(c) *Effects on cell membranes*—In experiments performed with isolated protoplasts taken from just behind the meristematic region of tomato seedling roots and also from *Avena* coleoptiles, Cocking[174,175], has shown that low concentrations of IAA led to enlargements in both the vacuoles and protoplasts, to an increased rate of protoplasmic streaming and to the eventual bursting of the protoplasts. It is of interest that the effective concentration for the root protoplast was 10^{-11} M and that for the *Avena* coleoptiles 10^{-5} M. The interpretation of these results is difficult but they establish that IAA exerts effects when the cell wall is absent and that membranes may be affected.

A close association between IAA and cell membranes has been inferred from the results of experiments to interpret the mode of action of a synthetic compound which interferes with auxin transport, α-naphthylphthalamic acid (NPA)[176]. This substance has been found to inhibit the movement of auxin through corn coleoptiles within 1 min of its application and also to bind itself to a particulate fraction of the coleoptile cells which is considered to consist primarily of plasma membrane vesicles[177]. Thompson *et al.* found that the NPA dissociated from its binding site when the particulate cell material was centrifuged through an NPA-free cushion and the NPA thus released could be used in another binding test without apparent change and was chromatographically unaltered. It would seem, therefore, that the NPA binding is reversible and non-covalent. It has been inferred from the above results that cell membranes are involved in auxin transport and that NPA interferes with this movement by occupying sites otherwise used by IAA.

Cleland[178] and Hager *et al.*[179] have shown that the rate of elongation of coleoptile segments can be increased by lowering the pH. Rayle and Cleland[180] have recently compared the effects of low pH and auxin on the growth of *Avena* coleoptiles and they find the following similarities: (a) they produce the same maximum growth rate and wall-extensibility, (b) in both cases wall extensibility began to rise at the time when rapid extension commenced but did not reach a maximum value until 1½–2 h later, (c) the Q_{10} for growth was high at 15–25°C and low at 25–35°C for both, (d) in both cases promotion ceased whenever the tension in the walls was reduced.

However, there were also distinct differences in the two responses, and of greatest importance is the fact that continued protein synthesis was needed for the auxin response but not for the growth induced by low pH. Rayle and Cleland speculate that the action of auxin may be to ensure the presence in the cell wall of a factor of unknown nature which is capable of causing the rupture of acid-labile cell wall bonds. This in turn they believe would lead to an increase in the extensibility of the wall and thus to cell extension. The way in which auxin exerts its effect on this factor and the identity of the acid-labile bonds are obscure.

Hager *et al.*[179] have studied the effect of low pH on cell elongation in auxin-starved *Helianthus* hypocotyls. Their experiments show that it is possible to induce elongation in a buffer solution kept at pH 4 and that the elongation is of the same order as that induced by auxin in air. The acid stimulation was rapid and could be switched on and off by appropriate pH changes, it could be prevented by chemicals which make the protoplasmic membranes permeable to protons and be induced by high energy phosphate (ATP) in an atmosphere of nitrogen, an effect which was greatly increased by prior incubation with auxin in the air.

In the light of these results Hager *et al.* postulate that (a) wall-softening enzymes are activated by high proton concentrations in the wall compartment, (b) this effect is maintained by a membrane-bound anisotropic ATP-ase proton pump, (c) the function of auxin is to co-operate with high energy phosphates in the operation of this pump.

An interesting paper has recently been published by Pitt and Galpin[181] who describe how they have isolated lysosomes from dark-grown potato shoots and examined their properties. They found that the lysosomic fractions were rich in RNA and contained enzymes which were separated into fractions exhibiting various activities: acid phosphatase, phosphodiesterase, ribonuclease, carboxylicesterase and β-glycerophosphatase. They also found that the following treatments led to an increased enzyme activity: (a) freezing, thawing, high-speed blending and ultrasonication, (b) treatment with Triton X-10 and deoxycholate, (c) extremes of pH, and (d) crude snake venom—this was very rapid and effective in solubilising acid phosphatases. In the light of these results the authors postulate that plant lysosomes may be akin to those described by Koenig[182,183], for animal cells: namely, membrane-limited polyanionic lipo-protein granules, with the contained enzymes held in an inert state by electrostatic binding to acidic groups of the lipo-protein matrix, with their active sites unavailable for interaction with the substrate. It is suggested by Pitt and Galpin that the lysosomes of the potato cells contain enzymes similarly associated the lysosome membranes.

Although there is no information available on the effects of growth substances on plant lysosomes it is clear that this is an important field for study. It is feasible that the rapidity of the action of growth substances would be explicable if they act by effecting the release of enzymes bound to the lysosome membranes.

(d) *Effects on cyclic AMP*—As in the case of the action of GA_3 in aleurone cells, there is now some evidence which indicates that IAA might also exert its effects on cell elongation through cyclic AMP. Thus, Salomon and Mascarenhas[184] and Brewin and Northcote[185,186] have shown that treatment of *Avena* coleoptiles with IAA increased the production of cyclic AMP within minutes. That this effect may be important in the mediation of the effect of IAA on elongation is suggested by the results of Salomon and Mascarenhas[187] who found that cyclic AMP and IAA both stimulated RNA synthesis in cell-free extracts of *Avena* coleoptiles, and by those of Kamisaka and Masuda[185,189] who discovered that cyclic AMP and auxin acted synergistically to promote the growth of freshly-cut sections of the tuber tissue of Jerusalem artichoke. However, in contrast to these positive effects, neither cyclic AMP nor dibutyryl cyclic AMP has been found to stimulate the extension growth of *Avena* coleoptiles[185,190]. Brewin and Northcote therefore pose the question as to whether the cyclic nucleotides penetrated into the coleoptiles. The presence of cyclic AMP phosphodiesterase on the outside of plant cells has been demonstrated in soyabean callus[191] and barley endosperm[192], and it is suggested that the exogenously-applied cyclic AMP may be incapable of penetrating into the cell before being broken down.

It is of interest that Brewin and Northcote[185] found that cytokinins had no effect on the rapid rise in the intracellular concentrations of cyclic AMP in the period immediately after subculturing their soyabean callus into a new medium, but 20 h afterwards the cytokinins produced higher concentrations of cyclic AMP. They offer the explanation that the effect of the cytokinin may be a very indirect consequence of modifying the physiology of the cells towards mitosis and/or that the cytokinins must first be converted to an active form.

The limited number of experiments carried out to date on the relationship between IAA and cyclic AMP in cell elongation are extremely interesting and this clearly represents a field of study meriting intensive investigation.

4.5 CONCLUSIONS

It will be seen from the above discussion that the understanding of the modes of action of the phytohormones in both the aleurone layer and cell elongation systems is still incomplete and confusing. It is difficult at the moment (a) to distinguish between primary, secondary, tertiary . . . . effects, (b) to determine how far the various effects are linked either directly or indirectly, and (c) to ascertain how far one substance may affect more than one aspect of the complex machinery regulating the individual processes.

Future research will clearly need to solve these problems but the work is difficult and costly in terms of both equipment and manpower. It will call for carefully-planned investigations correlating endogenous concentrations of phytohormones in different tissues with physiological effects, as well as a close study of the microstructure and metabolism of the cells as soon as possible after treatment and at regular intervals thereafter. Team work would seem to be desirable, and indeed inevitable, in this research in order to provide the necessary expertise in the fields of plant physiology, biochemistry, biophysics, anatomy and mathematics/statistics; all of these disciplines will be needed for the development and application of suitable experimental designs and techniques as well as for the interpretation of the results.

References

1. Audus, L. J. (1973). *Plant Growth Substances* (London: Leonard Hill)
2. Thimann, K. V. (1972). *Plant Physiology* (F. C. Steward, editor) (New York and London: Academic Press)
3. Scott, T. K. (1972). *Annu. Rev. Pl. Physiol.*, **23,** 235
4. Lang, A. (1970). *Annu. Rev. Pl. Physiol.*, **21,** 537
5. Cross, B. E. (1969). *Progress in Phytochemistry*, **1,** 195
6. Bailiss, K. W. (1971). *Bot. Rev.*, **37,** 437
7. Helgesson, J. P. (1968). *Science*, **161,** 974
8. Skoog, F. and Armstrong, D. J. (1970). *Annu. Rev. Pl. Physiol.*, **21,** 259
9. Skoog, F. and Schmidtz, R. Y. (1972). *Plant Physiology*, (F. C. Steward, editor) (New York and London: Academic Press)
10. Abeles, F. B. (1972). *Annu. Rev. Pl. Physiol.*, **23,** 259
11. Mapson, L. W., (1969). *Biol. Rev.*, **44,** 155
12. Pratt, H. K. and Goeschl, J. D. (1969). *Annu. Rev. Pl. Physiol.*, **20,** 54
13. Addicott, F. T. and Lyon, J. L. (1969). *Annu. Rev. Pl. Physiol.*, **20,** 139
14. Addicott, F. T. (1970). *Biol. Rev.*, **45,** 485

15a. Schneider, G. (1970). *Annu. Rev. Pl. Physiol.*, **21,** 499

15b. Morgan, D. G. (1968). *Euphytica*, 17 (Suppl. 1), 189

16. Kefeli, V. I. and Kadyrov, C. Sh. (1972). *Annu. Rev. Pl. Physiol.*, **23,** 185
17. Erdmann, N. and Schwiewer, U. (1971). *Planta*, **97,** 135
18. Sheldrake, A. R. and Northcote, D. H. (1968). *Planta*, **80,** 227
19. Sheldrake, A. R. and Northcote, D. H. (1968). *New Phytologist*, **67,** 1
20. Sheldrake, A. R. and Northcote, D. H. (1968). *J. Exp. Botany*, **19,** 681
21. Sheldrake, A. R. and Northcote, D. H. (1968). *Nature* (*London*), **217,** 195
22. Northcote, D. H. (1971). *Symposia. Soc. Exp. Biol.*, **25,** 51
23. Libbert, E. and Manteuffel, R. (1970). *Physiol. Plantarum*, **23,** 928
24. Libbert, E. and Silhengst, P. (1970). *Physiol. Plantarum*, **23,** 480
25. Libbert, E., Menteuffel, R. and Siegl, E. (1970). *Physiol. Plantarum*, **23,** 784
26. Libbert, E., Fischer, E., Drawert, A. and Schröder, R. (1970). *Physiol. Plantarum*, **23,** 784
27. Libbert, E., Fischer, E., Drawert, A. and Schröder, R. (1970). *Physiol. Plantarum*, **23,** 287
28. Murofushi, N., Yokota, T. and Takahashi, N. (1970). *Agr. Biol. Chem.*, **34,** 1436
29. Yamaguchi, J., Yokata, N., Murofushi, N., Ogawa, Y. and Takahashi, N. (1970). *Agr. Biol. Chem.*, **34,** 1439
30. Takahashi, N., Murofushi, N. and Yokota, T. (1972). *Plant Growth Substances.* 1970, 175. (D. J. Carr, editor) (Berlin, Heidelberg, New York: Springer Verlag)
31. Yamane, H., Yamaguchi, N., Murofushi, N., Ogawa, Y. and Takahashi, N. (1970). *Agric. Biol. Chem.*, **34,** 1144
32. Bearder, J. R. and MacMillan, J. (1972). *Agr. Biol. Chem.*, **36,** 342
33. MacMillan, J. (1972). *Hormonal Regulation in Plant Growth and Development*, 175 (H. Kaldewey and Y. Varder, editors) (Weinheim, Verlag Chemie)
34. MacMillan, J. (1971). Aspects of Terpenoid Chemistry and Biochemistry. 153, (T. W. Goodwin, editor) (London and New York: Academic Press)
35. West, C. A., Oster, M., Robinson, D. R., Lew, F. and Murphy, P. (1969). *Biochemistry and Physiology of Plant Growth Substances*, 313 (Ottawa: Runge Press)

36. Graebe, J. E., Bowen, D. H. and MacMillan, J. (1972). *Planta*, **102**, 261
37. Leopold, A. C. (1972). *Hormonal Regulation in Plant Growth and Development*, 245 (H. Kaldewey and Y. Varder, editors) (Weinheim: Verlag Chemie)
38. Bennet-Clark, T. A. and Kefford, N. P. (1953). *Nature (London)*, **171**, 645
39. Milborrow, B. W. (1969). *Sci. Progress, Oxf.*, **57**, 533
40. *Bibliography on Abscisic Acid*. (F. Hoffman-La Roche & Co. Ltd., Dept. VI/VEF, P.O.B. CH 4002 Basel, Switzerland)
41. Dörffling, K. (1972). *Hormonal Regulation in Plant Growth and Development*, 281 (H. Kaldewey, Y. Vardar, editors) (Weinheim: Verlag Chemie)
42. Addicott, F. T. (1972). *Plant Growth Substances 1970*, 272, (D. J. Carr, editor) (Berlin, Heidelberg, New York: Springer Verlag)
43. Milborrow, B. W. (1967). *Planta*, **76**, 93
44. Milborrow, B. V. (1970). *J. Exp. Bot.*, **21**, 17
45. Davis, L. A., Heinz, D. E. and Addicott, F. T. (1968). *Pl. Physiol.*, **43**, 1389
46. Gaskin, P. and MacMillan, J. (1968). *Phytochem.*, **7**, 1699
47. Mousseron-Canet, M., Mani, J. C., Dalle, J. P. and Olivé, J. L. (1966). *Bull. Soc. Chim. Fr.*, 12, 3874
48. Milborrow, B. V. (1968). *Biochemistry and Physiology of Plant Growth Substances*, 1531 (F. Wightman and G. Setterfield, editors) (Ottawa: Runge Press)
49. Milborrow, B. V. (1971). *Aspects of Terpenoid Chemistry and Biochemistry. Proc. Phytochem. Soc. Symp. Liverpool 1970*, 137, (T. W. Goodwin, editor) (London: Academic Press)
50. Lenton, J. R., Bowen, M. R. and Saunders, P. F. (1968). *Nature (London)*, **220**, 86
51. Lenton, J. R., Perry, V. M. and Saunders, P. F. (1971). *Planta*, **96**, 271
52. Wareing, P. F. and Ryback, G. (1970). *Endeavour*, **29**, 84
53. Taylor, H. F. and Smith, T. A. (1967). *Nature (London)*, **215**, 1513
54. Milborrow, B. V. and Robinson, D. R. (1973). *J. Exp. Bot.*, **24**, 537
55. Rudnicki, R. and Pieniazek, J. (1971). *Bull. Acad. Pol. Sci., Cl. V. Sér. Sci. biol.*, **19**, 421
56. Noddle, R. C. and Robinson, D. R. (1969). *Biochem. J.*, **112**, 547
57. Robinson, D. R. and Ryback, G. (1969). *Biochem. J.*, **113**, 895
58. Wright, S. T. C. (1969). *Planta*, **86**, 10
59. Wright, S. T. C. and Hiron, R. W. P. (1969). *Nature (London)*, **224**, 719
60. Milborrow, B. V. and Noddle, R. C. (1970). *Biochem. J.*, **119**, 729
61. Tamura, S. and Nagao, M. (1969). *Planta*, **85**, 209
62. Milborrow, B. V. (1972). *Plant Growth Substances 1970*, 281, (D. J. Carr, editor) (Berlin, Heidelberg, New York: Springer Verlag)
63. Koshimizu, K., Inui, M., Fukui, H. and Mitsui, T. (1968). *Agric. Biol. Chem.*, **32**, 789
64. Koshimizu, K., Mitsui, T. and Ogawa, Y. (1966). *Agric. Biol. Chem.*, **30**, 941
65. Milborrow, B. V. (1969). *Chem. Commun.*, 966
66. MacMillan, J. and Pryce, R. J. (1968). *Chem. Commun.*, 124
67. Davis, L. A., Lyon, J. L. and Addicott, F. T. (1972). *Planta*, **102**, 294
68. Walton, D. C. and Sondheimer. E. (1972). *Pl. Physiol.*, **49**, 285
69. Walton, D. C. and Sondheimer, E. (1972). *Pl. Physiol.*, **49**, 290
70. Tamura, S. and Nagao, M. (1970). *Agric. Biol. Chem.*, **34**, 1393
71. Oritani, T. and Yamashita, K. (1970). *Agric. Biol. Chem.*, **34**, 108
72. Sondheimer, E. and Walton, D. C. (1970). *Plant Physiol.*, **45**, 244
73. McWha, J. A., Philipson, J. J., Hillman, J. R. and Wilkins, M. B. (1973). *Planta*, **109**, 327
74. Popoff, I. C., Sachs, R. M. and Gibbs, J. B. (1972). *J. Agric. Food Chem.*, **20**, 665
75. Taylor, H. F. (1968). *Plant growth regulators. Society of Chemical Industry. Monograph No. 31*, 22 (London)
76. Taylor, H. F. and Burden, R. S. (1970). *Phytochemistry*, **9**, 2217
77. Burden, R. S. and Taylor, H. F. (1970). *Tetrahedron Lett.*, 4071
78. Taylor, H. F. and Burden, R. S. (1972). *Proc. Roy. Soc. (London) B*, **180**, 317
79. Taylor, H. F. and Burden, R. S. (1970). *Nature (London)*, **227**, 302
80. Firn, R. D., Burden, R. S. and Taylor, H. F. (1972). *Planta*, **102**, 115
81. Burden, R. S., Firn, R. D., Hiron, R. W. P., Taylor, H. F. and Wright, S. T. C. (1971). *Nature New Biol.*, **234**, 95
82. Dicks, J. W. and Friend, J. (1967). *Phytochemistry*, **6**, 1193
83. Dicks, J. W. (1970). *Phytochem.*, **9**, 1433

84. Firn, R. D. and Friend, J. (1972). *Planta*, **103,** 263
85. Pryce, R. J. (1971). *Planta*, **97,** 354
86. Valio, I. F. M. and Schwabe, W. W. (1970). *J. Exp. Bot.*, **21,** 138
87. Fries, K. (1964). *Beitr. Biol. Pflanz.*, **40,** 177
88. Pryce, R. J. (1972). *Phytochem.*, **11,** 1759
89. Valio, I. F. M., Burden, R. S. and Schwabe, W. W. (1969). *Nature* (*London*), **223,** 1176
90. Pryce, R. J. (1971). *Phytochem.*, **10,** 2679
91. Osborne, D. J. (1955). *Nature* (*London*), **176,** 1161
92. Osborne, D. J. (1958). *Trop. Agric.*, **35,** 145
93. Jacobs, W. P., Shield, J. A. and Osborne, D. J. (1962). *Plant Physiol.*, **37,** 104
94. Osborne, D. J., Jackson, M. B. and Milborrow, B. V. (1972). *Nature New Biol.*, **240,** 98
95. Böttger, M. (1970). *Planta*, **93,** 205
96. Greenwood, M. S., Shaw, S., Hillman, J. R., Ritchie, A. and Wilkins, M. B. (1972). *Planta*, **108,** 179
97. MacMillan, J. and Pryce, R. J. (1968). *Soc. Chem. Ind. Monograph.*, **31,** 36
98. Binks, R., Cleaver, R. L., Littler, J. S. and MacMillan, J. (1970). *Chemistry in Britain*, **7,** 8
99. MacMillan, J. (1972). *Plant Growth Substances 1970*, 790, (D. J. Carr, editor) (Berlin, Heidelberg, New York: Springer Verlag)
100. Binks, R., MacMillan, J. and Pryce, R. J. (1969). *Phytochem.*, **8,** 271
101. Williams, P. M., Ross, J. D. and Bradbeer, J. W. (1973). *Planta*, **110,** 303
102. Dedio, W. and Zalik, S. (1966). *Anal. Biochem.*, **16,** 36
103. Rathbone, M. P. and Hall, R. H. (1972). *Planta*, **108,** 93
104. Jackson, M. B. and Osborne, D. J. (1972). *J. Exp. Bot.*, **23,** 849
105. Durley, R. C., MacMillan, J. and Pryce, R. J. (1971). *Phytochemistry*, **10,** 1891
106. Sembder, G., Weiland, J., Aurich, O. and Schreiber, K. (1968). *Plant Growth Regulators*. S.C.I. Monograph No. 31, 70
107. Crozier, A., Bowen, D. H., MacMillan, J., Reid, D. M. and Most, B. H. (1971). *Planta*, **97,** 142
108. Short, K. C. and Torrey, J. C. (1972). *J. Exp. Bot.*, **23,** 1099
109. Wright, S. T. C. and Hiron, R. W. P. (1969). *Nature* (*London*), **224,** 719
110. Wright, S. T. C. and Hiron, R. W. P. (1972). *Plant Growth Substances*, 1970, 291 (D. J. Carr, editor) (Berlin, Heidelberg, New York: Springer Verlag)
111. Zeevaart, J. A. D. (1971). *Pl. Physiol.*, **48,** 86
112. Simpson, G. M. and Saunders, P. F.. (1972). *Planta*, **102,** 272
113. Little, C. H. A. and Eidt, D. C. (1968). *Nature* (*London*), **220,** 498
114. Mittelhauser, C. J. and van Steveninck, R. F. M. (1969). *Nature* (*London*), **221,** 281
115. Tucker, D. J. and Mansfield, T. A. (1971). *Planta*, **98,** 157
116. Jones, R. J. and Mansfield, T. A. (1970). *J. Exp. Bot.*, **21,** 714
117. Phillips, I. D. J. (1964). *Ann. Bot. NS.*, **28,** 36
118. Tal, M. and Imber, D. (1971). *Pl. Physiol.*, **47,** 849
119. Itai, C. and Vaardia, Y. (1965). *Pl. Physiol.*, **18,** 941
120. Itai, C. and Vaardia, Y. (1971). *Pl. Physiol.*, **47,** 87
121. Goeschl, J. D., Pratt, H. K. and Bonner, B. A. (1967). *Pl. Physiol.*, **42,** 1077
122. Wareing, P. F. and Phillips, I. D. J. (1970). *The Control of Growth and Development in Plants*. (Oxford: Pergamon Press)
123. Wilkins, M. B. (1969). *The Physiology of Plant Growth and Development* (London: McGraw Hill)
124. Hill, T. A. (1973). *Endogenous Plant Growth Substances* (London: Arnold)
125. Takahashi, K. (1972). *Nature New Biol.*, **238,** 92
126. Altman, A. and Goren, R. (1971). *Plant Physiol.*, **46,** 844
127. Ting-Yon, C., Meyer, M. M. Jr. and Beevers, L. (1969). *Planta*, **88,** 192
128. Cathey, H. M. (1964). *Annu. Rev. Pl. Physiol.*, **15,** 271
129. Halevey, A. H. and Wittwer, S. H. (1965). *Naturwissenschaften*, **52,** 310
130. Halevey, A. H. and Shilo, R. (1970). *Physiol. Plantarum*, **23,** 820
131. Wright, S. T. C. (1969). *Biochemistry and Physiology of Plant Growth Substances*, 521 (Ottawa: Runge Press)
132. Sorokin, H. and Thimann, K. V. (1966). *Protoplasma*, **59,** 326
133. Sachs, T. (1969). *Ann. Bot.*, **33,** 263

134. Sachs, T. (1970). *Israel J. Bot.*, **19,** 484
135. Wardlaw, I. F. and Mortimer, D. C. (1970). *Can. J. Bot.*, **48,** 229
136. Ali, A. and Fletcher, R. A. (1971). *Can. J. Bot.*, **49,** 1727
137. Wright, K. and Northcote, D. H. (1972). *J. Cell. Sci.*, **11,** 319
138. Jeffs, R. A. and Northcote, D. H. (1967). *J. Cell. Sci.*, **2,** 77
139. Kaur-Sawhney, R. and Galston, A. W. (1972). *Hormonal Regulation in Plant Growth and Development.* 27 (H. Kaldewey and Y. Varder, editors) (Weinheim: Verlag Chemie)
140. Paleg, L. G. and West, C. A. (1972). *Plant Physiology*, 146 (F. C. Steward, editor) (New York, London: Academic Press)
141. Filner, P. and Varner, J. E. (1967). *Proc. Nat. Acad. Sci. (USA)*, **58,** 1520
142. Koblitz, H. (1969). *Biol. Zentr.*, **88,** 283
143. Koblitz, H. (1969). *Biol. Zentr.*, **88,** 409
144. Scala, J., Patrick, C. and Macbeth, G. (1969). *Phytochemistry*, **8,** 37
145. Reid, P. D. and Marsh, H. V. Jnr. (1969). *Z. Pflanzenphysiol.*, **61,** 170
146. Dufus, C. M. (1969). *Phytochemistry*, **8,** 1205
147. Groat, J. I. and Briggs, D. E. (1969). *Phytochemistry*, **8,** 1615
148. Pollard, C. J. (1971). *Biochim. Biophys. Acta*, **252,** 553
149. Johnson, K. D. and Kende, H. (1971). *Proc. Nat. Acad. Sci. (USA)*, **68,** 2674
150a. Evans, W. H. and Varner, J. E. (1971). *Proc. Nat. Acad. Sci. (USA)*, **68,** 1631
150b. Evans, W. H. and Varner, J. E. (1972). *Plant Physiol.*, **49,** 348
151. Pollard, C. J. (1970). *Biochem. Biophys. Acta.*, **201,** 511
152. Nicholls, M. W., Schaefer, G. M. and Galsky, A. G. (1971). *Plant Cell Physiol. (Tokyo)*, **12,** 717
153. Earle, K. M. and Galsky, A. G. (1971). *Plant Cell Physiol. (Tokyo)*, **12,** 727
154. Heyn, A. N. J. (1969). *Arch. Biochim. Biophys.*, **132,** 442
155. Tanimoto, E. and Masuda, Y. (1968). *Physiol. Plantarum*, **21,** 820
156. Wada, S. E., Tanimoto, E. and Masuda, Y. (1968). *Plant and Cell Physiol. (Tokyo)*, **9,** 369
157. Ruesink, A. W. (1969). *Planta*, **89,** 95
158a. Ridge, J. and Osborne, D. J. (1970). *J. Exp. Bot.*, **21,** 843
158b. Ridge, J. and Osborne, D. J. (1971). *Nature New Biol.*, **229,** 205
159. Sargeant, J. A., Alack, A. V. and Osborne, D. J. (1973). *Planta*, **109,** 185
160. Nooden, L. D. (1968). *Plant Physiol.*, **43,** 140
161. Trewavas, A. J. (1968). *Arch. Biochem. Biophys.*, **123,** 324
162. Trewavas, A. J. (1968). *Phytochemistry*, **7,** 673
163. O'Brien, T. J., Jarvis, B. C., Cherry, J. H. and Hanson, J. B. (1968). *Biochim. Biophys. Acta*, **169,** 35
164. Key, J. L. (1969). *Annu. Rev. Pl. Physiol.*, **20,** 449
165. Nissl, D. F. and Zenk, M. H. (1969). *Planta*, **89,** 323
166. Durand, J. and Zenk, M. H. (1972). *Plant Growth Substances, 1970*, 62 (D. J. Carr, editor) (Berlin, Heidelberg, New York: Springer Verlag)
167. Evans, M. L. and Ray, D. L. (1969). *J. Gen. Physiol.*, **53,** 1
168. Evans, M. L. and Hokanson, R. (1969). *Planta*, **85,** 85
169. Uhrström, I. (1969). *Physiol. Plantarum*, **22,** 271
170. Rayle, D. L., Evans, M. L. and Hertl, R. (1970). *Proc. Nat. Acad. Sci. (USA)*, **65,** 184
171. Barkley, G. M. and Evans, M. L. (1970). *Plant Physiol.*, **45,** 143
172. Evans, M. L. and Rayle, D. L. (1970). *Plant Physiol.*, **45,** 240
173. de la Fuente and Leopold, A. C. (1970). *Plant Physiol.*, **46,** 186
174. Cocking, E. C. (1972). *Hormonal Regulation in Plant Growth and Development*, 19 (H. Kaldewey and Y. Varder, editors) (Weinheim: Verlag Chemie)
175. Power, J. B. and Cocking, E. C. (1970). *J. Exp. Bot.*, **21,** 64
176. Morgan, D. G. and Söding, H. (1958). *Planta*, **52,** 235
177. Thomson, K. S., Hertel, R. and Müller, S. (1973). *Planta*, **109,** 337
178. Rayle, D. L. and Cleland, R. (1970). *Plant Physiol.*, **46,** 250
179. Hager, A., Menzel, H. and Krauss, A. (1971). *Planta*, **100,** 47
180. Rayle, D. L. and Cleland, R. (1972). *Plant Growth Substances 1970*, 44 (D. J. Carr, editor) (Berlin, Heidelberg, New York: Springer Verlag)
181. Pitt, D. and Galpin, M. (1973). *Planta*, **109,** 233

182. Koenig, H. (1962). *Nature (London)*, **195,** 782
183. Koenig, H. and Gray, R. (1964)' *J. Cell. Biol.*, **23,** 50
184. Salomon, D. and Mascarenhas, J. P. (1971). *Life Sci.*, **10,** 879
185. Brewin, N. J. and Northcote, D. H. (1973). *J. Exp. Bot.* In the press
186. Gilman, A. G. (1970). *Proc. Nat. Acad. Sci.* (*USA*), **67,** 305
187. Salomon, D. and Mascarenhas, J. P. (1972). *Biochem. Biophys. Res. Commun.*, **47,** 134
188. Kamisaka, S. and Masuda, Y. (1970). *Naturwissenschaften*, **57,** 546
189. Kamisaka, S. (1972). *Plant Growth Substances 1970*, 654 (D. J. Carr, editor) (Berlin, Heidelberg, New York: Springer Verlag)
190. Weintraub, R. L. and Lowson, V. R. (1972). *Plant Physiol.* (*Suppl.*) **49,** 30
191. Brewin, N. J. and Northcote, D. H. (1973). *Biochim. Biophys. Acta*, **320,** 104
192. Pollard, C. J. (1971). *Biochim. Biophys. Acta*, **252,** 553
193. Ryback, G. (1972). *Chem. Comm.*, 1190
194. Sondheimer, E., Galson, E. C., Chang, Y. P. and Walton, D. C. (1971). *Science*, **174,** 829
195. Tinelli, E. T., Sondheimer, E., Walton, D. C., Gaskin, P. and MacMillan, J. (1973). *Tetrahedron Lett.*, 139
196. Milborrow, B. V. and Garmston, M. (1973). *Phytochem.* **12,** 1597
197. Burden, R. S., Dawson, G. W. and Taylor, H. F. (1972). *Phytochem.* **11,** 2259

5
The Biochemistry of Photomorphogenesis

H. SMITH
University of Nottingham

5.1 INTRODUCTION

Photomorphogenesis is a paradigm of development in the higher plant. The absorption of light by the plant evokes a precise, specific, and often profound, change in the pattern of development. The overall process begins with the perception of a radiant energy stimulus, proceeds through the transduction of this stimulus within the cells in some way to modify the mechanisms regulating development, and culminates in the ultimate morphogenic changes themselves. Over the last half-century, photomorphogenesis has attracted increasing attention, not only for its own intrinsic interest, but also because of its great value as a model system for investigations into the regulation of development. Light treatments may be applied to plants and removed without residual effect (in contrast to hormone applications, for example), and the discovery that very small amounts of light can be effective greatly enhanced the analytical power of this approach. Thus investigations into photomorphogenesis are not only concerned with understanding the mechanisms by which light controls development, but also hopefully with gaining an insight into the wider problem of developmental regulation itself.

Indeed, since Garner and Allard[1,2] first identified the process of photoperiodism in the 1920s, an enormous amount of information has been collected concerning the two ends of the photomorphogenic response system, i.e. the perception of the light stimulus and the nature of the final morphogenic changes. It is now known, for example, that light is capable of regulating virtually every aspect of plant development ranging from seed and spore germination, stem elongation, leaf expansion, root initiation, chloroplast development, and epidermal hair development through both phototropism and geotropism, leaf and chloroplast movements, to flowering, fruiting, tuber formation and bud dormancy. In addition photomorphogenic phenomena have been found in all classes of living plants.

This is largely descriptive work, however, and most of the real advances have been concerned with the mechanisms of perception of the light stimulus. At least two photoreceptive substances responsible for photomorphogenic phenomena are known to exist. One absorbs principally in the blue region of the spectrum and has not been identified chemically although it is probably either a carotenoid or a flavin compound. The other, principally due to its remarkable property of existing in two spectrally different forms which are photo-interconvertible, has been isolated, purified and identified chemically and is known as phytochrome. Phytochrome is a bluish chromoprotein with a molecular weight of *ca.* 120 000 daltons, has a linear bilitriene chromophore and exists in two stable forms; Pr, which has an absorption maximum at 660 nm, and Pfr, which absorbs maximally at 730 nm. Absorption of light by either form leads to photoconversion to the other form. Dark grown seedlings apparently contain only Pr, and absorption of red light (*ca.* 660 nm) photoconverts part of the Pr to Pfr and initiates the various morphogenic changes. This is usually depicted by the following scheme:

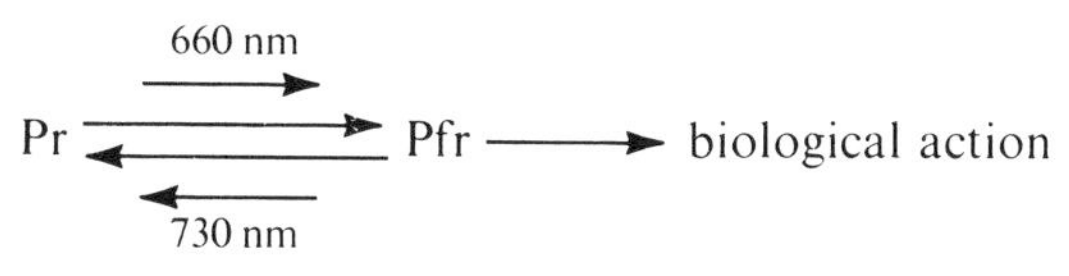

although it has never been proved that Pfr is the biologically active moiety *per se*[3]. Other photomorphogenic phenomena may be initiated by treatment with continuous far-red light (*ca.* 700–730 nm), which apparently acts, by virtue of the long wavelenth absorption tail of Pr, to maintain a small proportion of total phytochrome as Pfr for a long period[4]. It is not the function of this article to review the properties and physiology of phytochrome and the reader is referred to the several accounts already published [3,5-9], particularly the excellent review by Briggs and Rice[5] which deals in detail with the chemical nature of phytochrome and its reactions. Very little work has been possible on the nature of the blue-absorbing photoreceptor, but many of the responses to blue light appear to be at least phenomenologically similar to those mediated by phytochrome.

Although a great deal of progress has been made in understanding the mechanism of light perception, and in describing the final morphogenic manifestations, very little is really known about the partial processes that link light perception and its manifestations. The primary question here is: how do the photoreceptors interact with the cellular and molecular mechanisms regulating development? To answer this question fully presupposes a clear understanding of the regulatory mechanisms of development which, of course, does not yet exist. However, most biologists would now accept that development involves the spatial and temporal control of gene expression. In operational terms, this means the control of those processes which lead to the action of specific enzymes within the cell. It is worth remembering that there are several levels at which the ultimate expression of a gene could be controlled: namely, transcription, translation, and enzyme activation or inactivation.

The concentration of ideas on gene expression stemmed from the discoveries of molecular biology and led Mohr[10] to propose in 1966 the hypothesis that phytochrome regulates development by controlling gene expression at the genome level. In its simplest form, the hypothesis proposes that Pfr interacts directly with the genome and induces the transcription of certain genes whilst repressing the transcription of others. In more recent publications, the proposed direct interaction of Pfr with the genome has been de-emphasised, allowing the possibility of an indirect effect mediated perhaps by other substances which themselves interact with Pfr[9].

Any direct effect of phytochrome on gene expression implies a rather slow response time, since the synthesis of new enzymes in higher plant cells necessarily takes a finite time. The discovery of very rapid effects of light mediated by phytochrome, consequently caused some authorities to reject the idea of an intimate relationship between the photoreceptor and the genome. In 1967, Hendricks and Borthwick[11] postulated that phytochrome acts by controlling membrane permeability, thus allowing for the rapid effects achieved. This hypothesis does not, of course, attempt to explain the morphogenic effects of light and in any case, is not necessarily in conflict with the generalised version of Mohr's gene expression hypothesis. It is conceivable that phytochrome, operating initially through a change in the properties of certain critical membranes, may cause the release of some other substance(s) which itself interacts with the mechanisms controlling gene expression, and thus leads to both the rapid effects on membrane permeability and the longer term changes in development.

It is with this question that this article is concerned. I have attempted here to draw together all the relevant information pertaining to those processes which intervene between the primary action of the photoreceptor and the ultimate developmental changes. Most of the information is concerned with phytochrome, although some observations relating to the effects of blue light are important. In order to provide a logical theme the events are discussed in the order in which they apparently occur after light perception; however, no causal relationship is implied or intended. Contemporary with this article, Mohr has published a review on a closely similar topic (the role of phytochrome in controlling enzyme levels in plants)[12]. Since the views expressed by Mohr[12], and those contained here, are radically different, the duplication is more apparent than real.

5.2 RAPID EFFECTS OF LIGHT

5.2.1 Rapid effects apparently associated with membranes

5.2.1.1 Bioelectric potentials

The earliest known event to succeed the perception of light by phytochrome is the change in electric potential of the etiolated oat coleoptile. Newman and Briggs[13], using a sensitive flowing-drop technique which obviates the problems associated with direct contact between the electrode and the plant tissue, showed that red light caused an increase in the positive potential existing between the upper part and the base of the coleoptile. The lag in this response is < 15 s and the increases are of the order of 5–10 mV, which enables them to be reliably measured. In subsequent darkness, the potential returns to the original level within *ca.* 12 min after which far-red light can be shown to cause a significant decrease, again with a lag of less than 15 s.

Maximum response only occurs when the whole coleoptile is irradiated, suggesting that the changes in potential represent an integration of the responses of many cells.

Other phytochrome-mediated effects on bioelectric potentials are known. Jaffe[14], who was the first to observe such effects, found that red light caused the apex of mung bean root sections to become more electropositive, with a lag of < 30 s. The increases in potentials were considerably smaller (*ca.* 1 mV) than those later reported for the oat coleoptile[13], but this may have been due to different techniques. Red/far-red reversibility was observed thus showing that phytochrome was the photoreceptor. Both of these examples are consistent with the view that an early effect of phytochrome photoactivation is an alteration of membrane properties. It is likely that significant changes in bioelectric potential can only occur by the action of specific ion pumps which separate oppositely-charged ions on different sides of membranes.

5.2.1.2 Root–tip adhesion and acetylcholine

The above observations of rapid changes in bioelectric potentials can be related to (in fact they stem from) the earlier discovery by Tanada that phytochrome regulates the adhesion of barley[15] and mung bean[16] root tips to the surface of negatively-charged glass vessels. The adhesion, which occurs only at the apex and requires a complex bathing solution[17], is stimulated by red light with a lag of *ca.* 30 s. Subsequent far-red light causes release of the root tips. Adhesion is a rather difficult phenomenon to observe and quantify, but the recent observation that root tips will adhere to the cathode when electrodes are placed in the bathing solution enables more acceptable quantitative measurements to be made[18].

Phytochrome is not the only agency which can control the adhesion of root tips. Tanada[19] has shown, for example, that abscisic acid (ABA) can cause adhesion in darkness, whilst supra-optimal concentrations of indoleacetic acid (IAA) prevent adhesion even in the presence of red light. IAA and ABA apparently act antagonistically in this response. Another substance which can regulate the adhesion of root tips is the mammalian neurohumour, acetylcholine (ACh). Jaffe[20], using a specific clam-heart bioassay, showed that ACh was present in mung bean root tips and that red light caused both an increase in internal levels and efflux of ACh within 4 min. Subsequent far-red reduced the internal levels to those of the control. Added ACh substituted for red light in several responses, including the induction of root tip adhesion and hydrogen ion efflux, and the inhibition of secondary root initiation[21]. An inhibitor of ACh action in mammals, atropine, and an ACh-degrading enzyme, acetylcholinesterase, both reduced the red-light mediated induction of root tip adhesion; in contrast, eserine, an inhibitor of acetylcholinesterase, inhibited the far-red induced release of the root tips.

Although ACh causes sporulation in the fungus *Trichoderma*[22] (a light-initiated process) and has been implicated in the photoperiodic control of flowering in *Lemna*[23], little support has been forthcoming for a direct role in phytochrome action. Mohr *et al.*[24] found that ACh did not substitute for continuous far-red light in the photomorphogenesis of *Sinapis alba* even though eserine was present. A more cogent criticism comes from Tanada's observation that adhesion due to ACh could be prevented by increasing the K^+ ion concentration to 10^{-3}M[25]. It was suggested that ACh may be competing with K^+ for some site on the plasmalemma thereby preventing the detachment process, for which K^+ is essential. It therefore seems unlikely that ACh is acting hormonally to control membrane permeability in a manner analogous to its effect in mammalian nerve cells, but rather is acting unspecifically as a competing cation. As Tanada[25] points out, however, these observations in no way invalidate Jaffe's[20] finding of changed endogenous levels of ACh in the root tip upon light treatment.

Little further information is available on the effects of light on the levels of ACh in plant tissues. Hartmann[26] has detected an ACh-like substance in moss callus which is present in larger amounts in red light treated callus than in callus given red followed by far-red light. In contrast, Satter *et al.*[27] were unable to find any light-mediated changes in ACh-like substances in several tissues of various legume species (this work is discussed below in connection with leaflet movements). The real role of ACh in the early events of photomorphogenesis therefore remains obscure. It is certain that ACh, or at least pharmacologically similar substances, exist in plants, and there are two reports of effect of light on the levels of these substances. However, Jaffe's[20, 28] hypothesis that phytochrome acts by regulating the synthesis and degradation of ACh, which in its turn acts as a second messenger to modify membrane properties and to initiate morphogenic processes, is not supported by independent investigations. Clearly, intensive efforts should be made to achieve a satisfactory interpretation of the importance of ACh.

5.2.1.3 Nyctinastic leaflet closure

The phytochrome control of nyctinastic leaflet closure was first reported by Fondeville *et al.*[29] who showed that far-red light prevented closure of *Mimosa pudica* leaflets whilst immediate subsequent red light re-established the closing process. The time lag in this response is *ca.* 5 min. Similar phenomena have been observed in a range of related species[30] with particular attention being given to *Albizzia julibrissin*[31]. The perception of the light stimulus occurs in the pulvinules[32] and the closing response is known to be associated with depolarisation across a membrane[33].

In *Albizzia julibrissin*, the closure response can be investigated in leaflet pairs excised from the plant together with a small piece of rachilla. Under these conditions, red light leads to a significant increase in the efflux of electrolytes from the severed ends of the rachilla[31]. More recent work using electron microprobe analysis has shown that red light promotes and far-red inhibits the efflux of K^+ ions from the ventral motor cells of the pulvinule[34]. Furthermore, Satter and Galston have shown that K^+ changes correlate not only with phytochrome-mediated leaflet movements[35], but also with movements regulated by endogenous rhythms[36]. These observations have led Satter *et al.*[34, 37] to postulate that phytochrome, situated in the ventral motor cell membranes, regulates the efflux of K^+ from the cell which in turn affects the osmotic potential. The consequent transfer of water from the ventral motor cells causes the collapse of the cells and the closure of the leaflets. It is also suggested that the movement of K^+ involves the action of an energy-dependent ion pump since both closure and K^+ movement is inhibited by sodium nitrite and dinitrophenol.

This picture is somewhat complicated by the light microscope observations of Setty and Jaffe[38] who showed that the movement of *Mimosa pudica* leaflets was correlated with the contraction of specialised contractile vacuoles found within the central vacuole of the pulvinule motor cells. Irradiation of a small part of the pulvinule with a microbeam of red light caused the contraction of the contractile vacuole in other, non-irradiated parts. This was taken to indicate that a second messenger is released from irradiated cells that stimulates all the motor cells in the pulvinus. In related work on the seismonastic closing of *Mimosa pudica* leaves, evidence was obtained for the migration of calcium from the surface of the contractile vacuole into the rest of the cell and indeed out of the cell[39]. It was suggested that Ca^{2+} migration to the tonoplast and plasmalemma might change their conformation and thus lead to altered permeability characteristics. The observed efflux of K^+ from the motor cells would thus be due to the Ca^{2+} effects on the tonoplast and plasmalemma. Again, K^+ was thought likely to be the osmotic agent drawing water out of the cells and causing leaflet closure.

5.2.1.4 Phytochrome and membrane properties: conclusions

The evidence described above supports the view that one of the earliest events following photon absorption by phytochrome is the modification of membrane properties. There is, as yet, no direct evidence which locates phytochrome as an actual component of membranes in higher plants and indeed much of Jaffe's work implies action *on* membranes via a second messenger rather than action *in* membranes directly. Whatever the mechanism, however, phytochrome appears to regulate the movement of K^+ (and possibly other substances) across the membranes of certain cells. It is not known as yet how general this phenomenon is, and it should be stressed that direct observation of phytochrome-mediated ion fluxes has only been made in the highly specialised motor cells of pulvini. Furthermore, there is no reason necessarily to suppose that effects on membranes are always prerequisites for changes in the pattern of development. Mohr has pointed out, with some justification, that the phrase 'phytochrome acts on a system such as membrane permeability' is nebulous and of little heuristic value (see Ref. 9, p. 87). He urges that this concept be transformed into a solid model which may be subjected to experimental test. An essential feature of any such model will be the processes linking the initial changes in membrane properties and the first events which can be associated with development, i.e. changes in enzyme levels. An interesting analogy at this point is the effect of auxins on both membrane properties and protein synthesis. Hardin *et al.*[40] have recently shown that auxin interacts with soybean plasmalemma fractions *in vitro* and releases a factor which stimulates the rate of RNA synthesis using soybean chromatin and RNA polymerase. Thus it is not inconceivable that primary action at a membrane site could lead to secondary action at transcription, translation or enzyme activation/inactivation. Clearly, Jaffe's concept of a second messenger finds a place here, although there is not yet sufficient evidence for acetylcholine fulfilling this role.

5.2.2 Rapid effects not obviously associated with membranes

5.2.2.1 Changes in ATP, ADP and c-AMP

Recently, there have been two reports of very rapid changes in the concentrations of ATP and ADP in plant tissues in response to red light. In secondary root tips of mung bean, 4 min of red light markedly decreased the levels of ATP with no comparable effects on ADP[21]. In oat mesocotyl tissue, on the other hand, red light caused a marked increase in ATP and a concomitant (and almost stoichiometric) drop in ADP levels[41]. In the latter case the changes were complete within one minute, and considerable action had taken place within 30 s; in addition, the concentration of ATP and ADP returned to the original dark level within 5 min of switching the red light off and thus classical red/far-red photoreversibility experiments could not be carried out. A second effect of red light was seen in oat mesocotyl sections; 1–2 h after irradiation, ATP levels began to fall significantly without the levels of ADP changing. Thus the apparently contradictory results in mung bean roots and oat mesocotyls may merely be a reflection of different time courses of a single process.

The significance of these findings is difficult to evaluate until further work is done. Although changes in the energy charge of tissues in response to red light could lead to major changes in metabolism, there are at present no conceivable mechanisms which could link changes in ATP and ADP with developmental changes. Nevertheless, the effects of light on ATP, ADP and other adenine nucleotides could with benefit be investigated in a range of photomorphogenic test materials. It is perhaps relevant at this point to refer to the recent report of changes in cyclic-3′,5′-AMP (c-AMP) in mustard seedlings in response to phytochrome photoactivation[42]. This extremely short note refers to results but does not give an account of the methods used either to quantify or identify the c-AMP in the tissues. c-AMP is currently a highly fashionable substance and it could only have been a matter of time before it would be linked to photomorphogenesis; however, the identification, isolation and measurement of c-AMP is a notoriously difficult procedure and the reported results cannot be evaluated until the methods and the controls used are published in full.

5.2.2.2 Phytochrome and NAD-kinase

Tezuka and Yamamoto[43] in 1969 reported that a brief irradiation with red light given in the middle of the night to light-grown *Pharbitis nil* seedlings caused the tissue concentration of NADP to rise. The most significant feature of these experiments was the finding that a partially purified phytochrome preparation from etiolated peas had NAD kinase activity which could be stimulated *in vitro* by red light. The effect of red light was to lower the K_M of the NAD kinase for NAD, and it was originally suggested, as one of several possibilities, that phytochrome might possess NAD-kinase activity. It was later shown, however, that phytochrome and the NAD-kinase activity could be separated on calcium phosphate gels, and thus the effects of red light *in vitro* appear to represent a light-mediated interaction between the two proteins[44, 45].

These findings clearly could be of great importance, since if confirmed they represent the only truly *in vitro* activity of phytochrome other than the Pr $\rightleftharpoons$ Pfr interconversions. Unfortunately, the effects on NAD-kinase have not been confirmed although several laboratories have tried (W. R. Briggs, personal communication; C. B. Johnson and H. Smith, unpublished results).

5.2.2.3 *Gibberellin changes in cereal leaves and homogenates*

When dark-grown cereal seedlings are irradiated with red light, a surge of gibberellin activity can be detected in the leaves within 10–20 min[46-49]. The rapidity of the effect has led to the suggestion that release of gibberellin from a bound form occurs, rather than a stimulation of gibberellin synthesis[49]. On the other hand, applications of (2-chloroethyl)trimethylammonium chloride (CCC) an inhibitor of gibberellin synthesis, prevented the red light effect. In addition, inhibitors of both RNA and protein synthesis significantly inhibited the increase in gibberellin activity[46]. Recently, Reid *et al.*[50] reported that irradiation of homogenates of etiolated barley leaves with red light significantly increased the extractable gibberellin activity within *ca.* 16 min. In addition, the homogenates were capable of converting [^{3}H]GA$_9$ into other substances which co-chromatographed with gibberellin-active substances, and this conversion was stimulated by red light. The inference is that red light stimulates the interconversion of gibberellins and thus leads to increased gibberellin activity in bioassays, due perhaps to the differential activity of the different gibberellins in the bioassays. The nature of the homogenate (prepared in a Waring blender and filtered once) was not described in the paper, and thus it is not safe to assume that this response is a 'cell-free' activity—many intact cells would probably survive the treatment. Furthermore, the possible presence of micro-organisms is not commented upon. In spite of these possible criticisms, the response is clearly promising as a way of investigating rapid effects of light and the use of the new g.l.c.–m.s. methods for identifying the newly-formed gibberellins would probably be very valuable here. In a speculative mood, it would not be difficult to imagine a newly-formed gibberellin acting as the 'second-messenger' discussed in Section 5.2.1.

5.3 LIGHT-MEDIATED CHANGES IN ENZYME LEVELS

5.3.1 General aspects of the effects of light on enzyme levels

5.3.1.1 *The range of enzymes controlled by light*

Very many investigations into the effect of light on enzyme activities have been carried out in recent years. Unfortunately, much of the work has been of a descriptive nature and very few of these investigations have been carried through to the point at which they yield useful information on the mechanisms underlying the observed enzyme changes. A list of the enzymes whose extractable activities are known to be under photocontrol is given in Table 5.1. A wide range of metabolic activities including photosynthesis, photorespiration, chlorophyll synthesis, fat degradation, starch degradation, nitrate assimilation, nucleic acid synthesis and degradation and secondary product synthesis may thus be under photocontrol exerted at the level of specific enzyme activities. Table 5.1 also gives information on the approximate lag phases which precede the first detectable changes in enzyme activity. Clearly, most of the reported enzyme changes occur only after a considerable period of time and thus can only be secondary effects of the primary action of the photomorphogenic photoreceptors.

With enzymes which change over a shorter time-course, however, a more detailed analysis may provide useful information on the primary action of the photoreceptor, although even here, it seems unlikely that the photoreceptor *directly* modifies the level of these enzymes. The only enzymes which respond to light with a sufficiently short lag phase are lipoxygenase, inorganic pyrophosphatase and phenylalanine ammonia-lyase (PAL). Of these, only lipoxygenase and PAL have been investigated in any real detail; in any case they are of especial interest since phytochrome apparently acts to depress the activity of lipoxygenase whilst it elevates the activity of PAL. Before discussing these two interesting responses in detail a few cautionary comments are necessary.

5.3.1.2 Processes contributing to changes in enzyme activities

The possible processes that can contribute to a change in the amount of any particular enzyme within a cell are enzyme synthesis, enzyme degradation, enzyme activation and enzyme inactivation. The first two processes obviously result in the formation of new enzyme molecules, or the breakdown of existing enzyme molecules and thus require the activity of complex metabolic sequences. Enzyme activation and inactivation, on the other hand, are processes which result in the *modification* of pre-existing enzyme molecules to make them catalytically more or less active respectively. These modifications may involve covalent changes in the enzyme molecules (e.g. phosphorylation or removal of a polypeptide), or non-covalent allosteric interactions effected by small metabolites. Clearly, when investigating a light-mediated change in the extractable activity of an enzyme, it is important to determine which one, or more, of these four possible processes is responsible for the change. As will be stressed later, only when a change in the rate of *de novo* synthesis of an enzyme is proved can it be considered possible that the light stimulus is operating through the regulation of gene expression at the transcription or translation level.

It is not easy to determine whether or not enzyme synthesis, degradation, activation or inactivation is occurring in respect of any specific enzyme. The level of an enzyme in a cell may at any one point be determined by any or all of these processes. For example, a steady-state level of apparent enzyme

Table 5.1 Phytochrome-mediated changes in enzyme activity

Enzyme	*Plant*	*Effect*	*Lag*	*Ref.*
Intermediary metabolism				
NAD-kinase (*in vitro*)	Pea	+	0	43
Lipoxygenase	Mustard	–	0	51
Amylase	Mustard	+	~6 h	52
Ascorbic acid oxidase	Mustard	+	~3 h	53
Galactosyl transferase	Mustard	+	~12 h	54
NAD^+-linked glyceraldehyde 3-phosphate dehydrogenase	Bean	+	<12 h	55
Nitrate reductase	Pea	+	<2 h	56
Nucleic acid and protein metabolism				
RNA polymerase (nuclear)	Pea	+	4 h	57
Ribonuclease	Lupin	+	4 h	58
Amino acid activating enzymes	Pea	+	—	59
Photosynthesis and chlorophyll synthesis				
Ribulose 1,5-diphosphate carboxylase	Bean	+	<24 h	55
Transketolase	Rye	+	—	60
$NADP^+$-linked glyceraldehyde phosphate dehydrogenase	Bean	+	<12 h	55
Alkaline fructose 1,6-diphosphatase	Pea	+	—	61
Inorganic pyrophosphatase	Maize	+	~2 h	62
Adenylate kinase	Maize	+	—	62
Succinyl CoA synthetase	Bean	+	—	63
Peroxisome and glyoxisome enzymes				
Peroxidase	Mustard	+	72 h	64
Glycollate oxidase	Mustard	+	6 h	65
Glyoxylate reductase	Mustard	+	6 h	65
Isocitrate lyase	Mustard	0	—	66
Catalase	Mustard	0	—	67
Secondary product synthesis				
Phenylalanine ammonia-lyase	Peas (many others)	+	1.5 h	68
Cinnamate hydroxylase	Peas	+	—	69

activity may be achieved by a balance of equal rates of synthesis and degradation, or a similar balance between synthesis and inactivation. A sudden increase in apparent enzyme activity may be caused by an increase in synthesis rate, a decrease in degradation rate, the initiation of enzyme activation or a combination of any or all of these processes. Similar considerations apply to sudden depressions in apparent enzyme activity.

5.3.1.3 Terminology and its dangers

The terms synthesis, degradation, activation and inactivation as applied to enzymes are capable of precise definition, as above. Unfortunately, much of the work on the photocontrol of enzyme levels is characterised by a rather loose application of these terms. In many papers, for example, the term 'enzyme synthesis' is used continually, although the evidence supporting the actual involvement of true synthesis is minimal, as is discussed below.

A similar criticism applies to the application of the terms 'induction' and 'repression' to those phenomena in which light either raises or lowers, respectively, the extractable activity of an enzyme. Although these terms were defined originally in operational terms, most biochemists would agree that 'induction' means the initiation of the transcription of a particular gene by the action of a low molecular weight metabolite (usually the substrate of the enzyme coded by the gene); whilst 'repression' means the cessation of the transcription of a gene again by the action of a low molecular weight metabolite. This view of the meaning of these terms implies that the control mechanisms operate qualitatively, i.e. switching transcription on or off, rather than quantitatively, i.e. modulating the rates of transcription. The continued use of these terms in the context of photomorphogenesis suggests that a conclusion has been reached in which photocontrol is known to be exerted qualitatively at the level of transcription. As will be seen, there is at present no evidence whatsoever to support such a hypothesis.

5.3.2 The photocontrol of PAL activity

PAL catalyses the deamination of phenylalanine to cinnamic acid with the liberation of ammonia. The enzyme has been found in a wide range of plants[70] and has been extensively purified from potatoes[71] and maize[72] where it has a molecular weight of *ca.* 320 000 daltons. It appears to have regulatory properties as evidenced by unusual kinetic behaviour and by end-product inhibition[73]. PAL, although of esoteric interest, is an important enzyme in secondary metabolism since it catalyses the branching reaction from the main stream of protein synthesis leading to an enormous range of secondary products including cinnamic acid derivatives, simple phenols, lignin, acetophenones, coumarins, flavonoids and isoflavonoids.

The extractable activity of PAL is subject to photocontrol in a wide variety of species (Table 5.2). The photoreceptor involved is often, but not always phytochrome and in several cases the most marked increases in enzyme activity are due to the blue-absorbing photoreceptor. In non-etiolated tissues

Table 5.2 The photocontrol of PAL and other enzymes of flavonoid biosynthesis

Region of pathway	*Enzyme*	*Plant*	*Effect of light*	*Ref.*
Shikimic acid pathway	5-Dehydroquinase	Mung bean	No effect	74
	5-Dehydroquinase	Pea	Stimulation	74
	Shikimate: NADP oxidoreductase	Mung bean	No effect	74
	Shikimate: NADP oxidoreductase	Pea	Stimulation	74
	Shikimate: NADP oxidoreductase	Pea	No effect	75
B-ring synthesis	Phenylalanine ammonia-lyase (PAL)	Potato	Stimulation	76
	PAL	Gherkin	Stimulation	77
	PAL	Buckwheat	Stimulation	78
	PAL	Mustard	Stimulation	79
	PAL	Pea	Stimulation	75
	PAL	Artichoke	Stimulation	80
	PAL	Cocklebur	Stimulation	81
	PAL	Strawberry	Stimulation	82
	PAL	Parsley	Stimulation	83
	PAL	Mung bean	Stimulation	74
	PAL	Red cabbage	Stimulation	84
	PAL	Radish	Stimulation	85
	Cinnamate hydroxylase	Pea	Stimulation	86
	Cinnamate hydroxylase	Buckwheat	Stimulation	87
	Cinnamate hydroxylase	Soybean	Stimulation	88
	p-Coumarate: co-enzyme A ligase	Parsley	Stimulation	89
	p-Coumarate: co-enzyme A ligase	Soybean	Stimulation	88
A-ring Synthesis	Acetate: co-enzyme A ligase	Parsley	No effect	89
	Acetate: co-enzyme A ligase	Soybean	No effect	88
Flavonoid modification	Chalcone–flavanone isomerase	Parsley	Stimulation*	90
	UDP-apiose synthetase	Parsley	Stimulation	83
Glycosylation	Apiosyl–transferase	Parsley	Stimulation*	90
	Glucosyl–transferase	Parsley	Stimulation*	90

* In these cases, the experiments were not designed to show whether light affected enzyme levels, but the results indicate that a stimulatory effect of light is likely.

light appears to stimulate PAL levels through photosynthetic pigments. In etiolated tissues, the light-mediated rise in PAL activity tends to follow a similarly shaped time course, irrespective of the photoreceptor. In each case, the onset of irradiation is followed by a lag phase, after which a phase of steady increase in extractable PAL activity occurs. In many cases the peak of enzyme activity is followed by a rapid decline, often reaching the original level found in dark-grown seedlings.

In most species tested, the lag phases are of similar duration (*ca.* 60–90 min), but the duration of the phases of increase and decrease is very different. In gherkin hypocotyls, with continuous blue light, maximum enzyme activity is achieved at *ca.* 4 h followed by a rapid decline[77]; in pea terminal buds,

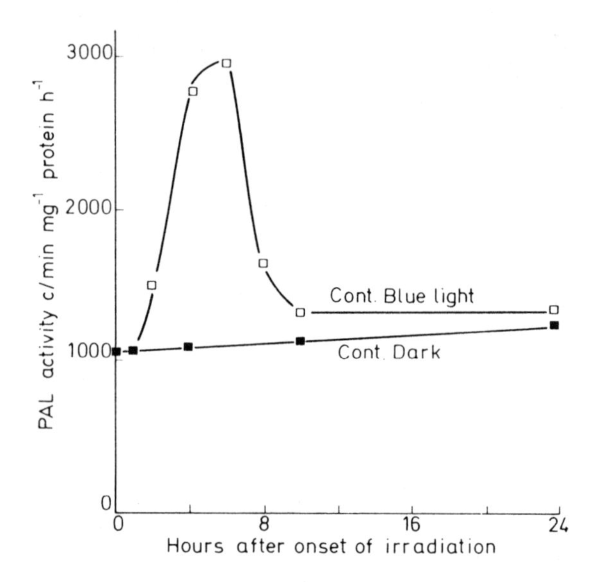

Figure 5.1 The time-course of the changes in PAL activity in gherkin hypocotyl irradiated with continuous blue light. (From T. H. Attridge, unpublished data.)

after a brief red light treatment, maximum activity is at 6–7 h, again followed by a rapid decline, but not down to the dark level[75]; and in mustard hypocotyls, with continuous far-red light, maximum activity is not reached for *ca.* 24 h, and the subsequent decline is correspondingly much slower[79]. In some species, e.g. red cabbage, the increase in activity is not followed by a fall to lower levels[84], but this behaviour is not common.

The general pattern of the response to light, irrespective of photoreceptor, is therefore as follows and as shown in Figure 5.1 which gives some data from gherkin to serve as an example: (a) a lag phase (usually *ca.* 60–90 min; (b) a phase of rapid increase in extractable activity; (c) a phase of decline in extractable activity (not always seen). In order to fully understand the response to light, it is clearly necessary to discover the processes going on in each of these three phases.

5.3.2.1 The lag phase

At present virtually nothing is known of the processes occurring between the first perception of the light stimulus and the first detectable rise in enzyme activity. Engelsma[91] has shown that certain substances of a redox nature, in particular glutathione, can cause increases of PAL in isolated gherkin hypocotyls in darkness. This response may be similar to the earlier finding of Klein and Edsall[92], that various reducing agents can mimic photomorphogenesis in dark-grown bean leaf discs. Glutathione apparently was not tested. Although these observations are intriguing, no investigations into possible light-mediated changes in endogenous reducing or thiol reagents have so far been carried out.

In mustard seedlings, the lag phase on first irradiating with far-red light is of the order of 45–60 min[93]. However, when seedlings were pretreated for several hours with far-red light followed by a period of darkness, subsequent far-red light elicited an immediate rise in PAL[94]. It has been suggested that this response can be accounted for by a dual action of phytochrome; an initial role at the level of transcription and a subsequent effect on translation[9]. This view is based mainly on the effects of RNA and protein synthesis inhibitors[94]. A further interesting aspect of the PAL response in mustard is that the lag phase gradually diminishes as the seedlings age[95]. At 36 h a lag of *ca.* 1 h is seen whereas at 72 h no lag can be detected. Engelsma[84], however, was unable to repeat these results with red cabbage seedlings, where a second irradiation with far-red light caused a second rise in PAL, but only after a considerable lag.

5.3.2.2 The phase of increase: methods and results

Basically we wish to know whether the transient increases in PAL are due to effects on synthesis or degradation rate or to the activation of pre-existing inactive enzymes. As stated above, it is not a simple matter to determine which of these processes might be occurring as a brief outline of the methods currently available will indicate. These are (a) the use of selective inhibitors, (b) immunology, (c) radiolabelling and (d) density labelling. Inhibitors of RNA and protein synthesis have been used a great deal in photomorphogenesis on the principle that judicious applications of differentially-selective inhibitors should provide evidence on the locus of the controlling step. Unfortunately, as is now well known, none of the inhibitors is wholly specific when used with higher plants and side-effects are common[96]. These manifest themselves in the inhibition of respiration, uncoupling of oxidative phosphorylation, and effects on the uptake and transport of metabolites. Another problem with inhibitors is the blanket nature of their action. If light were to activate a particular enzyme via an effect on another protein whose turnover was very rapid, then an inhibitor of protein synthesis would prevent the activation. This result would be indistinguishable from an effect of light on the *de novo* synthesis of the enzyme itself. For these very cogent reasons, evidence from inhibitor experiments can only be circumstantial; it can never prove the *de novo* synthesis of a particular enzyme. The best that can be said of inhibitors is that they have a certain negative value; if an increase in enzyme activity occurs in the presence of saturating concentrations of a protein synthesis inhibitor, then it is reasonably certain that *de novo* synthesis is not involved.

The other methods available are all much better in that they can all be used to obtain an unequivocal demonstration of enzyme synthesis. They do, however, have drawbacks. Immunology and radiolabelling both have the basic disadvantage that the enzyme must be purified to a single homogeneous protein. In density labelling, on the other hand, although purification is not necessary, it is not easy to arrange for substantial amounts of the density label to be present in tissues during, and only during, the time when the increase in enzyme activity occurs. Nevertheless, these three methods represent the only certain ways at present of answering the questions raised at the beginning of this section.

Many workers have shown that inhibitors of protein synthesis will prevent the increase in PAL activity when applied during the lag phase or the early parts of the phase of increase[76-79, 81, 97-99]. In a few cases, the inhibitor of RNA synthesis, actinomycin D, has been used but only incomplete inhibition of the rise in PAL has been demonstrated[100, 101]. Although these results are consistent with *de novo* synthesis of PAL during the phase of increase, because of the problems mentioned above they by no means prove the case.

Attempts to demonstrate directly the *de novo* synthesis of PAL have been made by both the radiolabelling and the density-labelling methods. Zucker[102] has reported the incorporation of radiolabel into PAL in *Xanthium* leaf disc. PAL was purified to a single homogeneous protein to remove the label associated with other proteins, but it was not specifically degraded to polypeptides to demonstrate that incorporation of labelled amino acids was random and not merely tagged on at the end during chain completion. Thus, although this is highly suggestive evidence for PAL synthesis, it is not completely unequivocal. In addition, radiolabel was found in PAL from dark-treated discs, indicating that *de novo* synthesis was also proceeding in darkness. If this evidence is accepted as proof of synthesis, it means that light is not acting to *switch-on* synthesis, but merely to modulate either the rate of synthesis or the rate of degradation. Of these two possibilities, it seems likely that light, acting in this case through the photosynthetic machinery, decreases the rate of PAL degradation, rather than increases its rate of synthesis, since Zucker[103] found that the loss of radioactivity from preformed PAL was greater in discs incubated in darkness, than in discs incubated in the light.

In a different tissue, potato tuber discs, PAL has been shown to be synthesised by density labelling. Sacher, Towers and Davies[104] rinsed discs in 97% D_2O, dried them, and repeated the treatment several times in order to ensure the uptake of significant amounts of D_2O into the cells. They then incubated the discs in either white light or darkness. In both cases, the extracted enzyme had a significantly higher buoyant density than the PAL from H_2O incubated discs, showing unequivocally *de novo* synthesis of PAL in both light and dark treated tissues. Here again therefore there is no question of light *switching-on* PAL synthesis and we must look either to a modulation of the synthesis and/or degradation rates, or to a mechanism of activation to account for the observed changes in extractable PAL activity.

Both of the above examples, *Xanthium* leaf discs[102,103] and potato tuber discs[104], are complicated since they almost certainly involve wound reactions, i.e. abnormal metabolic responses to the stresses imposed by slicing the tubers or cutting the leaves. It may not be wise therefore to generalise on the basis of this information.

What is required is an analysis by density or radiolabelling of PAL in intact seedlings. In one published report, Schopfer and Hock[105] imbibed dry mustard seeds in D_2O and grew them in the label for more than 3 days before the actinic light was given. At the end of the light period the enzyme was found to have a higher buoyant density than that from water-grown seedlings. It would indeed have been rather surprising if the enzyme had not been density-labelled by this treatment, since only if it had pre-existed in the dry seed could it have been synthesised in the absence of D_2O. This evidence therefore provides no indications as to the mechanism of the light action; it only demonstrates that PAL is synthesised some time after germination. Unfortunately, this result has already been used several times quite unjustifiably as support for the hypothesis that phytochrome acts through the control of enzyme synthesis at the level of transcription[9,12,105,106].

The only way to obviate the criticisms levelled at the above work is to introduce the density label only during the period in which the enzyme activity increases. If the enzyme becomes density labelled within this period, then it can be concluded that *de novo* synthesis was occurring; even then this does not necessarily prove that the light treatment initiated or even stimulated the synthesis of the enzyme. If D_2O is used as the density label, experiments of this sort clearly require the transfer of seedlings to D_2O after significant periods of growth in H_2O. We have for some time been attempting to carry out such experiments in this laboratory and have found that using H_2O-imbibed gherkin seedlings, it is very difficult to ensure adequate penetration of the density label.

Early experiments, published as a preliminary (and premature) report[107], indicated that a significant shift occurred within 4 h of transfer to D_2O if light was given at the same time and thus led us to conclude that *de novo* synthesis occurred during the light treatment. Further work has caused us to revise this view[108] and we have found that the amounts of label incorporated during these H_2O/D_2O transfers are too small to allow reliable measurements to be made using swinging-bucket rotors[109]. The major problem here is the low degree of resolution and reliability obtained when swinging-bucket rotors are used for density-gradient centrifugation. By using fixed angle rotors, which, establish a much shallower gradient, however, we have shown that resolution, and accordingly reliability, can be increased sixfold[110]. Using this method, we have recently been able to show that *de novo* synthesis is not involved in the blue-light mediated increase of PAL in gherkin seedlings[111].

The strategy of this experiment was to imbibe seeds in H_2O and to grow them for 24, 48, 72 or 96 h also in H_2O. The seedlings were then transferred to 100% D_2O with vacuum infiltration after which they were grown for 72, 48, 24 and 0 h, respectively in 100% D_2O, followed by a 4 h blue-light treatment. Enzyme extracts were made, centrifuged in a CsCl gradient in a fixed-angle rotor, fractionated and assayed both for PAL, which is increased by the light treatment (see Figure 5.1) and acid phosphatase, which increases

Table 5.3 Lack of effect of blue light on the *de novo* synthesis of PAL in gherkin hypocotyls

Seeds were imbibed in H_2O (Expts. 1–6) or D_2O (Expt. 7) and transferred to D_2O at the stated times by vacuum infiltration. Batches were either given blue light for the time period 96–100 h (Light) or were left in darkness (Dark). In Expt. 6, 60% D_2O was used as higher concentrations prevented germination; in the transfer experiments (Expts. 2–5) 100% D_2O was used. Enzyme extracts were prepared at time 100 h and centrifuged for 40 h at 45 000 rev/min in a Type 65 fixed-angle rotor on a Beckman L2-65B ultracentrifuge. Gradients were assayed for PAL and/or acid phosphatase. Results are in terms of the buoyant densities (ρ) and the difference between the buoyant densities of the enzymes from D_2O treated plants and H_2O controls ($\Delta\rho$). Data from reference 111

	Treatments	*PAL*				*APase*	
		Dark		*Light*			
Expt. No.	hours 0 24 48 72 96 100	ρ	$\Delta\rho$	ρ	$\Delta\rho$	ρ	$\Delta\rho$
1	H_2O, H_2O	1.295	0.000	1.295	0.000	1.324	0.000
2	H_2O, D_2O	1.300	0.005	1.293	−0.002		
3	H_2O, D_2O, D_2O	1.301	0.006	1.299	0.004	1.329	0.005
4	H_2O, D_2O, D_2O	1.305	0.010	1.303	0.008	1.333	0.009
5	H_2O, D_2O, D_2O	1.305	0.010	1.302	0.007	1.334	0.010
6	D_2O, D_2O	1.311	0.016	1.311	0.016	1.335	0.011

during the first 48 h in darkness and is not affected by light. The results, summarised in Table 5.3, show that a significant density shift occurred in acid phosphatase in those seedlings grown in D_2O for 72 h, with much smaller shifts when D_2O was present for shorter times. This proves that D_2O penetrated the tissues in sufficient amounts for it to be incorporated in significant amounts into any proteins which were being synthesised. Thus if light acts to stimulate the *de novo* synthesis of PAL it should be detected by a significant shift in buoyant density. No such shift is apparent in PAL when D_2O is only present during the light period, and although increases in buoyant density are seen in longer incubations in D_2O, they are if anything greater in the dark-treated than in the light-treated seedlings. There appears to be a slow rate of PAL synthesis in dark-grown seedlings. If light acted to stimulate synthesis, then it would lead to an increased pool of 'heavy' PAL in the tissues which would manifest itself as an increased buoyant density over that of the enzyme from the dark-grown seedlings. Thus, with acid phosphatase acting as an internal control, and with the high degree of accuracy and reproducibility afforded by the fixed-angle rotor, it can be concluded that *de novo* synthesis is not involved in the increase of PAL in gherkin seedlings in response to blue light.

Clearly, then, there is no support here for the view that light operates at the level of transcription (or translation for that matter). The most likely possibility is that light activates pre-existing inactive PAL and, as is discussed below, there is other evidence for this hypothesis, at least for gherkin seedlings. Gherkins, however, respond maximally to blue light, which is absorbed by an as yet unknown photoreceptor which might well act via a

Table 5.4 Lack of effect of far-red light on the *de novo* synthesis of PAL in mustard hypocotyls

Seeds were imbibed in H_2O for 48 h whereupon they were either irradiated with continuous far-red light for a further 48 h (Light) or left in darkness for 48 h (Dark). In Expt. 1, seedlings were maintained in H_2O during the irradiation period, whilst in Expt. 2 seedlings were transferred with vacuum infiltration to 100% D_2O at 48 h and held in 100% D_2O until 96 h. Enzyme extracts were prepared at 96 h and centrifuged for 40 h at 45 000 rev/min in a Type 65 fixed-angle rotor on a Beckman L2-65B ultracentrifuge. Gradients were assayed for PAL and acid phosphatase. Results are in terms of the buoyant densities (ρ). Two replicates of each experiment are given. (From T. H. Attridge, C. B. Johnson and H. Smith, unpublished data.)

Treatments			*PAL*		*APase*	
Expt. No.	hours 0–48	hours 48–96	*Dark*	*Light*	*Dark*	*Light*
1	H_2O	H_2O	1.296	—	1.330	—
			1.295	—	1.334	—
2	H_2O	D_2O	1.321	1.314	1.345	1.343
			1.320	1.313	1.347	1.345

different mechanism than phytochrome. Preliminary experiments with mustard seedlings, on the other hand, have shown similar results to those on gherkin (Table 5.4). The density shifts of PAL were considerably larger in dark-grown seedlings than in those irradiated with far-red light for the 48 h of D_2O incubation. These results indicate that *de novo* synthesis of PAL occurs in both dark and far-red light treated mustard seedlings. The lower buoyant density of the enzyme from the irradiated plants can best be explained by a light-mediated activation of pre-existing PAL which has a low buoyant density since it was synthesised in the absence of D_2O. Thus, as far as PAL is concerned, neither the blue-absorbing photoreceptor, nor phytochrome appear to operate by a direct effect on the *de novo* synthesis of the enzyme.

5.3.2.3 The existence of inactive PAL in gherkins

The above results (Table 5.3) are best explained in terms of a light-mediated activation of pre-existing inactive PAL. Evidence for the reversible inactivation of PAL in light-treated gherkins was reported originally by Engelsma[97] and similar evidence for potato tuber discs was obtained by Zucker[99]. These findings, which are discussed later in relation to the phase of decrease in enzyme activity, suggested that inactive PAL might also be present in dark-grown seedlings. Recent experiments here have shown that this is the case and that the inactive PAL can be revealed by treating the seedlings with cycloheximide and/or subjecting the seedlings to a period of low temperature[112] (Figure 5.2). Spraying with this protein synthesis inhibitor leads to an

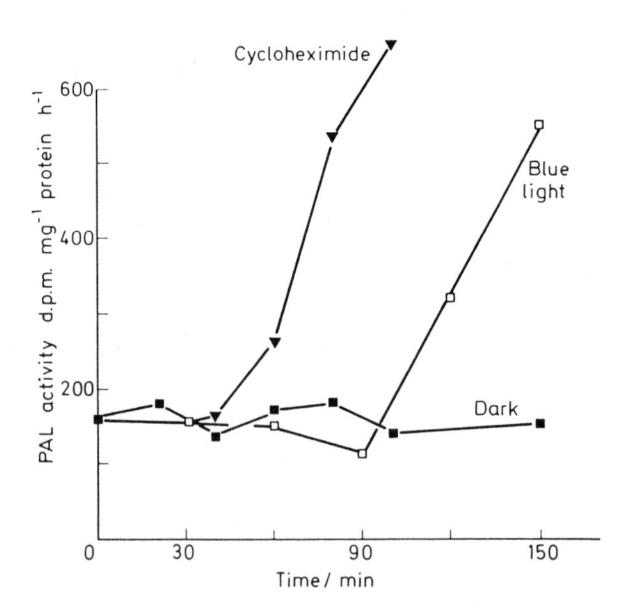

Figure 5.2 The cycloheximide-induced increase in the extractable PAL activity of dark-grown gherkin hypocotyls. (From Attridge and Smith[112], by courtesy of *Phytochemistry*.)

enormous increase in extractable PAL (much greater than the light mediated increases). In contrast to the enzyme present after light treatment, the enzyme resulting from cycloheximide treatment is remarkably stable *in vivo*. We assume that cycloheximide, acting either through the inhibition of protein synthesis or through one of its side effects, prevents the synthesis of a substance (perhaps a protein) which is necessary for the maintenance of PAL in an inactive state. If this substance is normally turning over very rapidly, then the cessation of its synthesis will allow all the accumulated, hitherto inactive, PAL to become active. The situation, however, is not too simple, since cycloheximide will also inhibit (but not completely) the blue light-mediated increase in enzyme activity—and this means that light must also inhibit the cycloheximide induced increase!

It is not possible at the present time to account for all these effects on a simple model, and it will probably not become possible until the nature of the activation/inactivation process is understood. Engelsma and van Bruggen have made a fleeting reference to a non-dialysable substance leached from excised gherkin hypocotyls, which when added back to hypocotyls prevented rises in PAL activity. Little further information is yet available about this factor although we have confirmed its presence both in eluates and extracts of hypocotyls (C. J. French, unpublished work).

Thus the situation is far from clear in gherkins. Some other observations have led to the conclusion that light activates PAL in peas. Attridge and Smith[114] found that PAL extracted from white-light-treated peas had quite different properties than PAL from dark-treated seedlings. The enzyme from the light-treated plants was very much more unstable and more susceptible to inhibition by quercetin than the enzyme from the dark controls. No other differences in physical properties were detectable and the two enzymes could not be separated by chromatographic or electrophoretic methods. These differences in properties therefore appear to be consistent with a light-mediated modification of pre-existing less active enzyme molecules. There is, therefore, considerable evidence which supports the view that PAL is formed in darkness in an inactive form and activated by light.

5.3.2.4 The phase of enzyme decrease

The decrease in extractable PAL activity often seen following the light-mediated increase is probably due to the re-inactivation, or possibly the degradation of the light-activated enzyme molecules. Both Engelsma[97] and Zucker[99] have shown that treatment with protein synthesis inhibitors (particularly cycloheximide) at the peak of the light response prevents the subsequent fall in activity. Engelsma[115] suggested that the loss of activity may thus be due to the complexing of PAL with a proteinaceous inactivator analogous to the potato invertase inactivator. This view was supported by the following experiments. Gherkin seedlings were given blue light and the PAL activity was allowed to rise and fall again; the seedlings were then transferred to 4 °C in darkness for 24 h after which they were returned to 25 °C still in darkness. PAL levels were seen to rise upon returning to 25 °C to a level approximately equivalent to the maximum level reached after the initial light treatment; this increase, however, could not be prevented by cycloheximide (cf. Figure 5.2). Engelsma[115] concluded from this that the postulated complex of PAL and inactivator was altered by the low-temperature treatment such that it dissociated after the temperature was raised to 25 °C, revealing the existence of active PAL. In another series of experiments, it was shown that seedlings grown at low temperatures (9–14 °C) accumulated considerable amounts of extractable PAL activity in total darkness, suggesting that the rate of synthesis of the presumed inactivator was not equivalent to that of PAL at these low temperatures[116]. In spite of all this circumstantial evidence for an inactivator, however, no substance having the correct properties has yet been isolated. It is also true that its proteinaceous nature is only a presumption based on the use of protein synthesis inhibitors—it is quite possible that the inactivator is a small metabolite whose existence within the tissues is dependent on the activity of an enzyme which turns over very rapidly.

5.3.2.5 Conclusions regarding the photocontrol of PAL activity

There is as yet no evidence, other than inhibitor experiments, which supports the view that light regulates PAL levels through effects on *de novo* synthesis. In contrast, density labelling experiments in gherkins have shown that blue light does not operate at the level of enzyme synthesis, the most likely possibility being that light activates pre-existing inactive PAL. The density-labelling experiments carried out on other species so far do not provide any evidence for or against an action of light on *de novo* synthesis. In dark-grown gherkin seedlings, relatively large pools of inactive PAL exist, and it is possible that the inactive state is maintained by complexing of the enzyme with a proteinaceous inhibitor.

If these conclusions are valid, and light activates PAL rather than stimulates its synthesis, the inhibition of the light effect by the protein synthesis

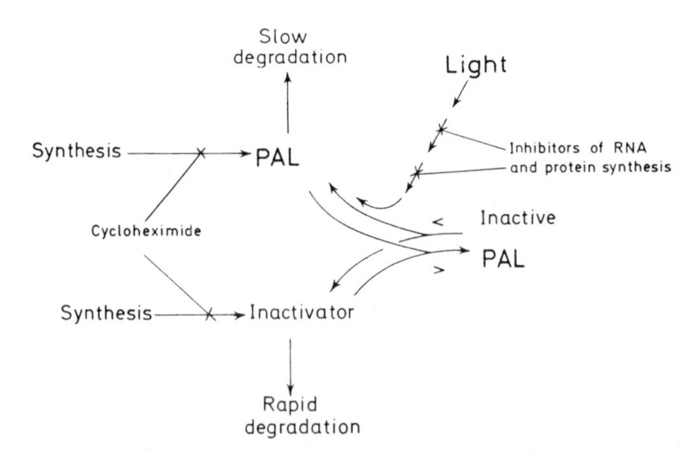

Figure 5.3 Scheme for the control of PAL activity in gherkin hypocotyls (Modified from Smith[108], by courtesy of Academic Press.)

inhibitors must be accounted for. It is possible that these inhibitor effects are due to the side effects of the antibiotics as mentioned above, but it is not necessary to invoke these side effects. The light-activation process could conceivably require the action of one or more specific enzymes (or proteins) which turn over relatively rapidly, or whose synthesis is required before the activation can occur. Thus, the mere fact that light does not control PAL synthesis does not necessarily mean that effects on the synthesis of other proteins are not involved. Clearly then, although the density-labelling experiments do not support action of light on protein synthesis, they only disprove it as far as PAL is concerned; action on the synthesis of other proteins is still possible.

The photocontrol of PAL levels in gherkins can be drawn into a relatively simple model, shown in Figure 5.3 which is a modification of an earlier proposal[108]. The real situation is certainly more complex, however, since this model does not account for the observed light inhibition of the PAL increase evoked by cycloheximide treatment.

5.3.3 The photocontrol of lipoxygenase activity in mustard

Lipoxygenase catalyses the oxidation of unsaturated fatty acids containing a methylene-interrupted multiple-unsaturated system in which the double bonds are all *cis*. Examples are linoleic and linolenic acids and the action of the enzyme is to convert them to the conjugated *cis–trans* hydroperoxide. The physiological role of lipoxygenase is at present obscure but the photocontrol of its extractable activity has been studied intensively. In mustard cotyledons[51, 117], lipoxygenase activity increases steadily during growth in the dark. If continuous far-red light is given, there is no change in the time course of increase in enzyme activity until just over 33 h after the start of imbibition.

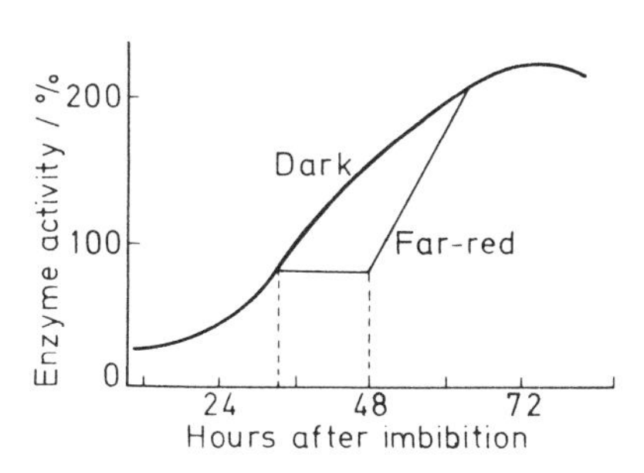

Figure 5.4 The photocontrol of lipoxygenase activity in mustard seedlings. Seedlings were grown in either continuous darkness or continuous far-red light from the start of imbibition. (From Oelze-Karow and Mohr[117], by courtesy of *Z. Naturforsch.*)

At this point, far-red completely and suddenly prevents all further increase in enzyme activity for a period of *ca.* 15 h. At about 48 h after imbibition, the enzyme activity begins to increase, even in far-red light, at a rate higher than that found in the dark (Figure 5.4).

This phenomenon is clearly a most impressive case of the phytochrome regulation of enzyme activity. The response to far-red is virtually instantaneous when given between 33.25 and 48 h after the onset of imbibition; given at any other time, far-red is totally ineffective. The mechanism which controls the level of lipoxygenase activity appears to go through a phase of sensitivity to phytochrome and the transitions into and out of this phase appear to be very abrupt. By very ingenious experiments, it was concluded that this response represents a threshold response to Pfr, the critical photostationary state (i.e. Pfr/P_{total}) being 1.25%. During the sensitive phase, if the radiation conditions are such that $Pfr/P_{total} > 1.25\%$, no further increase in lipoxygenase are seen; if $Pfr/P_{total} < 1.25\%$, the increase proceeds unabated. If a high Pfr/P_{total} is established, the enzyme increase is stopped immediately with no detectable lag phase. Similarly, if a Pfr/P_{total} less than 1.25% is established either by manipulating the radiation conditions or allowing the loss of Pfr by the process of destruction, then the enzyme increase is resumed again without a detectable lag. Under these conditions, as shown in Figure 5.4 the resumed rate of increase is greater than the rate in darkness and the enzyme activity 'catches up' with the dark controls very rapidly.

These extremely precise observations have been used as crucial supporting evidence for the concept that phytochrome may act to control the level of certain enzymes by gene repression[9, 12, 106]. Since repression implies cessation of messenger-RNA synthesis, its control of enzyme synthesis is necessarily slow and one would expect both the cessation of enzyme increase and its resumption to be smooth and gradual transitions. The rapid and abrupt nature of the transitions observed seem more suggestive of effects on later steps of enzyme synthesis (i.e. translation) or even on the activity of the enzyme. This is clearly a case where the use of the density-labelling technique during the phases of increase in enzyme activity and during far-red inhibition of the increase could well prove extremely valuable.

5.3.4 Conclusions regarding the photocontrol of enzyme activity

The only conclusion that can be derived at present is that there is no single piece of evidence which unequivocally supports the view that light acts to control the synthesis of enzymes. On the other hand, this does not mean that light does not act in this way in some cases, and indeed the possibility will never be ruled out until every enzyme is tested! Positive evidence does exist, however, for photoactivation of enzymes and the possible generality of this phenomenon would bear further investigation.

5.4 NUCLEIC ACID AND PROTEIN SYNTHESIS IN RELATION TO PHOTOMORPHOGENESIS

5.4.1 Light and nucleic acid synthesis

Although the above conclusions derived from the study of specific enzymes provide little support for the gene expression theory, they do not disprove it, and the theory has been a strong force in determining the approach of many investigations of the biochemistry of photomorphogenesis. It is not surprising therefore that some considerable effort has been expended in searching for light-mediated changes in nucleic acid synthesis occurring with a very short lag phase. The gene expression hypothesis, however, implies that the change in gene transcription will be relatively small, and that stimulation of the transcription of one set of genes might occur in association with inhibition of the transcription of other sets of genes. Thus, if phytochrome were to act in the way proposed in the hypothesis, only very small changes in the rate of synthesis of total messenger-RNA would be expected. Messenger-RNA comprises only *ca.* 5% of total cell RNA and at present there are no reliable techniques for separating messenger-RNA from the rest. The separation of individual messenger-RNAs from each other is an even more daunting problem, at present quite unapproachable.

With hindsight, therefore, it can be said that attempts to obtain evidence relating to the initial mode of action of phytochrome by investigating the effects of light on nucleic acid synthesis were doomed from the start. Early investigations were restricted to the measurement of total nucleic acid levels in seedlings given actinic light treatment. For example, in mustard cotyledons treated with continuous far-red light, a considerable increase in total RNA was observed over a 24 h period[118]. The increase had a lag phase of 6 h and thus must be a secondary effect of the primary changes. In any case, it is likely that the bulk of the increase was due to increased numbers of ribosomes rather than to changes in messenger-RNA synthesis.

Later work has concentrated on shorter term experiments designed to test for rapid effects on the synthesis of specific fractions of cellular nucleic acids. As mentioned above, however, the fractionation methods do not as yet allow separation and quantitisation of the most interesting RNAs. Dittes and Mohr[119] pursued the mustard cotyledon response by incubating tissues in radioactive precursors of the nucleic acids for 20 min after the onset of far-red light. The nucleic acids were then extracted and separated by MAK-chromatography. No differences could be observed in any fraction of nucleic acid from the columns. This result may indeed reflect the true situation but, as the authors point out, MAK-chromatography is a very insensitive technique which gives only poor separation of the major types of nucleic acids.

In another investigation, Koller and Smith[120] measured the rates of synthesis of ribosomal-RNA in three photomorphogenic test tissues and concluded that no causal relationship existed between the effects on nucleic acid synthesis and the subsequent developmental changes. RNA was separated here by acrylamide gel electrophoresis which enables complete separation of all ribosomal-RNA species but not of messenger-RNAs. In the terminal buds of etiolated peas where brief red light leads to a large increase in leaf growth, ribosomal-RNA synthesis was significantly stimulated, starting *ca.* 2–3 h after light treatment and reaching a peak at *ca.* 6 h (Figure 5.5). In stem sections of etiolated peas, on the other hand, where red light inhibits extension growth, a corresponding decrease in ribosomal-RNA synthesis occurred (Figure 5.5). Finally, in apical sections of oat coleoptiles, where red light stimulates extension growth but does not increase cell number, no effects on ribosomal-RNA synthesis were detectable (Figure 5.5). These results suggest that the observed changes in ribosomal-RNA were associated with the subsequent growth changes and merely reflected the synthesis of new ribosomes as new cells were formed. It was shown that 5-fluorouracil, a metabolic analogue of uracil which preferentially inhibits ribosomal-RNA synthesis, did not prevent the red-light-induced growth changes in any of the three test materials. It was thus concluded that the phytochrome effects on ribosomal-RNA synthesis were not essential prerequisites for the ultimate developmental changes.

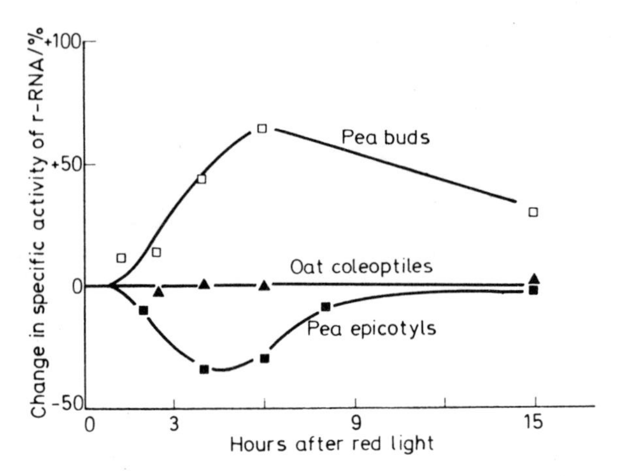

Figure 5.5 Effects of red light on the synthesis of ribosomal-RNA in pea terminal buds, pea epicotyls and apical sections of oat coleoptiles (From Koller and Smith[120], by courtesy of *Phytochemistry*.)

Phytochrome has also recently been shown to cause an increase in the proportion of ribosomes present as polysomes. Using etiolated bean leaves, Pine and Klein[121] showed that brief red light caused a three fold increase in the proportion of cytoplasmic polysomes, starting *ca.* 2 h after light treatment and reaching a new steady state at *ca.* 10 h. At the same time, a greater increase in plastid polysomes occurred. In both cases, the effects were reversible by brief far-red light, proving the involvement of phytochrome. These results were obtained using a rather inefficient method of polysome extraction in which only a small proportion of the total ribosomes were found as polysomes. Recently, a much improved technique has been developed[122] and we have used this technique in an attempt to confirm Pine and Klein's[121] observations. Results, shown in Figure 5.6, illustrate that red light does indeed increase the proportion of polysomes in bean leaves, and that white light has an even greater effect. Similar results were obtained with pea leaves. These findings confirm the earlier results of Williams and Novelli, who showed that white light caused a marked rise in the polysomal proportions of ribosome preparations from etiolated maize leaves[123].

Pine and Klein[121], in considering the mechanism of the increase in polysomal proportions, rejected the possibilities that light causes either a sudden assembly of ribosomes onto pre-made messenger-RNA strands, or a piling-up of extra ribosomes onto pre-existing polysomes. The first possibility would imply a very short time-lag, and the second an increase in the average number of ribosomes per polysome, neither of which were found. They

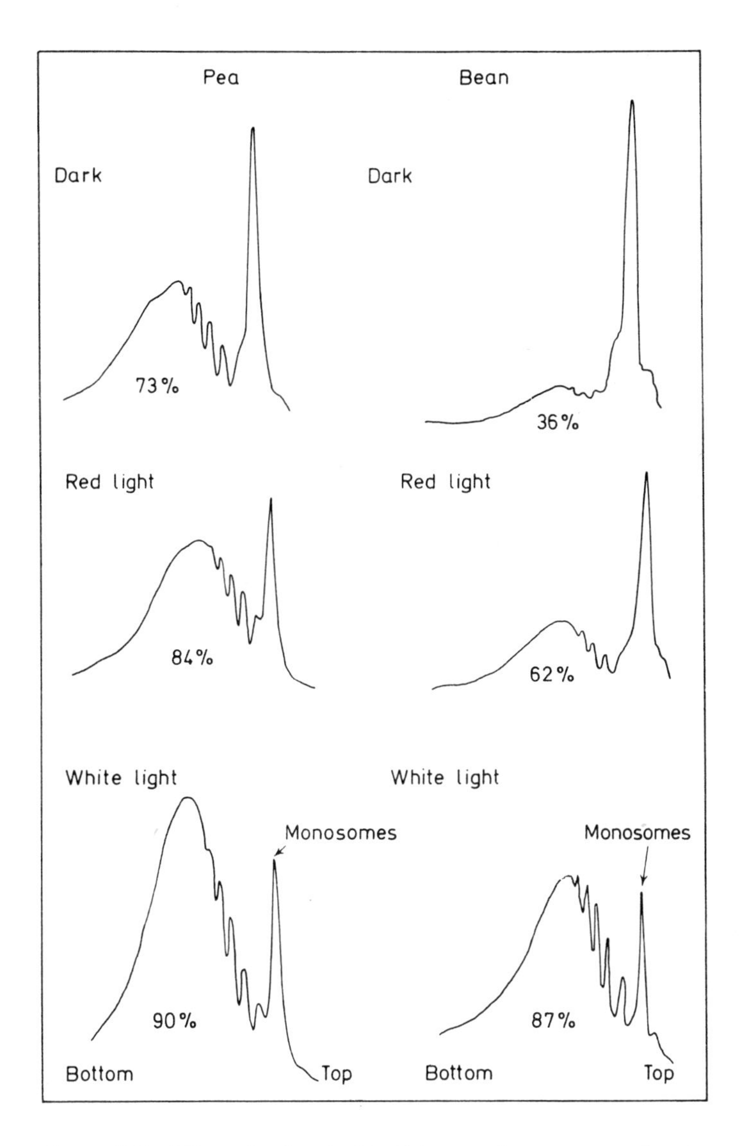

Figure 5.6 Effects of red and white light on polysome proportions in etiolated leaves of pea and bean. Seedlings were grown in darkness for 7 days and either irradiated with 10 min red light and returned to darkness for 16 h or irradiated with white light for 16 h or left in darkness for 16 h. Polysomes were then extracted and analysed by sucrose density-gradient centrifugation. The numbers under the curves represent the proportions of total ribosomes present as polysomes

concluded that the most likely mechanism is that the messenger-RNA becomes more stable, i.e. its synthesis continues at the same rate whilst its degradation is slowed. This would allow for a higher proportion of polysomes on a steady-state basis but the length of time required to accumulate a new stable level of polysomes might be several hours.

Other workers have shown red/far-red light effects on enzymes of RNA metabolism. Bottomley[57] isolated nuclear and plastid RNA polymerase from etiolated pea seedling terminal buds previously treated with light. Both red and far-red light increased the plastid polymerase activity by *ca.* 50% over the dark control, and far-red reversibility of the red effect was not detected. Both red and far-red light increased the activity of the nuclear polymerase also, but red light was more effective, and subsequent far-red reversed the effect down to the far-red control value. Thus the nuclear polymerase activity appears to be increased via a phytochrome mediated mechanism whereas although the plastid polymerase activity is also increased by light, phytochrome is apparently not the sole photoreceptor. The increases in polymerase activity did not become detectable until *ca.* 4 h after light treatment, and it was therefore concluded that they were not manifestations of the primary action of phytochrome.

Increases in the activity of ribonuclease, an enzyme which degrades RNA, also occur in response to phytochrome photoactivation, and with a similar time course. Acton[58] has shown, using lupin seedlings, that a ribonuclease isozyme associated with the ribosomes is significantly increased by red light after a lag of *ca.* 4 h. The effect is red/far-red reversible. Thus, both enzymes of RNA synthesis and RNA degradation are controlled by phytochrome, but only as secondary responses.

Photomorphogenesis is clearly associated with changes in nucleic acid metabolism although it is not certain that the two processes are causally related. The light-mediated increases in ribosomal-RNA synthesis appear to be associated with the formation of new cells rather than with the earlier events of photomorphogenesis. The increases in polysomal proportions, and in RNA-polymerase and ribonuclease activities all occur somewhat too late for them to be considered as primary steps in photomorphogenesis and here again they may be associated with the production of new cells.

5.4.2 Protein synthesis and white light

Little direct investigation of the possible phytochrome control of protein synthesis has been carried out. This is rather surprising in view of the manifold effects of phytochrome on enzyme activities. However, there is considerable evidence on the effects of white light on protein synthesis and some tantalising indications of the mechanism of the effect. Unfortunately, most of this work has been carried out by biochemists interested in the control of protein synthesis and unconcerned about the nature of the photoreceptor. The white light treatments have commonly been relatively short (*ca.* 2–3 h) and the effects normally occur within this time period. They are therefore quite rapid compared with many of the known biochemical manifestations of photomorphogenesis. The plants, however, are usually subjected to high irradiances during this period and the possible involvement of photosynthesis, or at least of light perception by the photosynthetic photoreceptors looms large. Whether these effects can therefore be attributed to phytochrome, to the blue-absorbing photoreceptor or to protochlorophyll/chlorophyll is as yet anybody's guess. Nevertheless they are of great relevance to any consideration of the biochemistry of photomorphogenesis.

Effects of white light on total protein levels were first observed in 1954, long before phytochrome was discovered[124]. Ten years later Williams and Novelli showed that ribosomes prepared from white light treated maize, bean and soybean leaves had a greatly enhanced capacity to incorporate [^{14}C]- leucine into a protein-like product *in vitro*. The lag phase in maize shoots was *ca.* 2 h and maximum effect was achieved by 3 h. The light effect appeared to be an intrinsic property of the ribosomes since the same supernatant fraction (i.e. containing transfer-RNAs, aminoacyl transfer-RNA synthetases etc.) was used in all cases. Subsequently, the same authors investigated this response further by assaying the capacity of ribosomes to support the incorporation of phenylalanine into poly-phenylalanine using polyuridylic acid (poly(U)) as an artificial messenger[123]. Again, light did not affect the capacity of the soluble supernatant to support phenylalanine incorporation, but did increase the ribosomal activity by *ca.* 35%. Thus the effect was again shown to be due to an intrinsic property of the ribosomes. Recently, this work has been followed up by Travis *et al.*[126] who showed that 3 h of white light enhanced the ability of maize shoot ribosomes to incorporate phenylalanine into polypeptide, (using poly(U) as messenger) by *ca.* 100% depending on the Mg^{2+} concentration. Light grown plants yielded ribosomes with a much larger Mg^{2+} optimum than dark-grown plants.

In order to determine the nature of this difference in ribosomal properties, the effects of puromycin were tested. Puromycin attaches to ribosomes and releases a peptidyl–transfer-RNA complex that is essential for the binding of phenylalanine–transfer-RNA to ribosomes at low Mg^{2+} concentrations. When the light-treated ribosomes were incubated in puromycin, the high rates of phenylalanine incorporation at low Mg^{2+} were lost and the ribosomes appeared identical to those from dark-grown plants, although puromycin depressed the activity of the 'dark' ribosomes somewhat. Thus, it appears that one of the effects of light is to enhance the amounts of a ribosome-associated peptidyl–transfer-RNA which acts as an initiation factor for phenylalanine incorporation. Other initiation factors may also be involved in the light response. When ribosomes were 'washed' in high concentrations of KCl, which removes associated proteins but not the peptidyl–transfer-RNA, the 'light' ribosomes showed a much higher Mg^{2+} optimum and were reduced in activity, but were still considerably more active than the 'dark' ribosomes. When ribosomes were both KCl-washed and puromycin-treated, both Mg^{2+} optima and activities were identical.

The conclusion to be derived from these findings is that light may activate protein synthesis by direct effects on the ribosomal machinery, particularly on one or more initiation factors which are more or less loosely bound to the ribosomes. In view of the considerations mentioned above concerning the photoreceptors for this response, it would be extremely dangerous to draw conclusions about the mechanism of action of the photomorphogenic photoreceptors on the basis of this elegant work. What can be said, however, is that similar experiments ought to be performed from the viewpoint of the photomorphogenecist—that is, the conditions of the light treatment should be controlled and manipulated in order to obtain information on the photoreceptors involved.

5.4.3 Conclusions

The lag phases of all the responses described in this section are too long for them to be involved in the primary mechanisms of photomorphogenesis. They thus provide no support for the gene expression hypothesis in its original form. On the other hand, the intervening events between the immediate action of the photoreceptor and the ultimate developmental displays most probably involve the integrated formation and functioning of a range of proteins. The time course of these events will vary from tissue to tissue, but lag phases are likely to be of the order of hours rather than minutes. The changes described here therefore may well represent partial processes of essential importance to the overall transition rather than initial casual events in the photomorphogenic response system. Thus, although changes in RNA and protein synthesis may well be important aspects of the overall photomorphogenic transitions, there is no reason as yet to suppose that other changes (e.g. in the stability or activity of specific RNA and protein molecules) do not also take part.

5.5 METABOLITE CHANGES

The reader who has progressed this far will have realised that the biochemistry of photomorphogenesis is a fragmentary collection of isolated items of information. This is nowhere more true than in the study of the photocontrol of the levels of various metabolites. A wide range of substances has been investigated in a similarly wide range of plants, but from the point of view of mechanisms, the search has not been particularly rewarding. Since I am concerned principally with mechanisms, no attempt will be made to give encyclopaedic coverage of this rather confused subject. There are, however, a few cases in which attempts have been made to obtain evidence relating to mechanisms; those substances studied in most detail in this respect have been flavonoids, ascorbic acid and carotenoids.

5.5.1 Flavonoids

Flavonoids are secondary products with a basic C_{15} structure comprising two aromatic rings. One ring is synthesised by head-to-tail condensation of acetate units and the other from the shikimic acid pathway via phenylalanine. There are several different classes of flavonoids distinguished by the oxidation level of the bridge carbons; the flavonols and anthocyanidins are the two most important classes. These are found in an extremely wide range of plants in many of which their synthesis is controlled by light. Related substances also often controlled by light are the phenylpropanoids, which are C_6–C_3 compounds biosynthetically derived from the shikimic acid pathway.

The photocontrol of flavonoid levels is exemplified by the situation in mustard seedlings where, after a lag of *ca.* 3–4 h, continuous far-red causes a massive increase in the level of anthocyanin[127]. Puromycin inhibits synthesis in the presence of continuous far-red light irrespective of the time at which the inhibitor is applied[128]. The effects of the inhibitor take several hours to manifest themselves and this has been taken to indicate that continued anthocyanin synthesis is dependent on one or more critical enzymes whose half-life is the order of a few hours (Ref. 9, p. 57). The obvious candidate for the critical enzyme is PAL, but although PAL activity is regulated by light (as discussed above) the levels of PAL are not always correlated closely with the rates of anthocyanin synthesis (see Ref. 9, p. 143 and Ref. 116). It thus appears that other enzymes in the pathway may also be limiting the rate of anthocyanin synthesis under certain conditions.

Mohr and colleagues have also investigated the effects of actinomycin D on phytochrome-mediated anthocyanin synthesis in some detail, and have concluded that specific induction of messenger-RNA synthesis is involved[129]. It was found that a pre-incubation of the seedlings in actinomycin D for 3 h before the onset of the irradiation completely abolished the light-mediated synthesis of anthocyanin. On the other hand, a 3 h incubation in actinomycin D (in darkness) given after 6 h of irradiation, only partially inhibited the increase in anthocyanin upon returning to continuous far-red light. From these and related experiments it was concluded that actinomycin D could block the primary processes of the light response if given at or before exposure of the tissues to the light stimulus, but permitted continued synthesis of anthocyanin if the synthetic process had begun before application of the inhibitor. This is generally consistent with the concept that light acts to switch on selectively the transcription of the genes coding for the limiting enzymes in anthocyanin synthesis. There are, however, other possible interpretations.

The requirement for pre-incubation in actinomycin D in order to inhibit fully the light effect could mean that the inhibitor acts by preventing synthesis of a messenger-RNA that is necessary for light action[107]. On this view, actinomycin D would need to be added sufficiently long before the light treatment for the pre-existing messenger-RNA to be removed by turnover. The function of phytochrome would thus be to affect either the messenger-RNA itself, or the protein-synthesising machinery, in such a way that a greater rate of enzyme synthesis could be achieved. In this respect, this interpretation of the data might be said to fit in with what is known of the changes in ribosome properties brought about by continuous white light and described in the previous section. The effects of protein and nucleic acid synthesis inhibitors on anthocyanin synthesis therefore can be interpreted in at least two different ways. When it is remembered that all experiments with such inhibitors are suspect, and in addition that there is as yet no evidence at all that phytochrome acts on enzyme synthesis rather than activation, it is clear that no respectable conclusion can yet be reached regarding the mechanism of the photocontrol of anthocyanin levels.

5.5.2 Ascorbic acid and carotenoids

These two substances are completely unrelated both chemically and biosynthetically, but nevertheless they exhibit similar control by phytochrome in mustard seedlings[130, 131]. In both cases there is quite a high rate of synthesis in dark-grown seedlings, but far-red light increases this rate significantly. Also in both cases, if the far-red light is switched off the rate of synthesis falls quite rapidly to the dark level. Actinomycin D has no effect whatever on the rate of accumulation of ascorbic acid or carotenoids either in darkness or in far-red light. Mohr (Ref. 9, pp. 77–81) has proposed that this type of photocontrol represents a 'modulation' of pre-existing activities, and thus is in principle different from the control of anthocyanin synthesis, where in favourable circumstances phytochrome appears to 'switch on' a previously non-existent activity.

Here again, however, an alternative explanation is possible. If phytochrome acts to control the rate of synthesis of specific enzymes by changing ribosomal properties, or to activate pre-existing inactive enzymes, the observed effects on ascorbic acid and carotenoid synthesis could easily be accounted for. It would be necessary to assume that the messenger-RNAs for the as yet unknown limiting enzymes in the two pathways were quite stable over long periods; if this were the case, actinomycin D would have no effect on the rates of final product formation. On this view, it is no longer necessary to distinguish between modulatory and differentiational effects of phytochrome.

5.5.3 Chlorophyll

The biosynthesis of chlorophyll in most higher plants is subject to a complex system of photocontrol. One of the later reactions in the pathway, the reduction of protochlorophyll (ide) to chlorophyll (ide) is a photochemical reaction with protochlorophyll as photoreceptor. The early part of the pathway, however, is also under photocontrol mediated by phytochrome. It is likely that this photocontrol is exerted on the synthesis or activity of δ-aminolevulinic acid (ALA) synthetase, although this enzyme has not yet been confirmed definitively as existing in plant cells. Nevertheless, circumstantial evidence is strongly in favour of its existence.

When etiolated leaves are placed in continuous white light, although there is an instantaneous conversion of protochlorophyllide to form a small amount of chlorophyll, there is normally a considerable lag phase before the major phase of chlorophyll synthesis occurs. This lag can be of the order of 2–4 h in certain cases. In 1956, Withrow, Wolff and Price[132], using etiolated bean leaves, showed that the lag in chlorophyll formation could be virtually abolished by pretreatment of the leaves with a very small amount of red light given between 5 and 15 h *before* the transfer to continuous white light. It was also found that the effect of the red light pretreatment could be reversed by immediate subsequent irradiation with far-red light. Virgin[133] in 1961 produced an accurate action spectrum for the elimination of the lag phase in wheat leaves showing a prominent maximum at 660 nm with shoulders on the lower wavelength side of this maximum. The evidence thus suggests that this effect of pre-irradiation with red light on the elimination of the lag phase in chlorophyll synthesis is a classical phytochrome phenomenon. This conclusion should, perhaps, be approached with a little caution, since protochlorophyllide also absorbs strongly at 660 nm and is probably photoreduced even by the very low energy pre-irradiation treatments. Furthermore, complete re-imposition of the lag phase by far-red light is very difficult to achieve and in most cases only 40–60 % reversal is obtained, although complete far-red reversal has been reported in mustard[134]. The general lack of complete reversibility may be due to one or more of several factors such as rapid escape from phytochrome control, extreme sensitivity to low concentrations of Pfr or some effect dependent directly on protochlorophyllide absorption in addition to phytochrome.

It has been suggested that phytochrome acts, over a long period, to elevate the levels of ALA synthetase (or, at least, the enzyme responsible for the formation of ALA) thus removing the block on chlorophyll synthesis at the beginning of the pathway. Evidence for this comes from two sources. In 1958, Virgin [135] found that etiolated wheat leaves which had been pretreated with red light several hours before they were given a brief flash of intense white light to photoreduce their protochlorophyllide, resumed protochlorophyllide synthesis immediately, rather than after a 5–10 min lag as observed in fully dark-grown seedlings. If the hypothesis that protochlorophyllide acts in this system as a feed-back inhibitor of ALA synthesis is accepted[136], then a shortening of the lag phase in the resumption of protochlorophyllide synthesis would most likely be due to an increased level of the enzyme responsible for ALA synthesis, rather than to changes in the activity of that enzyme. Supporting evidence for this view comes from the observation that the red light pretreatment effect on the elimination of the lag phase in chlorophyll synthesis can be replaced by supplying etiolated leaves with exogenous ALA[137]. Upon transfer to continuous white light, leaves fed in such a way show no lag phase in greening, and there is no detectable effect of a pretreatment with red light. These findings are in agreement with the view that phytochrome acts by stimulating ALA synthesis, possibly by causing an increase in the level of ALA synthetase, but it is also possible that phytochrome photoactivation leads to an increased supply of precursors of ALA synthesis, such as succinyl-CoA and glycine.

This problem was intensively investigated in etiolated barley seedlings by Nadler and Granick[138] in 1970. When 9-day-old etiolated leaves were fed with glycine and/or succinate, there was no decrease in the lag phase of chlorophyll synthesis upon subsequent exposure to white light, suggesting that the intermediates for ALA synthesis were not limiting. If, however, similar seedlings were fed with ALA and transferred to *dim* white light (to prevent photobleaching) the lag phase was eliminated. Furthermore, chlorophyll synthesis in dim light continued in the presence of ALA even when inhibitors of protein synthesis such as cycloheximide were also applied; similar doses of cycloheximide in the absence of ALA feeding prevented chlorophyll synthesis. These data suggest that 9-day-old etiolated leaves contain all the enzymes responsible for converting ALA to chlorophyll and that their levels are non-limiting. Also, the conversion of exogenously fed ALA to chlorophyll during the first few hours of light treatment shows that the holochrome protein, which is necessary for the photoreduction of protochlorophyllide to chlorophyllide, is also non-limiting. Both cycloheximide, and chloramphenicol prevented chlorophyll synthesis in the absence of exogenous ALA. Inhibition of chlorophyll synthesis in bean leaves by chloramphenicol has also been observed[139]. Chloramphenicol given at the time of red light pretreatment led to a reimposition of the lag phase in greening, whilst application at the onset of the continuous white light, although depressing the rate of synthesis, did not reimpose the lag phase. A similar result was observed by Nadler and Granick[138] in barley leaves with cycloheximide.

Nadler and Granick[138] have also applied various inhibitors of nucleic acid synthesis in attempts to determine whether light acts through inducing RNA synthesis. No inhibition of chlorophyll synthesis was observed with 5-fluorouracil, with mitomycin-C or with various analogues of the purine and pyrimidine bases. A certain amount of inhibition was observed with actinomycin D, but only when the tissues were preincubated with the antibiotic for 24 h before illumination. These experiments, of course, are not immune to the criticism applied here to other work based on inhibitors of protein and nucleic acid synthesis. They are, however, quite different in one sense since the most important conclusions are derived from situations in which the inhibitors did not inhibit the synthesis of chlorophyll; thus actinomycin D only inhibited after a long pretreatment and cycloheximide had no effect in the presence of ALA. Thus it can be said that nucleic acid synthesis is probably not required for the light effect on chlorophyll synthesis and that ALA allows chlorophyll synthesis in the absence of protein synthesis. These conclusions are valid even if the antibiotics are inhibiting other processes *in addition* to nucleic acid and protein synthesis.

From these results, Nadler and Granick[138] have proposed a model scheme for the control of chlorophyll synthesis in barley. The control on the rate of ALA synthesis, and thus of chlorophyll, is thought to depend, at least in part, on the synthesis of a limiting protein that forms ALA, and on the rate of its degradation. This protein is presumably ALA synthetase. The role of phytochrome on this model is to activate stored messenger-RNA for translation into requisite proteins for ALA synthesis. Other evidence indicates that the ALA synthesis system is relatively unstable and that breakdown proceeds with a half life of *ca.* 1.5 h. After formation of ALA, the production of chorophyll proceeds unchecked by the action of the remaining enzymes of the biosynthetic chain, these enzymes being non-limiting and stable for at least 6 h. The final steps in synthesis are dependent on light via the photochemical reduction of protochlorophyllide by the holochrome.

5.6 CONTROL MECHANISMS IN PHOTOMORPHOGENESIS

The aim of this article has been to draw together the significant information relating to the biochemical changes which occur in cells undergoing a photomorphogenic transition, in the hope that one or more unifying trends may emerge. As is abundantly clear from the discussion, little concrete information is available and much of it does not lend itself to facile interpretation. It would therefore be foolhardy to attempt to make hard-and-fast conclusions at the present stage but it does appear as if some negative statements can be made together with some tentative suggestions regarding possible control mechanisms.

5.6.1 Primary action of phytochrome

It must be considered to be almost certain now that the initial action of phytochrome is on the properties of certain cellular membranes. Whether phytochrome is itself a component of membranes, or is associated with them in some looser manner, cannot yet be determined. Nevertheless, the extremely rapid effects of light can only be explained on the basis of relatively massive effects on membrane properties. A major problem therefore is the nature of the link between the primary action on membranes and the later effects on enzyme levels. The time-lag between these two events is *ca.* 45–90 min in various responses and represents the area of the greatest ignorance in the field of photomorphogenesis.

The possibility of a second messenger, suggested specifically as acetylcholine by Jaffe[20, 28], but in more general terms by others earlier[3, 11], seems an acceptable working hypothesis. Most of the evidence appears to be against acetylcholine as a general second messenger for photomorphogenesis but the heuristic value of the hypothesis is evident. In any case, intensive studies on metabolic changes occurring within 0–60 min after the onset of light treatment are clearly needed.

5.6.2 Control of enzyme levels

At present there is no single piece of evidence which can only be interpreted in terms of light stimulating or initiating the *de novo* synthesis of any enzyme. In the case of PAL, there is now definitive evidence, at least for the action of blue light in gherkin seedlings and probably also for mustard, that light does *not* act by stimulating *de novo* synthesis, and the best interpretation is that light mediates an activation of pre-existing inactive PAL. In the case of lipoxygenase in mustard, the very precise time courses published cannot readily be interpreted in terms of effects on synthesis, and again control of enzyme activity seems a possibility.

This negative conclusion does not, of course, rule out the possibility that light regulates the *de novo* synthesis of other enzymes and the general increase in polysome levels, coupled with possible effects on ribosome properties, indicates that general protein synthesis is elevated within a few hours of the onset of light treatment. This increased protein synthesis may, however, be similar to the increased rates of ribosomal-RNA synthesis observed in pea leaves, and be related to the formation of new cells.

5.6.3 Transcriptional or translational control

Although, as stated above, there is no direct evidence for the photocontrol of enzyme synthesis, it cannot yet be ruled out, and much of the inhibitor work in the literature is certainly consistent with such a view. Even though inhibitor experiments can never be unequivocal, it is worth considering whether they are best interpreted in terms of control of enzyme synthesis at the transcriptional or the translational level. The results of the actinomycin D experiments on anthocyanin, ascorbic acid, carotenoid and chlorophyll synthesis reviewed above all have one thing in common: complete inhibition cannot be obtained when actinomycin D is given at the time of the light treatment, and the antibiotic has to be applied often some hours before to achieve complete inhibition. These findings do not support the view that control is exerted at transcription and are more in favour of effects on the stability or other properties of pre-existing messenger-RNA, or on its translation at the ribosome.

A further argument is that transcriptional control generally implies an 'all-or-nothing' response, whereas photomorphogenic phenomena are almost always quantitative rather than qualitative changes, at least when investigated at the enzyme level. Thus in virtually all cases, significant amounts of enzyme can be detected in dark-grown tissues and light acts to increase these amounts rather than to initiate the formation of an enzyme which was not previously present. The only reported example of an 'all-or-nothing' phytochrome-mediated change in enzyme levels is PAL in mustard cotyledons, which could not be detected in dark-grown material[101]. There is a technical explanation for this finding, however, since the spectrophotometric assay used was not particularly sensitive. If a sensitive radioactive assay is used, significant amounts of activity can be detected in fully-etiolated cotyledons, showing that the light-mediated response here is also quantitative rather than qualitative (T. H. Attridge, unpublished results).

On the basis of all these considerations it seems to this reviewer that the gene-expression hypothesis of phytochrome action is no longer tenable except in its widest and most generalised interpretation. It is certainly true that gene expression is regulated but there is no evidence either for a direct interaction of phytochrome with the genome, or for control of transcription; all the evidence is in favour of post-transcriptional control. The best interpretation of the currently available information is that phytochrome acts to modify the properties of certain membranes, leading to the release of a second messenger which has several sites of action including, possibly, the protein-synthesising machinery and the as yet unknown mechanisms modifying pre-existing inactive enzymes. This model has obvious similarities to the role of cyclic-AMP[140] in mammals and bacteria, and to the recent suggestions for the mechanism of action of auxin[110, 141] reaffirming a faith in the unity of biochemistry. It is to be hoped that the methods used in these related investigations will be applied with success to a search for the postulated second messenger of phytochrome action.

References

1. Garner, W. W. and Allard, H. A. (1920). *J. Agric. Res.*, **18,** 553
2. Garner, W. W. and Allard, H. A. (1920). *J. Agric. Res.*, **23,** 871
3. Smith, H. (1970). *Nature (London)*, **227,** 665

4. Mohr, H. (1969). *An Introduction to Photobiology*, 99 (C. P. Swanson, editor) (New Jersey: Prentice Hall)
5. Briggs, W. R. and Rice, H. V. (1972). *Ann. Rev. Plant. Physiol.*, **23,** 293
6. Mohr, H. (1969). *Physiology of Plant Growth and Development*, 507 (M. B. Wilkins, editor) (London: McGraw-Hill)
7. Shropshire, W., Jr. (1972). *Photophysiology*, Vol. 7 (A. C. Giese, editor) (New York: Academic Press)
8. Mitrakos, K. and Shropshire, W., Jr. (editors) (1972). *Phytochrome* (New York: Academic Press)
9. Mohr, H. (1972). *Lectures in Photomorphogenesis* (Berlin: Springer-Verlag)
10. Mohr, H. (1966). *Photochem. Photobiol.*, **5,** 469
11. Hendricks, S. B. and Borthwick, H. A. (1967). *Proc. Nat. Acad. Sci.* (*U.S.A.*), **58,** 2125
12. Mohr, H. (1973). *The Biochemistry of Differentiation, MTP International Review of Science* (J. Paul, editor) in the press (London: Butterworths)
13. Newman, I. A. and Briggs, W. R. (1972). *Plant Physiol.*, **50,** 687
14. Jaffe, M. J. (1968). *Science*, **162,** 1016
15. Tanada, T. (1968). *Proc. Nat. Acad. Sci.* (*U.S.A.*), **59,** 378
16. Tanada, T. (1968). *Plant Physiol.*, **41,** 467
17. Junghans, H. and Jaffe, M. J. (1970). *Physiol. Plant*, **23,** 1004
18. Racusen, R. and Miller, K. (1972). *Plant Physiol.*, **49,** 654
19. Tanada, T. (1972). *Nature* (*London*), **236,** 460
20. Jaffe, M. J. (1970). *Plant Physiol.*, **46,** 786
21. Junghans, H. and Jaffe, M. J. (1972). *Plant Physiol.*, **49,** 1
22. Gressel, J., Galun, E. and Strausbauch, L. (1971). *Nature* (*London*), **232,** 648
23. Kandeler, R. (1972). *Z. Pflanzenphysiologie*, **67,** 86
24. Kasemir, H. and Mohr, H. (1972). *Plant Physiol.*, **49,** 453
25. Tanada, T. (1972). *Plant Physiol.*, **49,** 860
26. Hartmann, E. (1971). *Planta*, **101,** 159
27. Satter, R. L., Applewhite, P. B. and Galston, A. W. (1972). *Plant Physiol.*, **50,** 523
28. Jaffe, M. J. (1972). *Recent Advances in Phytochemistry*, Vol. 5, 80 (V. C. Runeckles and T. C. Tso, editors) (New York: Academic Press)
29. Fondeville, J. C., Borthwick, H. A. and Hendricks, S. B. (1966). *Planta*, **69,** 357
30. Hillman, W. S. and Koukkari, W. L. (1967). *Plant Physiol.*, **42,** 1413
31. Jaffe, M. J. and Galston, A. W. (1967). *Planta*, **77,** 135
32. Koukkari, W. L. and Hillman, W. S. (1968). *Plant Physiol.*, **43,** 698
33. Sibaoka, T. (1966). *Symp. Soc. Exp. Biol.*, **20,** 49
34. Satter, R. L., Marinoff, P. and Galston, A. W. (1970). *Amer. J. Bot.*, **57,** 916
35. Satter, R. L. and Galston, A. W. (1971). *Science*, **174,** 518
36. Satter, R. L. and Galston, A. W. (1971). *Plant Physiol.*, **48,** 740
37. Galston, A. W. and Satter, R. L. (1972). *Recent Advances in Phytochemistry*, Vol. 5, 51 (V. C. Runeckles and T. C. Tso, editors) (New York: Academic Press)
38. Setty, F. and Jaffe, M. J. (1972). *Planta*, **108,** 127
39. Toriyama, H. and Jaffe, M. J. (1972). *Plant Physiol.*, **49,** 72
40. Hardin, J. W., Cherry, J. H., Morré, D. J. and Lembi, C. A. (1972). *Proc. Nat. Acad. Sci.* (*U.S.A.*), **69,** 3146
41. Sandmeier, M. and Ivart, J. (1972). *Photochem. Photobiol.*, **16,** 51
42. Janistyn, B. and Drumm, H. (1972). *Naturwissenschaften*, **59,** 218
43. Tezuka, T. and Yamamoto, Y. (1969). *Bot. Mag. Tokyo*, **82,** 130
44. Yamamoto, Y. and Tezuka, T. (1972). *Phytochrome*, 407 (K. Mitrakos and W. Shropshire, Jr., editors) (New York: Academic Press)
45. Tezuka, T. and Yamamoto, Y. (1972). *Plant Physiol.*, **50,** 458
46. Reid, D. M., Clements, J. B. and Carr, D. J. (1968). *Nature* (*London*), **217,** 580
47. Reid, D. M. and Clements, J. B. (1968). *Nature* (*London*), **217,** 580
48. Beevers, L., Loveys, B. R., Pearson, J. A. and Wareing, P. F. (1970). *Planta*, **90,** 80
49. Loveys, B. R. and Wareing, P. F. (1971). *Planta*, **98,** 109
50. Reid, D. M., Tuing, M. S., Durley, R. C. and Railton, I. D. (1972). *Planta*, **108,** 67
51. Oelze-Karow, H., Schopfer, P. and Mohr, H. (1970). *Proc. Nat. Acad. Sci.* (*U.S A.*), **65,** 51
52. Drumm, H., Elchinger, I., Möller, J., Peter, K. and Mohr, H. (1971). *Planta*, **99,** 265
53. Drumm, H., Brüning, K. and Mohr, H. (1972). *Planta*, **106,** 259

54. Unser, G. and Masoner, M. (1972). *Naturwissenschaften*, **59,** 39
55. Filner, B. and Klein, A. O. (1969). *Plant Physiol.*, **43,** 1587
56. Jones, R. W. and Sheard, R. W. (1972). *Nature New Biol.*, **238,** 221
57. Bottomley, W. (1970). *Plant Physiol.*, **45,** 608
58. Acton, G. J. (1972). *Nature New Biol.*, **236,** 255
59. Henshall, J. D. and Goodwin, T. W. (1964). *Phytochemistry*, **3,** 677
60. Feierabend, J. and Pirson, A. (1966). *Z. Pflanzenphysiologie*, **55,** 235
61. Graham, D., Grieve, A. M. and Smillie, R. M. (1968). *Nature* (*London*), **218,** 89
62. Butler, G. L. and Bennett, V. (1969). *Plant Physiol.*, **44,** 1285
63. Steer, B. T. and Gibbs, M. (1969). *Plant Physiol.*, **44,** 775
64. Schopfer, P. (1972). *Proc. Symp. Tihany, Symposia biologica Hungarica*, Vol. 13, Nucleic Acids and Proteins in Higher Plants (G. L. Farkas, editor) (Budapest: Hungarian Academy of Sciences)
65. van Poucke, M., Cerff, R., Barthe, F. and Mohr, H. (1969). *Naturwissenschaften*, **56,** 417
66. Karow, H. and Mohr, H. (1967). *Planta*, **72,** 170
67. Drumm, H., Falk, H., Möller, J. and Mohr, H. (1970). *Cytobiologie*, **2,** 335
68. Smith, H. and Attridge, T. H. (1970). *Phytochemistry*, **9,** 487
69. Russell, D. W. (1971). *J. Biol. Chem.*, **246,** 3870
70. Young, M. R., Towers, G. H. N. and Neish, A. C. (1966). *Can. J. Bot.*, **44,** 341
71. Havir, E. A. and Hanson, K. R. (1968). *Biochemistry*, **7,** 1904
72. Havir, H. and Hanson, K. R. (1968). *Biochemistry*, **7,** 1915
73. Attridge, T. H., Stewart, G. R. and Smith, H. (1971). *FEBS Lett.*, **17,** 84
74. Ahmed, S. I. and Swain, T. (1970). *Phytochemistry*, **9,** 2287
75. Attridge, T. H. and Smith, H. (1967). *Biochim. Biophys. Acta*, **148,** 805
76. Zucker, M. (1965). *Plant Physiol.*, **40,** 779
77. Engelsma, G. (1967). *Planta*, **75,** 207
78. Amrhein, N. and Zenk, M. H. (1971). *Z. Pflanzenphysiologie*, **64,** 145
79. Durst, F. and Mohr, H. (1966). *Naturwissenschaften*, **53,** 531
80. Nitsch, C. and Nitsch, J. P. (1966). *C. R. Acad. Sci. Paris*, **262,** 1102
81. Zucker, M. (1969). *Plant Physiol.*, **44,** 912
82. Creasy, L. L. (1968). *Phytochemistry*, **7,** 441
83. Hahlbrock, K. and Wellmann, E. (1970). *Planta*, **94,** 236
84. Engelsma, G. (1970). *Acta Bot. Neerl.*, **19,** 403
85. Bellini, E. and van Poucke, M. (1970). *Planta*, **93,** 60
86. Russell, D. W. and Conn, E. E. (1967). *Arch. Biochem. Biophys.*, **122,** 256
87. Amrhein, N. and Zenk, M. H. (1970). *Naturwissenschaften*, **57,** 312
88. Hahlbrock, K., Kuhlen, E. and Lindl, T. (1971). *Planta*, **99,** 311
89. Hahlbrock, K. and Grisebach, H. (1970). *FEBS Lett.*, **11,** 62
90. Hahlbrock, K., Sutter, A., Wellmann, E., Ortmann, R. and Grisebach, H. (1971). *Phytochemistry*, **10,** 109
91. Engelsma, G. (1968). *Planta*, **82,** 255
92. Klein, R. M. and Edsall, P. C. (1968). *Plant Physiol.*, **41,** 949
93. Schopfer, P. and Mohr, H. (1972). *Plant Physiol.*, **49,** 8
94. Rissland, I. and Mohr, H. (1967). *Planta*, **77,** 239
95. Mohr, H. (1970). *Naturw. Rundsch.*, **23,** 187
96. Ellis, R. J. and MacDonald, I. R. (1970). *Plant Physiol.*, **46,** 227
97. Engelsma, G. (1967). *Naturwissenschaften*, **54,** 319
98. Hadwiger, L. E. and Schwochau, M. E. (1971). *Plant Physiol.*, **47,** 588
99. Zucker, M. (1968). *Plant Physiol.*, **43,** 365
100. Durst, F. and Mohr, H. (1966). *Naturwissenschaften*, **53,** 707
101. Dittes, L., Rissland, I. and Mohr, H. (1971). *Z. Naturforsch.*, **26b,** 1175
102. Zucker, M. (1970). *Biochim. Biophys. Acta*, **208,** 331
103. Zucker, M. (1971). *Plant. Physiol.*, **47,** 442
104. Sacher, J. A., Towers, G. H. N. and Davies, D. D. (1972). *Phytochemistry*, **11,** 2383
105. Schopfer, P. and Hock, B. (1972). *Planta*, **96,** 248
106. Schopfer, P. (1972). *Phytochrome*, 485 (K. Mitrakos and W. Shropshire, Jr., editors) (New York: Academic Press)
107. Smith, H. (1972). *Phytochrome*, 433 (K. Mitrakos and W. Shropshire, Jr., editors) (New York: Academic Press)

108. Smith, H. (1972). *Biosynthesis and its Control in Plants*, 303 (B. V. Milborrow, editor) (London: Academic Press)
109. Iredale, S. E. and Smith, H. (1973). *Phytochemistry* (in the press)
110. Johnson, C. B., Attridge, T. H. and Smith, H. (1973). *Biochem. Biophys. Acta* (in the press)
111. Attridge, T. H. and Smith, H. (1973). *Phytochemistry* (in the press)
112. Attridge, T. H. and Smith, H. (1973). *Phytochemistry* (in the press)
113. Engelsma, G. and van Bruggen, J. M. H. (1971). *Plant Physiol.*, **48,** 94
114. Attridge, T. H. and Smith, H. (1973). *Plant Science Lett.* (in the press)
115. Engelsma, G. (1970). *Planta*, **91,** 246
116. Engelsma, G. (1970). *Planta*, **90,** 133
117. Oelze-Karow, H. and Mohr, H. (1970). *Z. Naturforsch.*, **25b** 1282
118. Weidner, M. and Mohr, H. (1967). *Planta*, **75,** 99
119. Dittes, H. and Mohr, H. (1970). *Z. Naturforsch.*, **25b,** 708
120. Koller, B. and Smith, H. (1972). *Phytochemistry*, **11,** 1295
121. Pine K. and Klein, A. O. (1972). *Devel. Biol.*, **28,** 280
122. Davies, E., Larkins, B. A. and Knight, R. H. (1972). *Plant Physiol.*, **50,** 581
123. Williams, G. R. and Novelli, G. D. (1968). *Biochim. Biophys. Acta*, **155,** 183
124. DeDeken-Grenson, M. (1954). *Biochim. Biophys. Acta*, **14,** 203
125. Williams, G. R. and Novelli, G. D. (1964). *Biochem. Biophys. Res. Commun.*, **17,** 23
126. Travis, R. L., Lin, C. Y. and Key, J. L. (1972). *Biochem. Biophys. Acta*, **277,** 606
127. Mohr, H. (1966). *Z. Pflanzenphysiologie*, **54,** 63
128. Mohr, H. and Senf, R. (1966). *Planta*, **71,** 195
129. Mohr, H. and Bienger, I. (1967). *Planta*, **75,** 180
130. Bienger, I. and Schopfer, P. (1970). *Planta*, **93,** 152
131. Schnarrenberger, C. and Mohr, H. (1970). *Planta*, **94,** 296
132. Withrow, R. B., Wolff, J. B. and Price, L. (1956). *Plant Physiol.*, **31,** xiii
133. Virgin, H. (1961). *Physiol. Plant.*, **14,** 439
134. Kasemir, H. (cited in Ref. 9 as footnote on p. 171)
135. Virgin, H. (1958). *Physiol. Plant*, **11,** 347
136. Granick, S. (1965). *Biochemistry of Chloroplasts*, Vol. 2, 373 (T. W. Goodwin, editor) (London: Academic Press)
137. Sisler, E. C. and Klein, W. H. (1963). *Physiol. Plant*, **16,** 315
138. Nadler, K. and Granick, S. (1970). *Plant Physiol.*, **46,** 240
139. Marguiles, M. M. (1967). *Plant Physiol.*, **42,** 218
140. Jost, J. P. and Rickenberg, H. V. (1971). *Ann. Rev. Biochem.*, **41,** 741
141. Mondal, H., Mandal, R. K. and Biswas, B. B. (1972). *Nature New Biol.*, **240,** 111

6
Aspects of Trace Element Requirements in Plants and Micro-organisms: The Metallo Enzymes of Nitrate and Nitrite Reduction

E. J. HEWITT
Long Ashton Research Station, University of Bristol

6.1 INTRODUCTION

A comparatively recent review could find no space to discuss molybdenum proteins. I have therefore dealt with one group, the nitrate reductases, which are of interest in several contexts. They have varied electron transport properties and recently revealed regulatory aspects. They provide a unique opportunity to study independent effects of a coordinated metal or of an inducing substrate on the *in vivo* production of holo enzymes under conditions of metabolic gratuity. The biosynthesis of complementing moieties having separate catalytic functions is controlled by separate genes, and *in vitro* reconstitution of defective mutant proteins can be shown. Different physiological purposes may be served by nitrate reductase in the same cell under different conditions but views that different enzymes are involved may be re-interpreted. Probably all contain molybdenum as the ultimate electron donor but not all are flavoproteins.

Nitrite reductase systems depend on iron or copper and produce either ammonia, or nitrogen or its oxides, as a dissimilatory process. The nature of the intermediates of reduction during the transfer of six electrons to produce ammonia, the number of separate enzymes involved, the mechanisms which differentiate between production of ammonia in stoichiometric yields or of nitrogen and its oxides and other products, distinctions between electron donor systems and specificity for nitrite, sulphite and hydroxylamine, pose several interesting problems.

6.2 NITRATE REDUCTION

6.2.1 Characterisation of nitrate reductases

6.2.1.1 Molecular weights and Mo content

Most are between 1.6 and 6×10^5 daltons, e.g. in bacteria[1-4], fungi[5-8], algae[9-12], and plants[13-17,17a]. Two about 2×10^4 daltons are from *Perilla frutescens*[18] and the nitrate-reducing fragment obtained from 'nitrosome' preparations of *Candida utilis*[19], and one (10^6 daltons) is from *E. coli*[20].

Dimers occur in *Micrococcus*[1], *Aerobacter*[3,4], and *Chlorella*[11] and may be likely in spinach[15,17] and *E. coli*[20,21]. Molybdenum is generally present[3,4,5,15,22,23] and where determined, 1 atom mol^{-1}, or less is found in *E. coli*[20], *Micrococcus*[24] and wheat[13], and uncertainly one or two in *N. crassa*[5].

6.2.1.2 Substrates

(a) *Nature and affinity*—Nitrate reductases often reduce chlorate competitively in bacteria[1,4,25-28], fungi[7,29], algae[30-32], plants[17] with nitrate, and also bromate equally well[26,28] but not iodate[26] or only slowly[27,28]. Nitrate is planar, the halogens are pyramidal. Bond angles are 120° (O–N–O) 107° (O–Cl–O) 112° (O–Br–O) but only 99° (O–I–O). Bond lengths (Å) are 1.24 (NO_3^-) but 1.57–1.82 for the halogens, so angle (or redox potential) may exclude iodate[26]. Values of V_{max} are often similar for nitrate or chlorate when saturated. The K_m values for nitrate range from about 15 μM (*A. nidulans*[29] or *Ps. aeruginosa*[28]) to about 1000 μM (*M. denitrificans*[33] or *N. agilis*[34]) with no phylogenetic associations[26-28]. Since at least one enzyme for each of these extremes[24,28] contains molybdenum, substrate binding involves additional factors. This is also shown by the *differences* in the ratios of K_m for nitrate to chlorate which range from 0.5 or 0.2 (*A. Nidulans*[7,29], *A. aerogenes*[26], *Ps. denitrificans*[27]) to 0.07 or 0.04 (*Ps. multivorans*[26], *C. vulgaris*[30] or spinach[17]). Electron donors appear sometimes to influence K_m values[5,35] as well as ageing[29,36].

(b) *Specificity*—In *A. aerogenes* and *A. denitrificans* and some other bacteria one or both of two nitrate reductases A and B distinguished by their properties are found[26,37-45,45a].

Chlorate is reduced as well as nitrate by type A, chlorate is not reduced by B but is an inhibitor of nitrate reduction. A is predominantly particulate while B is soluble. Activation energy is much greater for B, and sensitivity to cyanide and azide much less than for A. Type A shows competitive and type B mixed inhibition by chlorate. The differential sensitivity to azide suggests differences in the metal components. Electron donor (BV°, MV°, or $FMNH_2$) affinities are maximal for A. Type A is inducible by nitrate and repressed by oxygen and thus resembles the *E. coli* membrane system (Section 6.2.3.1). Type B may be either constitutive and unaffected by oxygen or like type A.

Type A is present alone in *A. aerogenes* (Strain L III-1) and B only is present in *Ps. putida* and *Providencia alcalifaciens*, whereas *M. denitrificans* (strain 4) has both. In *P. putida* the type B is constitutive and essentially non-repressible by oxygen and regarded as assimilatory, but in *P. alcalifaciens*, *Aeromonas hydrophila* and *Edwardsiella tarda* it is induced by nitrate, repressed by oxygen and regarded as principally respiratory in function. The activity of B is reversibly inhibited by oxygen *in vivo* in *P. putida* independently of the non-repressibility by oxygen.

Type C enzyme able to reduce chlorate but not nitrate was found in *Hafnia* 6/63, *Proteus vulgaris* and *Providencia stuarti*[40, 43-45] and in a mutant of *E. coli*[46], for which BV° was the best donor. It was not nitrate-inducible or oxygen repressible, and was insensitive to azide and cyanide[40,43,44a,45]. In some species mutants contained only one or two of the A, B or C types[45]. A mutant of *Ps. aeruginosa* lost A and ability to denitrify but grew on nitrate. Most species except *Ps. putida* having only B showed nitrate respiration.

6.2.1.3 Electron donation

(a) *Nicotinamide or flavin nucleotides*—Most nitrate reductases, whether complex or supposedly single proteins utilise NADPH or NADH as primary electron donors. Fungi tend to be near specific for NADPH[6,46a]. Higher plants[47], algae and bacteria more often utilise NADH. In *Ankistrodesmus braunii*[32], *Dunaliella tertiolecta*[12], *Cyanidium caldarium*[48, 49], *Hansenula anomala*[50] and soya bean[51], NADH and NADPH are comparable. Sonication destroyed NADH activity in *Anabaena cylindrica*[52], and *A. chroococcum*[405], *Rhizobium*[53]. *M. denitrificans*[33] and *Spirillum itersonii*[54] scarcely utilised NAD(P)H.

Flavins ($FMNH_2$ and $FADH_2$) are effective donors for *N. crassa*[5, 55, 56], *Chlorella fusca*[9, 10], *C. caldarium*[48], *D. tertiolecta*[12], spinach[35, 57, 58], wheat[59, 60], maize[35], broad bean[61], barley[14] but very poor for *A. cylindrica*[52] (see also Section 6.2.2.6). Activity with NAD(P)H is highly sensitive to mercurials or moderate heat whereas FMNH (or BV°, MV°) donation is often unaffected[5, 10, 35, 48, 56, 57, 62] (see Sections 6.2.2.1, 6.2.2.2) or rarely inhibited[405].

(b) *Pyridilium radicals (methyl and benzyl (MV°, BV°), viologens) and ferredoxin*—The terminal moiety of complex systems in which molybdenum is situated (Section 6.2.2) with few exceptions, functions with BV° or MV° as donors, e.g. *C. pepo*, maize, spinach[63-65], *Achromobacter fischeri*[66] *E. coli*[20], *Micrococcus* and *Aerobacter* spp.[42], *N. crassa*[5], *C. fusca*[9] *Hansenula anomala*[67], *C. caldarium*[48, 68], *A. cylindrica*[52, 69], *A. braunii*[32]. Highly purified enzymes of *A. aerogenes*[4], *M. denitrificans*[33], *E. coli* terminal moiety[20], *S. itersonii*[54], *R. japonicum*[53] and *A. chroococcum*[405] functioned practically only with MV° or BV°.

Initially submerged[70] or poorly aerated[71] *N. crassa* mycelia yielded nitrate reductase which was inactive with NADPH. It had no flavin requirement but functioned with BV° or MV°[70]. It depended on molybdenum and iron for formation and was particulate. NADPH-cytochrome c reductase was decreased. This system resembles the activity of nit. 3 mutants (Section 6.2.6.1(a). Synthesis of the moiety controlled by the nit.1 gene (NADPH cytochrome c reductase) may be repressible by anaerobic conditions.

In photosynthesis, nitrogenase, nitrite and sulphite reductases and hydrogenases, viologen radicals and non-haem iron ferredoxin proteins are often interchangeable. In spinach[72] or *C. fusca*[9], spinach ferredoxin reduced by chloroplasts was inactive for nitrate reductase. MV° (dithionite reduced) was inactive for *D. tertiolecta*[12] and possibly spinach when reduced by chloroplasts[72], but active with dithionite[65]. Ferredoxin reduced by chloroplasts or NADPH but not by dithionite was very active for *A. cylindrica*[52,69].

Viologens show selective inhibitory effects. BV (1.5 mM) reduced more than 40%, totally inhibited in *C. pepo*[64] but was reversible after partial re-oxidation[73] but not by oxidised BV. In *Hansenula*[67] preincubation of enzyme with 10 μM BV° reduced by hydrogenase caused instant inactivation without nitrate or progressively with nitrate; $FMNH_2$ similarly inactivated. In *A. aerogenes* or *M. denitrificans*, no inactivation by excess BV°[26] occurred. In *Klebsiella pneumoniae*[74] excess BV° (> 50 μM) reduced to equilibrium by hydrogenase inhibited the nitrogenase system with optimal ratio of the Fe + Mo and Fe proteins. Excess of the Fe + Mo protein mitigated inhibition by BV°, whereas MV° did not inhibit comparably.

(c) *Sulphite*—In *Thiobacillus denitrificans* purified nitrate reductase functioned best with MV° but also well both with sulphite as SO_3^{2-}[75] in addition to dithionite which are rarely active in other systems. A sulphite oxidase showing e.s.r. signals for molybdenum occurs in wheat germ and *Thiobacillus thioparas*[76] which apparently resembles the molybdenum protein of liver[77-79] and will not donate to nitrate but the wheat germ enzyme[76] is not tested.

6.2.2 Electron transport in nitrate reductase systems

In addition to molybdenum, some nitrate reductases contain iron in one or more forms as non-haem iron or as cytochromes or as dissociable ionic iron. Flavins may or may not be present. Quinones appear necessary in membrane systems. The enzymes are complex proteins with separate gene control of different components in fungi and bacteria but in algae and plants this is not yet shown. Most systems show two distinct activities, namely diaphorase or cytochrome c reductase and nitrate reductase according to the scheme in Figure 6.1 which covers most variants in electron transport.

6.2.2.1 Role of molybdenum in electron transport

Removal of molybdenum from the *Neurospora* enzyme with cyanide (Section 6.2.4.7), confirmed by analysis[23], showed that NADPH and FAD donated to the metal which was not required for diaphorase activity by NADPH or $FADH_2$, but was essential for nitrate reduction by all donors. Molybdate reduced to Mo^V with dithionite and identified chromatographically[80-82] was 80% as efficient as by NADPH[55,56]. For soya bean where molybdenum removal was not shown analytically, the cyanide treated enzyme was re-activated by MoO_3 or MoO_4^{2-} but dithionite-reduced molybdate did not re-activate the same enzyme. Nevertheless, Mo- free aldehyde oxidase[84] and xanthine oxidase[85] could be reactivated by MoO_3 but not by MoO_4^{2-}. The *N. crassa* enzyme also catalysed oxidation of $FMNH_2$ by exogenous molybdate[23].

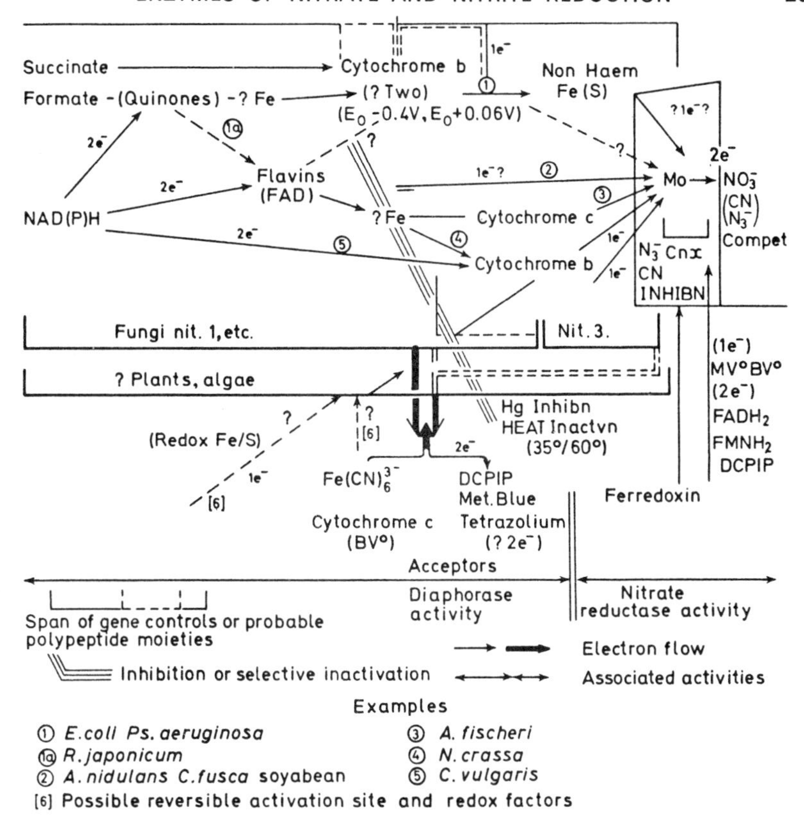

Figure 6.1 Generalised scheme for principal nitrate reductase systems with examples, and tentative representation of protein moieties, gene control and critical inhibitory susceptibilities

Hydrogen-reduced Mo^V was 25% as effective as NADH for *Ps. aeruginosa*[28]. Donation by Mo^V was not seen in *C. fusca* originally[86] or spinach[62] but when the *Chlorella* protein was heated at 45° for 5 min, which destroyed the NADH activity, Mo^V reduced nitrate enzymically[22]. Super activation by heat and mercurials of BV° donation to the terminal moiety in *N. crassa*[5] and *C. caldarium*[48, 68] may be analogous in exposing the molybdenum. The suggestion[31] that restoration of activity by molybdate after cyanide dialysis of the *Neurospora* enzyme[23] may be explained by oxidation of the cyanide complex by excess of MoO_4^{2-} (Section 6.2.4.7), implies that the metal had been removed from irrelevant protein such as a molybdenum carrier present in the partially purified enzyme. Molybdenum blue donated to the *E. coli* system[95] (6.2.2.5).

6.2.2.2 Haem iron with flavin nucleotides

(a) *Fungi*—The *N. crassa* enzyme contains cytochrome b 557, which remains in the protein of mol. wt. 2.3×10^5 daltons after > 500-fold purification and crystallisation[5, 87]. The cytochrome is reduced by NADPH only when FAD is also present and it can be reoxidised by nitrate[5]. Omission of FAD prevented reduction of nitrate or DCPIP by NADPH but $FADH_2$ functioned in the absence of NADPH. Reduced DCPIP reduced nitrate in the absence of NADPH or $FADH_2$. NADPH reduced FMN in the presence of enzyme[56]. Inhibition by oxine and *o*-phenanthroline[5] suggested that a separate metal, possibly iron, was required for both NADPH-nitrate and cytochrome c-reductase systems but not for $FADH_2$ or MV° nitrate reductase. Cytochrome c reduced by an unspecified manner did not reduce nitrate but potentials might be too close (ΔE 0.23V) for a one e^- donor.

The NADPH cytochrome c reductase (4.5 S) moiety in nit. 1 mutants (Section 6.2.6) is FAD dependent and probably retains the cytochrome b557. The electron transport sequence for *N. crassa* accords with Figure 6.1, omitting quinones and non-haem iron. Either cytochrome b or FAD may be the electron outlet for diaphorase action. The iron component in the dissimilatory enzyme from *N. crassa*[70, 71] was not characterised.

(b) *Bacteria*—In *Ps. aeruginosa*[28] cytochrome c (λ_{max}, 416, 520, 551 nm) which was removed by ammonium sulphate at pH 8.2 was a functional component, though a cytochrome b (λ_{max}, 426, 528, 559 nm) was also present. FAD was a component (1:1 with molybdenum) which linked NADH to cytochrome c. NADH, $FADH_2$, ferrocytochrome c and Mo^V were all effective electron donors for the complete system. Mo^{VI} and nitrate reoxidised both cytochromes. Removal of cytochrome c impaired the reaction with NADH or $FADH_2$ but not with Mo^V. Iron and molybdenum were needed for enzyme formation and accumulated in protein during purification in a ratio of 60 Fe:1 Mo. The high ratio of Fe:Mo may indicate additional non-haem iron. The particulate enzyme *R. japonicum* bacteroids[88] was thought to contain a cytochrome b and a flavin because antimycin A, acriflavin and u.v. irradiation inhibited with NADH or succinate. After solubilisation only BV° was effective[53]. (See also Section 6.2.2.5.)

6.2.2.3 Other haem iron systems (without flavins)

(a) *Algae*—Nitrate reductases of different *Chlorella* species appear to differ with respect to iron. The enzyme obtained from *C. vulgaris*[30, 89, 90] undoubtedly has a cytochrome b557 component. The haem was dissociable by acetone. Absorption peaks (and ε mM values) for the reduced form were: 423 nm (305), 527 (30.2), 557 (48.5). This haem did not react with carbon monoxide, 8-hydroxyquinoline-*N* oxide (HOQNO) or antimycin A. It was reduced by NADH and reoxidised by nitrate as in *N. crassa*[5]. The purified enzyme had characteristic diaphorase activities but no flavin requirements or flavin spectrum[89], thus differing from *N. crassa*.

(b) *Bacteria*—The nitrate reductase of *Ps. denitrificans*[27] is a membrane bound respiratory system which utilises formate or NADH as in *E. coli*. The solubilised system contained a cytochrome b (λ_{max} 560, 521 and 431 nm) and was unable to utilise either formate or NADH but BV° was a good donor. *A. fischeri* enzyme[66, 91] showed unusual features. The extensively purified protein had two components (4.5 S and 1.5 S) though the active one was not determined. Only BV° or cytochrome c functioned as donors. Immunity to cyanide is strange if molybdenum is present. The absorption spectrum showed a small peak at about 420 nm[91]. Carbon monoxide inhibited reversibility.

(c) *Plants*—Horse radish peroxidase with diethyl dithiocarbamate and $K_2SO_3 + K_2S_2O_5$ was reported to reduce nitrate whereas catalase, cytochrome c and haemoglobin were inert[92, 406] and NADH systems were slower.

6.2.2.4 *Non-haem iron (and molybdenum proteins)*

M. denitrificans enzyme[1, 33] of type A (6.2.1.2(b)) contained two forms of non-haem iron and labile sulphide (several atoms) and one atom Mo/mol of 1.6×10^5 daltons[24]. There was no flavin or haem component and the purified protein was brown with a weak absorption maximum (410–420 nm) (10% of *E* 280 nm) and utilised only MV° or BV° (Section 6.2.2). A cytochrome b was probably the electron donor[93] and not cytochrome c[94] and it resembles the *E. coli* system (Section 6.2.2.5).

6.2.2.5 *Haem and non-haem iron complex systems*

The complex formate-nitrate reductase of *E. coli*[20, 95, 96] is compatible with Figure 6.1. The physiological penultimate donor is an autoxidisable cytochrome b 559[97, 98] which requires menadione to link the system to formate (Sections 6.2.2.7(b), 6.2.3.1). The haem had bands at 599, 530 (ε mM 16.1) and 427 nm when reduced by dithionite. The haem-free homogeneous solubilised terminal moiety[95, 97, 98] of the particulate preparation had a mol. wt. of 10^6 daltons, and one atom molybdenum, and 40 of non-haem ferrous iron. The iron was apparently non-reactive with nitrate but was required for activity. Labile sulphide was not reported, and flavins were absent.

The cytochrome component was resolved into two identical spectral components, cytochrome b555 I and II with different redox levels and kinetics[96]. Component I was immediately reduced by formate (E_0-0.4 V) (but not NADH) and was linked to b555 II and the sequence was inhibited by HOQNO. Nitrate reoxidised I and II with biphasic kinetics. Ascorbate (E_0 + 0.06 V) reduction of nitrate was not inhibited by HOQNO and reduced component II only.

6.2.2.6 *Flavin systems without iron*

(a) *Micro-organisms*—In *C. fusca*, iron was thought unnecessary for activity or formation, unlike nitrite reductase[22, 99, 100], but molybdenum was an essential component[22, 101]. The *C. fusca* enzyme required dissociable FAD for both the NADH nitrate reductase and diaphorase activities[10], thereby resembling soya bean (6.2.2.6(b)). Light absorption originally showed neither haem nor flavin peaks[86] but now a shoulder at 410 nm may indicate a cytochrome[10, 11]. The reports require clarification. FAD (not FMN) protected the NADH nitrate reductase activity during heating for 5 min (45 °C)[10] which generally destroys NADH nitrate reductase and diaphorase activities[17, 59, 62, 86, 101], or at 60 °C in *Cyanidium*[48, 49, 60]. FMN similarly protected the enzyme from *Clostridium kluveri*[102]. The valid distinction between the *C. vulgaris* and *C. fusca* enzymes was established comparatively with regard to flavin dependence and spectrum[103].

The flavin dependent system of *Ankistrodesmus* has not been characterised[104], but can be labelled with ^{57}Fe and has a faint 410 nm peak[104a]. *A. nidulans* enzyme[6] had a peak at 420 nm. A flavoprotein was nevertheless inferred. A homogeneous preparation[8] had flavin peaks at 378 and 450 nm, bleached by NADH and restored by nitrate. No haem was present but an associated c type cytochrome explained the previous spectrum[6]. A simple flavoprotein having 1 mol FAD was suggested. A flavin is probably present for *H. anomala*[50] ($K_m < 0.1$ µM). A soluble preparation from *E. coli* utilising NADH required FAD (K_m 0.5 µM)[105].

(b) *Plants*—In soybean (*Soya max*)[51, 83] FAD is a dissociable co-factor, K_m 0.1 µM (3.7 µM for FMN) and is probably essential for wheat embryo[106] and sugar cane[107]. Spinach nitrate reductase utilises $FMNH_2$ directly, but K_m values are inexplicably varied (100 µM[35], × or 20 µM[58]) irrespective of using comparable methods. Although thought to be absent from spinach[62], agarose columns greatly decreased activity with NADH unless FAD was added[17]. Sephadex G.50 columns decreased maize activity[35] with NADH which was restored by cysteine; $FMNH_2$ activity was also enhanced. Sucrose-tris gradient centrifugation of barley enzyme[14] destroyed NADH- and most $FMNH_2$-activity unless EDTA, cysteine and FAD (10 µM) were present. Photochemically reduced FMN was superior to NADH for wheat[59, 60] and the physiological status of flavins is controversial[35, 58]. Stabilisation may be involved[10, 17], e.g. against thermal denaturation.

6.2.2.7 Other carriers

(a) *Metals*—Separate *E. coli* enzymes were stimulated up to sixfold by 1.25 mM Fe^{2+} ions[108, 109], even in the presence of NADH, FMN and menadione. *A. fisheri* enzyme[66] required ionic iron to link FMN or FAD to a c type cytochrome which was the physiological terminal donor. The *N. crassa* system[5] appeared to depend possibly on iron between the FAD or NADPH and the cytochrome b557, and especially for the diaphorase activity.

(b) *Quinones*—Menadione or 1,4-naphthoquinones are carriers in *E. coli* systems for which Vitamin K_2 may be the natural carrier[108] and 1 µM dicoumarol inhibited 100%. Menadione or K_3 stimulated, and dicoumarol inhibited, the solubilised *E. coli* system[20, 97, 98]. This factor linked reduction of nitrate by formate and simultaneous reduction of the cytochrome b. Menadione functioned in an aerobic system whereas a flavin was a carrier in an anaerobic system in *E. coli*[110, 111], and linked NADH to cytochrome b and nitrate reductase in *B. cereus*[112] whereas flavins, though active, were not components. The *Rhizobium* enzyme was inhibited by dicoumarol and menadione was needed when NADH but not succinate was the donor[88]. The lipid soluble quinones appear to be carriers in membrane bound complexes involving cytochromes.

6.2.3 Respiratory, membrane bound, and assimilatory systems

Several bacteria utilise nitrate both as a respiratory oxidant (nitrate respiration or dissimilation) and for nitrate assimilation, see reviews[95,112].

6.2.3.1 E. coli

Here[20,21,95,113,114] formate is the H donor for both activities in membrane bound fractions. Activity is suppressed by oxygen, but not totally in the presence of nitrate[21,115]. Synthesis of each component: formate dehydrogenase, cytochrome b[20] or b555 (types I and II)[96] and the terminal Fe/Mo nitrate reductase moiety is nitrate inducible. It is controlled either by related genes[116] or by a single pleiotropic gene, or the nitrate reductase protein influences the manifestation of the others by polarity[117], which might explain why a molybdenum requirement for formate dehydrogenase production and tungsten antagonism (Sections 6.2.4.4 and 6.2.4.5) occurs only if nitrate is present. Repression in aerobic conditions may depend on a redox sensitive repressor which is inactive at low redox potentials[21,115]. Restoration of activity by menadione or lipid soluble factors[108-110,111] may relate to integrity of the membrane-bound system. During purification the low E_0 cytochrome b555 appeared to be attached to formate dehydrogenase and the high E_0 b555 remained with the terminal moiety[96]. Their synthesis may depend on separate genes or their attachment may control the redox activities. Proteins of the respiratory and assimilatory systems were indistinguishable serologically when purified[118].

In chlorate resistant mutants (lacking nitrate (chlorate) reductase) isolated membrane proteins which normally held nitrate reductase were found to lack a low mol. wt. component (2×10^4 daltons) when separated by dodecyl sulphate acrylamide gel electrophoresis[119,120]. This fraction which was found in the wild strain was not induced by nitrate or correlated with formic dehydrogenase and was possibly structural. A mutant defective for formate dehydrogenase and nitrate reductase[121] had excess cytochrome c552 and normal cytochrome b559. Nitrate induced both in the wild strain in anaerobic conditions but suppressed cytochrome c in the mutant. Induction of c552 by low concentrations of nitrate in the wild strain was a secondary effect of nitrite which oxidised and induced c552[114] whereas excess nitrate suppressed cytochrome c552. Absorption bands appear to differ.

Differential effects of oxygen and nitrate on *E. coli* systems are compatible with one membrane bound complex. Thus oxygen may repress the operon controlling coordinate synthesis of the formate-nitrate reductase complex and reversibly inactivate the system by a metabolic redox factor, e.g. SS/SH or $NAD^+/NADH$[21,122,123,123a] (see Section 6.2.7.2). Oxygen suppressed nitrate-induced activity, especially in *Micrococcus*[124]. The transition from membrane-bound to soluble state in different conditions may be an artifact[120] or a result of changing redox conditions[21]. Suppression of hydrogen lyase activity by nitrate[115,125] may be explained by the suppressive effect of nitrate excess on cytochrome c552[114] and the probable link between hydrogen lyase and cytochrome c552[121]. Nitrate accumulation resulting from molybdenum deficiency or tungsten excess (Section 6.2.4.5) could suppress cytochrome c552 and account for loss of hydrogen lyase with molybdenum deficiency or excess of tungsten when nitrate is present[126].

6.2.3.2 Bacillus licheniformis

Multiple membrane proteins of chlorate resistant mutants of *B. licheniformis*[127] grown anaerobically with nitrate, differed electrophoretically from wild strains but not when grown aerobically where nitrate reductase was suppressed in wild strains. *B. licheniformis* differed from *E. coli* in that nitrate reductase formation depended only on the redox factor and not on nitrate[128].

6.2.3.3 Aerobacter aerogenes

In *A.* (*Klebsiella*) *aerogenes*[4] the membrane bound assimilatory and respiratory enzymes had the same terminal BV° nitrate reductase. The assimilatory system was thought to be inside and the respiratory one outside the membrane. Renewed growth after transfer from aerobic to anaerobic conditions or vice versa in the presence of nitrate required *de novo* protein synthesis[123, 129]. Nitrate appeared to induce formation of an *inactive* nitrate reductase which was activated when linked with other components of the respiratory or assimilatory pathways which are regulated independently by oxygen and ammonia. Unlike *E. coli* cytochrome b_1 was involved in respiratory but not in assimilatory nitrate reduction[129].

6.2.3.4 Proteus mirabilis

In the wild strain of *P. mirabilis* the type A reductase (Section 6.2.1.2 (b)) was reversibly repressed by aerobic conditions but remained active in a mutant defective in δ aminolaevulinic acid (ALA)[130, 131]. The repression by oxygen therefore depended on a haem component. Formate hydrogen lyase and formate dehydrogenase-nitrate reductase varied reciprocally. A component of the hydrogen lyase (which requires molybdenum for manifestation[125, 126, 132] (Section 6.2.4.4)) was thought to regulate nitrate reductase by a redox factor which was repressed in the reduced state. Alternatively, nitrate reductase combined with nitrate may regulate hydrogen lyase, because azide (which inhibited competitively with nitrate (Section 6.2.4.7)) did not prevent the formation of nitrate reductase, but reversed the repression of the hydrogen lyase by nitrate[133]. Formate nitrate reductase B and hydrogen lyase of the mutant were both inactivated after removal of ALA. Formate and BV° nitrate reductase A first increased and then declined as haem synthesis was impaired, possibly as a result of the polarity of a pleiotropic gene[117]. Activity of the membrane bound complex was possibly degraded when electron flow was diverted[134] and a similar mechanism may operate in *E. coli*[135, 136].

6.2.4 Metals in protein synthesis and enzyme activity

6.2.4.1 Molybdenum and nitrate reductase synthesis

(a) *Plants*—Restoration of nitrate reductase in molybdenum deficient plants occurred only when molybdenum was supplied *in vivo* to excised leaf tissues or intact plants whereas cell-free extracts never responded. Half maximal rate of response occurred with about 30–100 nM Mo in tissues. Responses to molybdenum or induction by nitrate both increased steadily over several hours and were inhibited substantially by cycloheximide, patulin, cycloserine, puromycin, L + azetidine-2-carboxylic acid and other amino acid analogues[137-143]. The response to molybdenum depended on intact cell structure and appeared to require concomitant protein synthesis. In molybdenum deficient spinach[144, 145], decreased nitrate reductase was associated with normal diaphorase estimated with DCPIP. Tetrazolium reduction after disc electrophoresis was low in the protein band having weak nitrate reductase but there was proliferation of other diaphorase bands. After molybdenum uptake for 16 h nitrate reductase increased greatly but total DCPIP diaphorase did not, whereas the tetrazolium reductase bands were decreased from nine to two and reinforced in the nitrate reductase band.

(b) *Algae*—In *C. fusca*[101] the diaphorase and nitrate reductase coincided in a sucrose density gradient. Whereas in normal cells NADH diaphorase and $FMNH_2$ and NADH nitrate reductase activities were all high, in molybdenum deficient cells the diaphorase was almost unchanged but the nitrate reductase was greatly decreased and a secondary peak of diaphorase appeared at a lower mol. wt. fraction. Molybdenum was concluded not to be required for synthesis of a diaphorase protein having a mol. wt. similar to the complete nitrate reductase, i.e. apoprotein was present in molybdenum deficient cells. When molybdenum was added, NADH nitrate reductase increased 4.3-fold in 4 h but 2.9-fold with 10 μg/ml cycloheximide as well (45% inhibition). Molybdenum was stated to be incorporated into preformed apoprotein in the deficient cells where protein synthesis was prevented, in contrast to the interpretation for plants above.

(c) *Fungi*—In similar experiments with wild type *N. crassa*[146] when grown with molybdenum there was the usual coincidence for nitrate-inducible NADPH cytochrome-c reductase and NADPH-nitrate reductase activities sedimenting at 7.8S. The constitutive NADPH cytochrome-c reductase at 12S and a small shoulder at 4S were observed. Without molybdenum the NADPH and MV° nitrate reductase decreased 70% but the 7.8 S NADPH cytochrome-c reductase and the shoulder at 4S scarcely changed. In nit. 1 mutants lacking nitrate reductase (Section 6.2.6.1(a)) nitrate inducible cytochrome c reductase was wholly in the 4S peak and was unaffected by molybdenum. In wild type entire NADPH-cytochrome c nitrate reductase apoprotein was concluded to be present without molybdenum as in *C. fusca*[101] but so conformed that it could not accept molybdenum *in vitro* unlike the cyanide-dialysed protein[23].

6.2.4.2 Molybdenum requirements in mutants

(a) *Aspergillus nidulans*—Some mutants of *A. nidulans* unable to grow on nitrate cannot produce nitrate reductase inducibly and lack xanthine dehydrogenase[147]. These mutants probably lack a common molybdenum containing (cnx) co-factor. Some 'leaky' mutants produced weak xanthine dehydrogenase or nitrate reductase when induced by nitrate. The cnxE mutant produced increased inducible NADPH and BV° nitrate reductase when supplied with 33 mM instead of 3.3 μM Mo in the medium, but not in the extracts[148]. Molybdenum activated the repaired enzyme hyperbolically. The K_m for nitrate for wild enzyme was 60 μM and 600 μM for repaired cnxE mutants so the repaired form was defective, but K_m NADPH was unchanged. Some mutants had nitrate inducible cytochrome c reductase (cnxE) but others (cnxF) which did not, were not repairable[148].

The cnx E_{14} strain showed appreciable 'repair' with the normal molybdenum level as in an *E. coli* mutant (below). Toxicity by 33 mM Mo was prevented by nitrate induction of either nitrate reductase or cytochrome c reductase according to the mutant or where nitrate reductase was constitutive, but was not prevented in cnx E by hypoxanthine which induced xanthine dehydrogenase. Synthesis of active or inactive nitrate reductase protein probably conferred resistance to molybdate toxicity but some mutants showed impaired molybdenum uptake or phosphatase activity[150].

The cnx (E) locus may code for a molybdenum inserting enzyme for nitrate reductase[148]. Coding for production of a molybdenum-containing moiety is also possible. The cnx locus may control aggregation of the 4.5S nitrate-inducible NADPH cytochrome c reductase to yield the 7.8S protein by linkage with the co-factor[151] either with or without prior insertion of molybdenum. The cnx mutant thus resembles somewhat the *N. crassa* nit 1. (Section 6.2.6.1(a)).

(b) *Escherichia coli*—Some *E. coli* mutants (Chl) are resistant to chlorate because they lack formate nitrate reductase. ChlD cells given 0.1 mM Mo *in vivo* produced formate and MV° nitrate reductase, formate dehydrogenase and formate hydrogen lyase comparable to wild strain given 1 μM or less[152], but 0.1 mM Mo (1% of the *A. nidulans* level) was not saturating for repair. Other Chl A and B mutants which complement (Section 6.2.6.1(b)) were not repairable. Molybdenum uptake was not involved but incorporation into a membrane fraction was increased in the repairable mutant. A molybdenum processing system was thought to be coded for by the ChlD locus.

6.2.4.3 Molybdenum incorporation into nitrate reductase

Enzymes from *M. denitrificans* and *N. crassa* showed a correlation between radio-activity ^{99}Mo[33] or total molybdenum[153] and enzyme specific activity in successive ammonium sulphate fractions. Statements that spinach nitrate reductase is not a molybdo protein[62, 86] were controverted[144, 145] by following radioactivity during fractionation and electrophoreses of protein from molybdenum deficient spinach given 150 μCi ^{99}Mo 16 h before harvesting. After removal of assumedly ionic molybdenum there was a constant ratio of radioactivity to enzyme activity and increasing radioactivity/mg protein which attained 18.7% of that supplied. In similar experiments with *C. fusca*[22] after purification and fractionation on agarose gel, only 1% of the molybdenum given (2 mCi) was recovered in the enzyme after 4 h growth of normal cells, from which molybdenum was omitted only 18 h before, thereby depressing net incorporation of labelled element[144]. The ratio ^{99}Mo/nitrate reductase declined during fractionation[22] suggesting possible loss of molybdenum bonding proteins[154, 155].

6.2.4.4 *Selenium and molybdenum in nitrate-formate metabolism*

After finding that formate dehydrogenase and hydrogen lyase activities of *E. coli* grown with nitrate, depended on molybdenum[126], unexpected loss of activity was restored by tap water, or boiler scale in which selenite was the active co-factor effective between 0.03 and 0.1 μM which provided 5–10 × 10^3 atoms Se/cell, and 0.01 μM molybdenum was optimal. Selenate was almost inert. Tellurate could not substitute. Vanadate, chromate, tungstate or uranyl ions could not replace molybdenum. Molybdate and selenite requirements were confirmed[156] and iron requirements for dehydrogenase (methylene blue acceptor) and lyase activities were differentiated.

Molybdate was needed to form nitrate-inducible cytochrome b555 in anaerobically grown cells. Without nitrate, molybdenum stimulated formation of a cytochrome c549[125] which is a possible link with hydrogen lyase[121]. The addition of molybdate and selenite in anaerobic nitrate medium were essential for and caused rapid increases of formate nitrate reductase and dehydrogenase activities. Molybdate as expected was needed for NADH- and BV° nitrate reductase. Selenite was stimulatory but possibly was not essential for BV° nitrate or chlorate reductase or for NADH nitrate reductase[125] and its effects here may arise from reciprocal polarity[117].

The inertness of selenate compared with selenite, selenide and selenocysteine may reflect failure of *E. coli* to reduce selenate[125, 157], or to instability of 5′-phosphoselenate[158], although selenite can replace sulphite in *E. coli* sulphite reductase[159]. Radioactive selenium was enriched in protein fractions most active in formate dehydrogenase[160]. Selenite and selenocysteine were most effective. Selenomethionine was 50% as effective as selenite in anaerobic cells and 25% in aerobic cells with methylene blue reduction and only 5% as effective for reduction of BV°. This was functional only in anaerobic cells, possibly because the terminal BV° nitrate reductase was suppressed aerobically and its function as a BV reductase prevented. The terminal moiety may be a non-haem iron sulphide or selenide protein. Selenide can replace sulphide in putidaredoxin of *Ps. putida* and parsley ferredoxin[161-163], which are functional but have altered redox values, and absorption spectra[162] or e.s.r. parameters[161].

6.2.4.5 Tungsten and vanadium substitution

(a) *Micro-organisms*—Tungstate but not vanadate competitively antagonised the molybdate requirement for formate dehydrogenase in *E. coli*[126]. In the absence of nitrate, tungsten had no effect. The BV° nitrate reductase was depressed by tungsten[132]. Tungsten (1 mM) with molybdenum (10 μM) competitively and reversibly inhibited (K_i 0.2 μM) the growth of *Azotobacter* 70 % with nitrogen and 50 % with nitrate. Vanadium inhibited growth severely but molybdenum could not reverse its effect[164]. Radioactively labelled tungsten was incorporated into protein from *A. vinelandii* or *A. chroococcum* in fractions normally containing molybdenum. There was a close correspondence between the tungsten and molybdenum peaks after electrophoresis[165-168] but two proteins may have been resolved[169].

Vanadium is unable to replace molybdenum in nitrogen fixation in certain species of *Azotobacter*[170-172], in *Rhizobia*[173], in myxophyceae[174, 175], or certain strains of *Clostridium*[176], but may substitute in *A. chroococcum* and *A. vinelandii*[172, 177] and in *Mycobacterium*[178] with up to 70 % efficiency. Vanadium was incorporated into protein of *A. vinelandii* and *A. chroococcum* grown in media free of molybdenum and was concentrated in fractions enriched with nitrogenase[154, 155, 179]. The specific activities with vanadium for nitrogen fixation, acetylene reduction or cyanide reduction were decreased to about 4 % of the molybdenum protein. The vanadium form was more thermolabile, but activation energies were similar for both. The K_m values were smaller for nitrogen and acetylene, affinity for carbon monoxide was greater and electron transfer to the substrate instead of to protons was more efficient in the molybdenum protein[179]. Tungsten inhibition of nitrogen fixation is explained by the incorporation of tungsten in place of molybdenum into *A. vinelandii* Mo/Fe nitrogenase protein to produce an inert analogue[169] but synthesis of the Fe nitrogenase was normal.

Tungsten inhibited the production of xanthine dehydrogenase activity by *Ps. aeruginosa*[180], competitively with molybdenum. Tungsten antagonised molybdenum for growth of *A. niger* with nitrate[181] and vanadium was not a substitute[182]. In *N. crassa*[146] tungsten antagonism resembled molybdenum deficiency (Section 6.2.4.1(c)) and NADPH cytochrome c reductase was still sedimented at 7.8 S in wild and at 4S in nit. 1 strains. There was a close correspondence in *C. fusca* between nitrate reductase and the fractionation of the ^{185}W labelled analogue. When given excess tungsten the NADH-ferricyanide diaphorase coincided with distribution of tungsten, but nitrate reductase was absent. In cells given tungsten and additional molybdenum nitrate reductase was restored and the tungsten protein decreased in a reciprocal manner[183].

Vanadium appeared to be essential in addition to molybdenum in *Scenedesmus obliquus*[184, 185] and stimulated oxygen evolution/mg chlorophyll especially at high light intensity, but could not replace molybdenum in *Anabaena* for growth on nitrate or atmospheric nitrogen[185].

(b) *Plants*—Tobacco cell cultures and barley seedlings grown with 0.1 mM tungstate and trace contamination levels of molybdenum had negligible nitrate reductase which was restored steadily over several hours in both species when given 0.1 mM molybdate[186]. Addition of molybdenum to tobacco callus cells previously grown in the presence of tungsten produced nitrate reductase in the presence of cycloheximide, which inhibited protein synthesis by 98%, indicating that *in vivo* replacement of tungsten by molybdenum occurred without protein synthesis. However, whereas L-azetidine-2-carboxylic acid, which inhibits nitrate reductase formation by substitution for proline[142], did not prevent incorporation of tungsten into nitrate reductase protein, puromycin which inhibits induction by nitrate[47] or by molybdenum[142] inhibited by 90% the incorporation of tungsten into nitrate reductase proteins[187, 407]. This shows that incorporation as distinct from exchange is dependent on protein synthesis in plants. This may explain why molybdenum appeared unable to reverse the effect of tungsten in tobacco cells if cycloheximide had been given together with the tungsten[188], because initial incorporation into protein had been prevented and there was no metal to exchange.

Sucrose gradient analysis of enzyme activities produced when barley plants were grown with tungsten and minimal molybdenum showed that both the 3.7S and 8S nitrate-inducible NADH cytochrome c reductases were superabundant[14] but production of the 8S NADH and $FMNH_2$ nitrate reductase was suppressed. Superabundance of cytochrome c reductases was a result of nitrate accumulation. Tungsten was shown to be incorporated into the nitrate reductase protein of spinach instead of molybdenum[15, 145] when molybdenum deficient plants with weak nitrate reductase were given ^{185}W-labelled tungstate for 16 h. The ^{185}W labelled protein behaved like the nitrate reductase during fractionation and electrophoresis and pH focusing.

The diaphorase activity with tetrazolium of the proteins separated by disc electrophoresis[144] after plants were given tungsten for 16 h was intermediate in pattern between molybdenum deficient plants and those given molybdenum. There was a reduction in the number of diaphorase bands from nine to about four compared with two for molybdenum and an increase in the activity of some, including that corresponding to nitrate reductase[145]. The presence of either metal appeared to aggregate or otherwise associate several possibly similar diaphorases differing only in charge. Their relevance to the 3.7S components[14] remain to be determined. In spite of the redistribution of diaphorase into fewer proteins the total diaphorase measured with DCPIP remained substantially unchanged after incorporation of tungsten or of molybdenum which specifically increased nitrate reductase activity[145] fourfold. The close similarity of the molybdenum and tungsten proteins obtained by *in vivo* incorporation of the metals provides a useful method for the study of the possible mechanism of metal incorporation and binding in the protein.

By contrast with tungsten in plants[145] or vanadium in nitrogenase[154, 155, 179], vanadium was not incorporated into protein associated with spinach nitrate reductase[189]. However, vanadium (30 μM) inhibited wheat embryo nitrate reductase *in vitro* but tungsten had no effect[106]. Uranium, but not tungsten, possibly replaced molybdenum with 10% effectiveness in cream xanthine oxidase[85] whereas tungsten had 30% of the activity of molybdenum in pig liver aldehyde oxidase[84].

(c) In vitro *stability and exchange of tungsten and molybdenum*—There was a greater spread of tungsten than of molybdenum relative to protein after disc electrophoresis[144, 145] and the tungsten protein may be less stable during electrophoresis with respect to retaining the metal. Tungsten was relatively easily removed from the protein of *C. fusca* during electrophoresis and migrated more rapidly like ionic tungsten but the stability of molybdenum in the protein was similar to that of the spinach enzyme[183]. It appeared that the tungsten was apparently not firmly bound by *Azotobacter* proteins[169]. In spite of evidence of *in vivo* exchange (Section 6.2.4.5(b)), exchange between tungsten and molybdenum *in vitro* was negligible for spinach[145].

6.2.4.6 *Molybdenum and tungsten in relation to nitrogen supply*

Several experiments with cauliflower and tomato plants indicated that molybdenum was still required when ammonium or other non-nitrate compounds of nitrogen were used instead of nitrate in non-sterile culture conditions. The molybdenum deficient plants contained abundant soluble nitrogen compounds and chlorophyll and relatively low concentrations of nitrate[190-195]. Nitrate reductase formation was negligible in these plants when given only nitrate but was significant when given only molybdenum. Both factors together resulted in more accelerated enzyme formation[140] and nitrate in leaf tissues was consistent with the concentrations required for induction of the enzyme[140].

Scenedesmus obliquus had no detectable requirement when grown with highly purified sterile media based on urea or ammonia, in contrast to nitrate but it was nevertheless considered certain[196] that the role of molybdenum in the nitrogen metabolism of green plants is not confined to the reduction of nitrate.

In cauliflower diagnostic symptoms known as whiptail[197] are produced under two clearly defined conditions:

(1) When plants are grown with nitrate and about 0.00005 p.p.m. Mo which is sufficient to permit limited nitrate assimilation and chlorophyll formation[198] but possibly insufficient for maximal formation of nitrate reductase holo enzyme induced by excess nitrate.

(2) When grown in unsterilised media with ammonium sulphate, urea, etc. at the same or much lower molybdenum concentrations[191]. The independent requirements for nitrate and molybdenum for nitrate reductase formation[137, 140] suggested[199] that molybdenum would not be required by plants grown with a nitrogen regime in which nitrate reductase was superfluous for nitrogen assimilation, and if also inducing (though otherwise gratuitous) concentrations of nitrate (or nitrite) were absent. When cauliflower plants were grown with ammonium sulphate using a sterile culture method which prevented nitrification, there were no detectable molybdenum requirements whereas in non-sterile conditions molybdenum deficiency developed[200].

Molybdenum therefore appears necessary when low (inducing) nitrate concentrations are present though they are not required for growth and accumulation is probably insignificant. Supernumary diaphorase moieties produced under these conditions[145] may influence cytochrome c reduction and its linkage to mitochondrial cytochrome oxidase might short-circuit oxidative phosphorylation. This might explain increases in ratios of P_i to ester P caused by molybdenum deficiency[192]. Brassicas produce methylcysteinesulphoxide in quantity[201, 202] which accumulates excessively in molybdenum deficient cauliflowers regardless of nitrogen source[203]. Its reactivity with the diaphorase systems has not been investigated. It is a potential analogue of aspartic acid[204]. Cauliflowers grown in non-sterile cultures which permitted nitrification of ammonia did not show expected molybdenum deficiency when 0.1–0.2 p.p.m. tungsten as purified sodium tungstate was given instead of molybdenum[205]. These plants had no detectable nitrate reductase but had normal diaphorase activity and normal chloroplasts, instead of severely disorganised ones produced when neither tungsten nor molybdenum was given[206]. Induction of diaphorases in the un-aggregated state appears to have serious metabolic consequences perhaps involving peroxidation of membrane hybrids.

6.2.4.7 Reactions with metal chelating inhibitors

The cyanide inhibition of *N. crassa* and soybean nitrate reductases which was reversed by molybdate and the removal of molybdenum from protein of *N. crassa* were reported[23, 83] (Section 6.2.2.1). These experiments could not be repeated with *Vicia faba* using cyanide[207], but dialysis against 0.2 M NH_4OH pH 11 caused inactivation, which was restored by molybdenum. The *V. faba* enzyme was functional with NADH or $FMNH_2$ equally but the activity with $FMNH_2$ was lost after dialysis and restoration of molybdenum whereas NADH was again functional. The *C. fusca* enzyme was reactivated by ferricyanide after dialysis in the presence of cyanide[31] and therefore the metal had not been removed, and interpretation of the soybean experiments[83] was questioned. Cyanide inhibited the spinach enzyme reversibly and dialysis against purified buffers or dissipation in air reactivated without addition of molybdenum[208], as occurred also for wheat embryo[106]. The K_i value was about 10 μM when the reaction was started by adding NADH after addition of cyanide. Tests with ^{99}Mo or ^{185}W labelled protein showed that cyanide did not remove the metal from nitrate reductase or the tungsten analogue[208]. Molybdenum was not removed from *Azotobacter* protein by dialysis against cyanide[167, 168]. The *Rhizobium* enzyme[88] showed a slow irreversible first-order inactivation by cyanide probably at two sites, though order of adding the reactants was not clear. Thiocyanate and toluenedithiol severely inhibited *Ps. denitrificans* enzyme[37].

The *T. denitrificans* sulphite donor system[75] with a cytochrome b component was inhibited 96 % by azide (5 μM), reversibly by carbon monoxide and also by 8-hydroxyquinoline -*N*.-oxide, antimycin A and piericidin. Unlike most nitrate reductases, except from *V. faba*[92], molybdenum in xanthine and aldehyde oxidases, which reduce nitrate and cytochrome c when molybdenum is present, is less tightly coordinated[84, 85]. It was removed by dialysis against ammonia or ageing and had a dissociation constant of 10^{-4}M.

Azide inhibited competitively with nitrate in the *C. vulgaris*, *C. fusca* and spinach enzymes[17, 31, 90]. K_i was 0.3–0.4 μM for *C. fusca* and spinach and 0.05 μM for *C. vulgaris*. Cyanate (K_i 0.22 μM) and thiocyanate (K_i 0.26 to 1 μM) were also competitive inhibitors for *Chlorella* sp.[31, 90]. Cyanide inhibited non-competitively and irreversibly with K_i 0.1–0.2 μM when NADH was added first[17, 31] or if pretreated with dithionite which is not a donor[31] but was reversible and competitive with nitrate added first[17] or on adding ferricyanide[31]. *N. crassa* showed the same behaviour[208a]. The competitive kinetics for cyanide, azide, thiocyanate and cyanate though not always seen[405] show combination with molybdenum. In sulphite oxidase Mo^{IV} was produced by sulphite and cyanide in the absence of oxidant[79] or by dithionite alone, but functioning sulphite oxidase was immune to addition of cyanide. Cyanide inhibition increased for some minutes when added to already functioning spinach[73] or *C. vulgaris*[90] systems pre-incubated with NADH, and slightly decreased when pre-incubated with nitrate[90] but similar expected transients were not reported with *C. fusca*[17]. The apparent failure of cyanide to inhibit *A. fischeri* enzyme with BV° as donor[66] might result from order of reactant pre-incubation and not indicate exceptional absence of molybdenum. Irreversibility after pre-incubation by NADH or dithionite[17, 31, 208a] might be caused by over reduction to Mo^{IV} which is highly stabilised by cyanide[209, 209a] or because the Mo^{V} cyanide complex is much more stable than Mo^{VI}[210]. The reversal of inhibition by ferricyanide treatment is variously interpreted. Either ferricyanide as an oxidant at the diaphorase site can reoxidise Mo^{V} or possibly Mo^{IV} complexed with cyanide whereas nitrate cannot[17, 31], or nitrate can achieve this but only when all trace of NADH has been demonstrably removed by ferricyanide[208a], although ferricyanide was stated to reactivate with excess NADH[31].

6.2.5 Mechanisms of nitrate reductase

6.2.5.1 Kinetic

The sulphite (donor) nitrate reductase enzyme from *M. denitrificans*[75] showed ordered ping-pong (bi bi) kinetics, but possibly changed as sulphite concentration approached 1mM and cooperativity may have been involved. Liver sulphite oxidase (O_2 acceptor) was also ping pong[77]. The spinach NADH donor system showed ping-pong (bi bi) kinetics[211]. The $FMNH_2$ and BV° systems have not been studied. Reciprocal plots for fixed and variant substrates showed no relationships between the variant and the K_m for the invariant substrate in *A. nidulans*[7] indicating that the reaction was not ordered with NADPH.

6.2.5.2 Catalytic

The electron transport sequences for *E. coli*, *A. fischeri*, *M. denitrificans*, *N. crassa*, *C. vulgaris*, already described show that the molybdenum-flavin complex is not representative for several nitrate reductases and several different transport sequences indicate non-specific reduction of molybdenum. The diverse K_m values for nitrate suggest protein (possibly hydrogen) bonding as well as by molybdenum must be important. As the BV° or $FMNH_2$ donation systems are relatively immune to organic mercurials[5, 86] which do not react with disulphides[212], the participation of a transient thiol group is excluded.

Complexes of Mo^{V} tend to be bimolecular[213, 214] and Mo^{V} tends to be dimeric[209, 215-217], but monomeric Mo^{V} complexes also occur[218]. Molybdenum analyses are rare for pure nitrate reductase but indicate uncertainly either one or two[5] or one atom/mol[13,20,24], for which electron transfer by a Mo^{VI}/Mo^{V} system must be sequential. The d orbital electrons of Mo^{V} are especially exposed to ligands[209] and as oxygen is involved in the electron transfer the active site is 'open sided'[219]. Dimeric Mo^{V} systems, though possible[5], would seem to be unlikely but Mo^{IV} must be considered and some other models are also discussed. The *M. denitrificans* enzyme showed an e.s.r. signal at 80 K due to monomeric Mo^{V} (g 1.985 and g 2.045) equal to 15% of the total Mo which disappeared in the presence of BV° and nitrate[24]. Dithionite reduction yielded a Mo^{III} signal for *M. denitrificans*[24] and Mo^{IV} in sulphite oxidase[79]. It was concluded that *monomeric* Mo^{V} is the reactive species in addition to non-haem iron for which other signals at 15 K were observed[24].

The free radicals BV°, MV° are highly active one e^- reductants in nitrate and nitrite reductase, hydrogenase and nitrogenase systems. Reduction of H^+ ions to nascent H close to activated nitrate might occur but H_2 evolution by nitrate reductase is unknown. Physiological donors have E_o values too high for hydrogen evolution and, unlike nitrogenase, ATP is not required as a possible energy or redox potential 'pump'. Optimal activity with BV° can occur above -0.25 V[64, 73]. Potassium ferrocyanide did not function with BV as a mediator which is detectably reduced non-enzymically[219a]. The ferro/ferricyanide couple E_o (+0.4 V) may be too close to the NO_3^-/NO_2^- couple (+0.44 V). The potential of the Mo^{V}/Mo^{VI} couple is probably between -0.2 and -0.4 V[239] and influenced by protein ligands.

A model one e^- sequential mechanism for nitrate reductase and monomeric Mo^{V} is based on a tartrate system at pH 2.2–3.5.

$$Mo^{V} + NO_3^- + H^+ \rightarrow NO_2 + Mo^{VI} + OH^- \qquad (6.1)^{220}$$

$$2NO_2 \rightleftarrows N_2O_4 \rightleftarrows NO_3^- + NO^+ \qquad (6.2)^{221}$$

$$NO^+ + OH^- \rightleftarrows HONO \rightleftarrows NO_2^- + H^+ \qquad (6.3)^{222}$$

Net reaction

$$2Mo^{V} + NO_3^- + H^+ \rightarrow 2Mo^{VI} + NO_2^- + OH^- \qquad (6.4)$$

or

$$Mo^{V} + \tfrac{1}{2}(NO_3^- + H^+) \rightarrow Mo^{VI} + \tfrac{1}{2}(NO_2^- + OH^-)$$

The further reaction

$$Mo^{V} + NO^+ \rightarrow Mo^{VI} + NO \qquad (6.5)$$

is rapid so that NO is the main non-enzymic product[220]. In the enzyme the reaction between NO^+ and Mo^{V} would be prevented if NO_3^- combined with Mo^{VI}[17, 31] before reduction to Mo^{V} and reaction (6.3) at pH 7 is far to the right. Reaction (6.1) requires a proton. In sulphite oxidase[79] and xanthine oxidase[223] a proton dissociating group is close but not bonded to the Mo.

Reversible redox systems based on flavin-Mo models[209, 215-217] are reported and are relevant only to the strict flavin-molybdenum nitrate reductase (Section 6.2.2.6) for which no molybdenum analyses are reported unless the wheat enzyme (one atom/mol)[13] is clasified thus. The two-electron mechanism involves both dimeric Mo^{V} and also Mo^{IV} in a disproportionation:

$$FMNH_2 + Mo^{VI} \rightleftarrows FMN + Mo^{IV} \tag{6.6}$$

$$Mo^{IV} + Mo^{VI} \rightleftarrows (Mo^{V})_2 \tag{6.7}$$

Net reaction: $$FMNH_2 + 2Mo^{VI} \rightleftarrows FMN + (Mo^{V})_2 \tag{6.8}$$

In phosphate buffer, which activates flavin and cytochrome nitrate reductases a monomeric Mo-flavin semiquinone is inferred[224, 225] and was the basis for the suggested mechanism for the flavin systems[112]:

$$Mo^{VI} + FMNH_2 \rightleftarrows FMNH^{\circ}Mo^{V} + H^+ \tag{6.9}$$

$$Mo^{V}FMNH^{\circ} + NO_3^- + H^+ \rightarrow FMN + Mo^{VI} + NO_2^- + H_2O \tag{6.10}$$

The participation of Mo^{IV} in molybdenum enzymes was suggested[226-228, 408] in which a ternary redox equilibrium exists between Mo^{VI}, Mo^{IV} and Mo^{V}. which was reported to be monomeric[228, 229]. These studies have not been carried out with nitrate as the oxidant[229] for which molybdenum was still required[84, 85]. Dimeric proteins with single Mo^{V} sites are now proposed[409].

A mechanism based on possible nitrato-molybdenum complexes by analogy with known nitrato-metal structures[230] is shown for nitrate reductase in Figure 6.2. For analyses of 1 atom Mo/mol discussion is limited to unidentate (I)

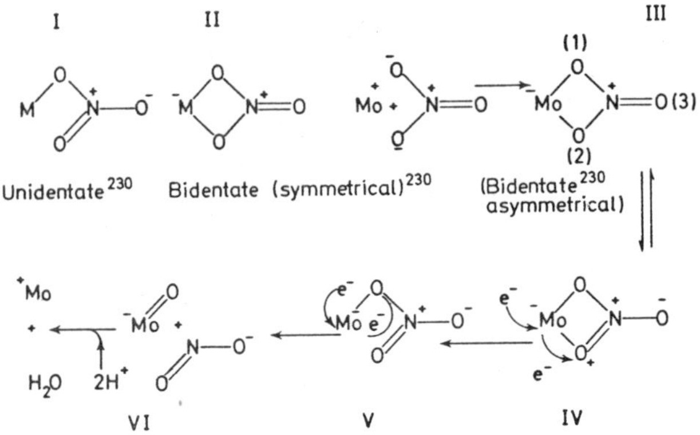

Bond lengths (Å) for asymmetrical structures[230], e.g. III

M—O(1) 1.9-2.1 M—O(2) 2.4-2.7
N—O(1) 1.25-1.34 N—O(2) 1.20-1.33 N—O(3) 1.18-1.28

Figure 6.2 Possible mechanism for nitrate reductase based on formation of Mo^- nitrato complexes. Nitrato structures drawn from or represented according to Addison *et al.* (1971)[230] with permission

or bidentate (symmetrical II or asymmetrical III) (planar) structures[230]. As K_m values vary, other (possibly hydrogen) bonding of nitrate to protein is assumed, which together with a complex Mo ligand field would favour an asymmetrical complex for which the bidentate structure (III) is postulated, having weakened N—O bonding and metal-oxygen bond lengths differing up to 35%[230] and N—O bonds possibly differing by 20% reciprocally[230] Tautomerisation envisaged for bidentate structures[230] is postulated (IV) and significant differences for Mo—O bond energies would facilitate asymmetrical e^- donation to yield a unidentate complex (V). A second e^- transfer could release nitrite leaving oxygen coordinated with molybdenum (VI). The adjacent proton dissociating group could provide H^+ ions for completion of the reaction. Molybdenum coordination by the protein is extreme[31, 106, 167, 168, 208] and probably of a high order[231]. A *C*-terminal histidine complex seems plausible[216, 232, 233] with other oxygen ligands provided by serine, threonine, glutamate, aspartate and aromatic residues. Cysteinyl Mo—S ligands[213, 234] as in xanthine oxidase[214, 235] would also be likely provided the bond is permanent and also not bimolecular for Mo[213].

6.2.6 Structural components of nitrate reductase

6.2.6.1 Nitrate reductase moieties in mutants

(a) *Fungi*—Nitrate-less mutants of *N. crassa*[236-243] and *A. nidulans*[147-149, 150, 151, 244-250] have been intensively studied (see also Section 6.2.4.2(a)). Six or more separate loci influence several aspects of the biosynthesis in heterocaryons of the nitrate reductase complex which is controlled by several separate genes in *N. crassa*[240] and *A. nidulans*[244] and separate polypeptide moieties for different functional agents corresponding with a simplified interpretation of Figure 6.1 were postulated[237, 238-244]. Both *N. crassa*[251] and *A. nidulans*[147] produce a constitutive NADPH cytochrome c reductase in wild and most mutant strains, which is not influenced by nitrate and has a high mol. wt. about 10–11S[238, 241, 243]. The wild strains induced by nitrate produce also NADPH cytochrome c reductase and $FMN(FAD)H_2$ (donor) and BV° MV° nitrate reductase. Following the terminology for *N. crassa*[237, 243], nit. 1 has only NADPH cytochrome c reductase, nit. 3 has only $FADH_2$ and MV° nitrate reductase, nit. 2 shows neither. The 10.6S constitutive NADPH cytochrome c reductase of *N. crassa* from the wild type of nit. 1 mutant was not influenced by freezing and thawing but the nitrate-inducible 6.8S wild type NADPH cytochrome c reductase disappeared after freezing and thawing and activity then sedimented at 4.5S and the 6.8S wild type nitrate reductase was lost altogether[238]. In nit. 1 nitrate-inducible NADPH cytochrome c reductase sedimented at 4.5S and there was no nitrate reductase. Freezing and thawing apparently disaggregated a complex having NADPH cytochrome c reductase and destroyed its nitrate reductase activity. Supra normal activity of 4.5S NADPH cytochrome c reductase was present in the nit. 1 mutant and was additionally activated by freezing and thawing[238]. Steapsin treatment of wild type nitrate and cytochrome c reductase destroyed both activities in the 6.8S fraction and enhanced NADPH cytochrome c reductase activity which sedimented at 3.8S whereas NADPH and BV° nitrate reductase were lost altogether[241]. In nitrate-induced nit. 1, NADPH cytochrome c reductase activity sedimented at 3.8S but NADPH and BV° nitrate reductase were absent. The nit. 3 mutant had BV° nitrate reductase but sedimentation was not reported.

This BV° activity was constitutive but was repressed by ammonia[242]. Two genes were considered to control separate synthesis of NADPH cytochrome c reductase and $FADH_2$ BV° Mo nitrate reductase[239-241].

In other experiments[243] wild type nitrate-inducible NADPH cytochrome c and NADPH, $FADH_2$ BV°—nitrate reductase co-sedimented at 7.9S. Nitrate-induced NADPH cytochrome c reductase in nit. 1 which had no nitrate reductase sedimented at 4.5S. The MV° and $FADH_2$ nitrate reductase in nit. 3 mutant was inducible by nitrate[243]. When obtained from uninduced mycelium it sedimented at 6.8S. In spite of apparent discrepancies[238-241, 243] it is clear that there are three NADPH cytochrome c reductases:— (i) constitutive (10–11S); (ii) nitrate-inducible and associated with wild type nitrate reductase (6.8–7.9S); (iii) nitrate-inducible in nit. 1 mutant and in wild type (3.8–4.5S) but absent from nit. 3. Both (ii) and (iii) require FAD as co-factor.

The MV° and $FADH_2$-nitrate reductase in nit. 3 lacking NADPH cytochrome c reductase was greatly increased compared with the wild type[243]. In a probably analogous manner, MV° and $FADH_2$ nitrate reductase activities from the wild type were activated by heating which destroyed NADPH cytochrome c and nitrate reductase activities[5]. Thus, elimination by mutant deletion or denaturation of one part of the complex makes the molybdenum site more available to exogenous donors as also happens with heating the *Chlorella* enzyme when Mo^V was used[22]. There appears to be no physiological donor for $FADH_2$ and BV° nitrate reductase in nit. 3. The possible suppression of the NADPH moiety by anaerobic conditions[70, 71] has been noted (Section 6.2.1.3(b)).

(b) *Bacteria*—The chlorate resistant mutants of *E. coli* (ChlA, ChlB) lacking nitrate reductase produced 50% of nitrate inducible cytochrome b present in the wild type, and ChlC 25%. The A and B mutants lack also formate hydrogen lyase which is retained by the C mutants[252]. Electrophoresis of proteins from wild type and mutants grown with or without nitrate showed complex differences but the principal protein fraction missing from the ChlC mutant corresponded with purified nitrate reductase from the wild type. In extracts of A and B mutants the fractions corresponding with wild type nitrate reductase were present, but enzyme activity was absent possibly as a result of defective selenium metabolism. An *E. coli* mutant, C98, lacked all nitrate reductase, soluble formate dehydrogenase, membrane bound formate cytochrome b reductase, and formate hydrogen lyase, but NADH cytochrome c reductase activity was 20 times normal[253]. The hydrogen lyase was restored by complementation of a soluble fraction from the wild type and a membrane fraction from the C98 mutant or the wild type. A mutant N16 was unable to grow on, or reduce nitrate with formate and lacked formate dehydrogenase, but contained MV° nitrate reductase[21]. This seems analogous to the nit. 3 mutant in *N. crassa* (Section 6.2.6.1(a)). Presumably, physiological donors for this system are not available, but nitrite reductase is usually present[254]. In several 'leaky' *E. coli* mutants[116] formate dehydrogenase, MV° nitrate reductase and cytochrome b, showed independently wide ranges for each. Either multiple genes code for each protein or products of a single pleiotropic gene are influenced differentially by other regulator factors coded for by the other genes. In two *E. coli* C type chlorate resistant mutants one (W3110) still retained BV°– nitrate and chlorate reductase but WC38 had none and neither had formate activity but a single gene was nevertheless thought to be responsible[117]. Lack of NAD(P)H systems may be analogous (see p. 203).

6.2.6.2 In vitro *complementation of nitrate reductase in mutants*

(a) *Fungi*—When extracts from induced nit. 1 and uninduced nit. 2 or nit. 3 *N. crassa* mutants (Section 6.2.6.1(a)) were mixed, wild type NADPH nitrate reductase was reconstituted sedimenting at 7.9S[243] and nit. 1 (4.5S) NADPH-cytochrome c reductase was decreased. Complementation was possible only between pH. 6.5 and 7 and was prevented by 5 min heating at 38 °C. The nit. 1 component was soluble and that of nit. 3 was particulate but the complemented system appeared to be soluble.

(b) *Bacteria*—Cell free extracts from *E. coli* mutants ChlA and B which are chlorate resistant and unable to reduce nitrate restore wild type nitrate and chlorate reductase activity when mixed[25, 119, 135, 136, 255-257]. This is normally membrane bound and particulate. Complementing moieties from the ChlA and B mutants were soluble but the complemented system was particulate. The K_m nitrate of the wild type was 0.31 mM and that of the complemented system 0.78 mM[25]. Complementation occurred at 32 °C during 2 h in the presence of 10^{-9} m Mg^{2+} only anaerobically but thiols were inhibitory. There was a sharp pH optimum between 7.0 and 7.6, and a critical ratio of the two proteins[135]. Nitrate or chlorate induced the complementing activity but the ChlB component was not nitrate-inducible[258] and may be structural[259]. The cytochrome b1 component was present in both mutants in excess of that in the wild type (but see 252) but after complementation the soret peak was obscured. In double deletion mutants ChlAB, AC and BC there was no complementation between any two but mixing extracts from all three resulted in complementation. Extracts from single mutants ChlA, B or C complemented with the reciprocal double mutants, e.g. A with BC etc.[260].

6.2.6.3 In vitro *reconstitution of nitrate reductase by denatured molybdo-proteins*

Lack of nitrate reductase caused by molybdenum deficiency or in defective mutants cannot be restored by adding molybdate to protein *in vitro* (Section 6.2.4.1). An *in vitro* repair of enzyme obtained from *N. crassa* nit. 1 mutant (Sections 6.2.6.1, 6.2.6.2) has been achieved by complementation with a denatured component of several molybdenum-containing proteins[261-263] but *A. nidulans* mutants may not utilise the metal[264]. When pure xanthine or aldehyde oxidase preparations treated at pH 2–3 in attempts to disaggregate them were then rapidly added to extracts of nitrate-induced nit. 1 at 6.5, significant wild type nitrate reductase was produced in 30 min[261]. The low pH values denatured the molybdo-proteins. Substitution of extracts from induced nit. 1 by uninduced nit. 1, uninduced wild type or any other mutants, induced or uninduced, prevented enzyme appearance with acidified xanthine oxidase. The molybdenum component was highly labile before complementation. As xanthine oxidase (and other Mo proteins below) have no cytochrome b557 this must be present in nit. 1 mutants. Nitrogenase Mo/Fe proteins of *A. vinelandii*, *Clostridium* and *Rhizobium*, liver sulphite oxidase, nitrate reductase from *Setaria faberii*, *E. coli*, *N. crassa* wild type and nit. 3 mutant were all active after low pH treatment[262]. Nitrogenases aged xanthine oxidase or bacterial extracts may function without acidification[261, 262, 410].

The nitrate inducible 4.5S cytochrome c reductase in nit. 1 was substantially decreased after reconstitution by the molybdenum containing fragments[262] as well as after complementation with nit. 3[243]. As so many diverse molybdenum proteins had similar restorative properties a small Mo moiety[410, 411] common to all was supposed to conform the reductase and cytochrome b557 to yield holo protein but molybdenum-amino acid complexes were inert[262] (see also Sections 6.2.4.1, 6.2.4.2, and 6.2.4.5). Protein from ChlA and B chlorate tolerant mutants of *E. coli* differed in their capacity to provide the reconstituting component[263]. The nitrate inducible A mutant was ineffective but the constitutive B mutant was successful. Electrophoresis showed that the protein fraction associated with wild type nitrate reductase[252] was present in both mutants[263]. Presumably a component which is common to all molybdoproteins and is necessary for nitrate reductase activity was not synthesised in mutant A. In *N. crassa* the 7.9S NADPH cytochrome c reductase of the wild type is fully manifested in molybdenum deficient conditions[146] so that aggregation, which may depend either on the molybdenum component[262] or on *cnx*[151] does not require the prior insertion of molybdenum to be effective.

6.2.7 Kinetic, functional and structural regulation

Nitrate reductase activity in the cell may be reversibly inhibited or activated by effectors or by the interaction between the diaphorase donors and substrates and probably a site on the enzyme which produces a switching effect on activity that is not spontaneously reversible. The combination of molybdenum and chelating agents is possibly involved in one aspect of possible regulation by this mechanism, and the diaphorase function may be important in physiological control. Activity may be independently regulated by slower processes of induction or repression of synthesis and probably by continuous turnover of the protein. The switching and the biosynthetic aspects of regulation have only recently been distinguished and are not easily differentiated.

6.2.7.1 Kinetic regulation

(a) *Carbamyl phosphate and cyanate*—Nitrate assimilation by *C. vulgaris* was suppressed by ammonia but recommenced quickly when the ammonia disappeared from the medium[265, 266]. Carbon dioxide and light, or a carbon source was necessary for suppression by ammonia, so a product, namely carbamyl phosphate was inferred to be involved. The inhibitory mechanism was concluded to result from its hydrolysis to cyanate which was severely inhibitory[267]. Carbamyl phosphate itself (K_i 60 μM) was a competitive inhibitor with nitrate for *C. fusca*[31] but cyanate also inhibited competitively (K_i 1 μM)[31] or 0.3 μM in *C. vulgaris*[90] and the true role of carbamyl phosphate[31] is not substantiated. Carbamyl phosphate was inferred to be a feed-back inhibitor produced from ammonia or nitrate by *C. utilis*[19]. It also inhibited competitively (K_i 18 μM) in maize[268] and in spinach[17] (K_i 15 μM) by cyanate (K_i 1.4 μM) was regarded as the active species[268] and neither inhibited for *A. chroococcum*[405].

(b) *ADP*—This inhibits several plant nitrate reductases[211,269-272]. Inhibition for spinach was mixed, being both non-competitive, and competitive with NADH[211,269]. In the presence of a thiol, e.g. GSH, the non-competitive aspect was abolished and inhibition was competitive with NADH. The effective concentration of thiol was influenced by oxygen and redox factors. The effects of ADP and the thiol were both cooperative. Although the K_i (0.1 mM) was high the complex kinetics suggested a physiological significance but another nucleotide might be the physiological species. The redox aspect of ADP inhibition may be related to other redox reactions discussed in Section 6.2.7.2.

(c) *Phosphate*—This is a general activator of nitrate reductases[29,88,106,211,251,271,273] and may be replaced by arsenate[251]. The requirement is never absolute, stimulation ranges between about 30% and 60% and after careful purification activity is still considerable without phosphate. The action[251] is principally on NAD(P)H or $FMNH_2$ nitrate reductase (Sections 6.2.1.3, 6.2.2.). Cytochrome c reductase is also activated[25], and its effect is enhanced by NADH[271].

6.2.7.2 Functional activation and inactivation

(a) *Chlorella*—The enzyme as extracted from *C. vulgaris* was almost inactive as nitrate reductase, but fully active as a ferricyanide or cytochrome c reductase[89,90]. It was slowly reactivated 100-fold by nitrate and phosphate additively at a low pH. Carbon monoxide inhibited nitrate-dependent photosynthesis[274] and nitrite accumulated probably because carbon monoxide inhibits nitrite reductase[11,275,276]. Carbon monoxide also inhibited aerobic reactivation of nitrate reductase *in vitro* in crude extracts, but not after purification[277]. Possibly, cytochrome oxidase was the activating oxidant but cytochrome c alone was inactive[278], unlike in *N. crassa*[208a]. Ferricyanide (250 μM) reactivated nitrate reductase 90% in about 2 min with a K_m about 25 μM[277] but for the diaphorase the K_m was 75 μM[90] possibly indicating a different site.

Unidentified redox compounds (not thiols) in the presence of NADPH inactivated the enzyme by reduction or activated it by oxidation[278] and a regulatory significance was suggested. A regulatory factor (10^3–10^4 daltons) was associated with non-haem iron and labile sulphide[279] and reacted via NADPH possibly at separate high or low potential control sites with first-order kinetics resulting in activation ($t_{\frac{1}{2}}$ 1 min) or inactivation ($t_{\frac{1}{2}}$ 3 min)[280]. Inactivation by ferrocyanide was rapid with NADPH but was prevented by nitrate or flavins. The *C. pyrenoidose* system was activated at 45°[412].

In *C. fusca* NADH nitrate reductase activity was soon suppressed by ammonia *in vivo*[281] whereas diaphorase persisted. Nitrate reductase reappeared *in vitro* on standing at 0 °C. Reactivation was prevented by treatment with Sephadex G 25 gel. Ammonia *in vitro* did not inactivate but NADPH caused biphasic first-order inactivation in the absence of nitrate[282] which reactivated reversibly after a lag. Ferricyanide reversed, and mercurials prevented inactivation by NADH. A functional NADH diaphorase appeared necessary for reversible activation. A physiological control mechanism was suggested whereby ammonia production uncoupled photophosphorylation and thereby modified cell redox values which then influenced enzyme activity by reactions at the diaphorase site[282]. ADP synergistically enhanced the reversible inactivation by NADH[282a] which was prevented by nitrate.

(b) *Chlamydomonas*—Nitrate assimilation was prevented by ammonia in *C. reinhardii* until the ammonia disappeared in the presence of acetate, or carbon dioxide in light[283,284]. In nitrate media removal of carbon dioxide, darkness or DCMU each caused rapid apparently first-order loss of BV° nitrate reductase ($t_{\frac{1}{2}}$ 30 min approx.) as in *C. vulgaris* in darkness[285]. NADH and $FMNH_2$ nitrate reductase but not diaphorase obtained from cells transferred for an hour to an ammonia or arsenate containing nutrient, or made anaerobic was reversibly inactivated *in vivo* and was also reactivated *in vitro* immediately by ferricyanide or slowly by nitrate[286,287]. Inactivation occurred *in vitro* with NAD(P)H alone and was prevented by nitrate. Contrary to experiments of an hour's darkness[283,284] DCMU, darkness, or lack of carbon dioxide did not inactivate *in vivo* after 15 min but prevented inactivation by arsenate or ammonia during 1 h. Lack of air inactivated in 15 min regardless of conditions[287]. After several hours in an ammonia nutrient the diaphorase as well as the NADH and $FMNH_2$ nitrate reductase activities were lost irreversibly by decay and repression and were re-induced by nitrate[286] or aspartate but not by nitrogen deficient conditions in a process dependent on protein synthesis[281,286]. By contrast in *C. fusca*[101] transfer to nitrogen-free media from ammonia resulted in de-repression of synthesis without the requirement for nitrate.

(c) *Cyanidium caldarium*—Heating the enzyme from nitrate grown cells for 5 min at 45°C destroyed both NAD(P)H activities but activated with first-order kinetics the BV° and $FMNH_2$ nitrate reductase about 50 to 400 %[48,68], and mercurial reagents also activated the BV° system as in *N. crassa*[5]. Phosphate or urea also activated latent NAD(P)H nitrate reductase from cells originally grown with nitrate and transferred to ammonia[49]. Activation by phosphate increased for 3 h and was probably distinct from kinetic activation (Section 6.2.7.1(c)). The latent BV° enzyme formed by transferring the cells to ammonia for an hour was reactivated by heating[48]. Reactivation by nitrate *in vivo* after 1 h in the presence of ammonia *in vivo* was not affected by cycloheximide, by contrast with re-induction after a longer period of repression by ammonia[48].

(d) *Fungi*—In *N. crassa* wild type NADPH nitrate reductase was suppressed by transfer to ammonia nutrition by two processes, namely inactivation and repression of biosynthesis after breakdown of existing enzyme[288]. Heating at 60 °C[5] did not reactivate the ammonia inactivated enzyme[288] unlike that of *Cyanidium*[48]. Nitrate stabilised the enzyme against first-order breakdown ($t_{\frac{1}{2}}$ 30 min) in the absence of ammonia but not against inactivation by ammonia[289]. The nitrate concentration required for stabilisation was much greater than for induction of *de novo* enzyme synthesis. When nit. 1 or nit. 3 mutants were transferred from nitrate to ammonia or nitrogen-free media, neither the nit. 1 NADPH cytochrome c reductase nor the nit. 3 BV° nitrate reductase changed in activity. Repression by ammonia and instability in the absence of nitrate are dependent on the integrity of the whole complex. A search for an alternative physiological role for the cytochrome c reductase in *A. nidulans* was without result[290].

(e) *Plants*—Repression by ammonia or a product occurred in barley roots[291-292] and *L. minor*[293] and by certain amino acids for tobacco callus cells[294-295] but had no effect in several other species[47, 140, 292, 294, 296]. Induction by nitrate is observed for practically every species, effective concentrations ranging from 10 μM[291] to 50 mM[297] in different tissues of barley. *De novo* protein synthesis was reasonably inferred in several experiments with antimetabolites[47, 138, 141-143, 291, 296-299]. It was conclusively shown in buoyant density studies of isotopically labelled enzyme induced in tobacco callus cells[16]. Enzymic loss in maize[413] and turnover[16] occur in the presence of nitrate[16]. First-order loss in its absence is often observed with $t_{\frac{1}{2}}$ about 3–6 h[16, 35, 188]. Inactivation by ammonia as found in algae is not known in plants but hydrolysis of the cyanogenic glycoside dhurrin caused inactivation in young sorghum[300]. This was reversed by nickel but physiological significance is not known. Hormones may mimic nitrate or act synergistically[414-419].

6.3 NITRITE, SULPHITE AND HYDROXYLAMINE REDUCTION

The earlier work up to 1964 on assimilatory nitrite reduction and denitrification has been reviewed[112, 301, 302]. Relationships and distinctions between major substrates for this group of enzymes and the significance of possible intermediates in nitrate reduction are discussed in *ad hoc* contexts.

6.3.1 Fungi and yeasts

6.3.1.1 Fungi

Two *N. crassa* mutants unable to grow on nitrite, excreted hydroxylamine in the culture medium[236] but other mutants did not, regardless of whether or not nitrate or nitrite could be utilised. In two mutants pyridoxine was needed for production of nitrite reductase activity, possibly for FAD synthesis as in its absence riboflavin or a related product was formed. The suggestion[236] that pyridoxine yielded an oxime with hydroxylamine which was reduced to an amine prior to transamination is not compatible with failure of wild type extracts to reduce pyridoxyl phosphate oxime or grow on hydroxylamine. Nitrite reductase from *N. crassa*[303, 304] utilised NAD(P)H with FAD (K_m 50 μM) as the natural co-factor, but BV° and MV° are more efficient donors without flavin participation[305]. Iron deficiency sharply depressed enzyme activity but manganese or molybdenum had no effect[304].

Copper and iron accumulated proportionately with specific activity during protein fractionation[304, 306, 307].

The product of nitrite reduction was stated to inhibit the enzyme[304]. Hyponitrite (about 0.5 μM) was inhibitory[306, 307] but was not shown to be a product. Activity as assayed[304] declined after 15 min but this was to be expected from K_m values. The conclusion that hyponitrite was the inhibitory product does not seem justified. Hydroxylamine was not inhibitory[306, 307] but was a possible product[308]. Results of simultaneous assays for nitrite, hyponitrite and hydroxylamine reductases, when considered in relation to the K_m for nitrite[304] and for various hydroxylamine reductases[309-311], do not reinforce but do not exclude the idea that hydroxylamine is a free equilibrated intermediate in nitrite reduction by *N. crassa*. Although hyponitrite was inhibitory its K_m might be relatively low, but hyponitrite reductase was not characterised sufficiently for its significance to be assessed[312]. Generalisations extended to plants[306, 307, 313], and based on inadequate kinetic studies with impure fungal enzymes, seem premature.

A *N. crassa* hydroxylamine reductase is also a sulphite reductase[310, 311]. A homogeneous enzyme from *A. nidulans*[314] reduced sulphite to sulphide quantitatively with MV° or BV° as donors whereas NAD(P)H and flavins were inactive. Hydroxylamine was also reduced and the K_m was 400 times greater. Nitrite reduction was not investigated. The homogeneous enzyme sedimented at 4.2 S and showed light absorption bands at 384 and 585 nm like other nitrite/sulphite reductases which probably indicated non-haem iron and possibly labile sulphide groups (Sections 6.3.1.2, 6.3.2.1 and 6.3.3).

6.3.1.2 Yeasts

The nitrite reductases of *S. cerevissiae*[315] and *C. utilis*[19] are both NADPH specific and probably flavin dependent and function well with BV° or MV°. After 300-fold purification[315] the ratio of nitrite (K_m 180 μM), hydroxylamine (K_m 4.5 mM) and sulphite (K_m 38 μM) reductase activities were unchanged. Substrates were mutually competitively inhibitory. NADPH oxidation, nitrite reduction and ammonia formation were stoichiometric. In *Candida*[19] the K_m for nitrite was 15 μM and for hydroxylamine 6.5 mM.

A homogeneous nitrite-sulphite reductase of *S. cerevissiae*[316-319] contained five or six atoms of non-haem iron[316], no haem iron and two or three labile sulphide atoms[317]. FMN (NADPH acceptor) and FAD, 1 mol each, were present for a total mol. wt. of 3.5×10^5 daltons. K_m values[319] were: sulphite; 14 μM, nitrite; 1mM and hydroxylamine; 4.5 mM. Light absorption at 455 nm was probably derived from the flavins. The 587 and 386 nm chromophore was possibly related to non-haem iron and was bleached at 587 nm by MV° or by NADPH and the flavins. Yeast sulphite-nitrite reductase synthesis is controlled by possibly six genes[318]. Some mutants lost NADPH activity and both flavin components but retained the MV° activity and the 587 nm chromophore in the non-haem iron protein terminal moiety which was no longer cyanide sensitive. Non-haem iron decreased from five or six to possibly two atoms proportionately with possibly one labile sulphide group in these mutants[318] with decrease from 14.8S (350 000) to 6.6S or 5.1S.

Therefore two non-haem iron proteins appear to be present. A third class of mutants retained FMN in the 6.6S component together with the terminal BV° activity. *T. nitratophila* unlike others[19, 315] is nitrite specific[420].

6.3.2 Bacteria

Bacteria show both assimilatory and dissimilatory (denitrifying) nitrite reductase activities. The products and intermediates and the enzyme systems appear quite different for these two physiological activities. Haem and non-haem iron, copper and flavins are variously involved.

6.3.2.1 Assimilatory nitrite (and sulphite) reductase systems

An autoxidisable c type cytochrome-containing protein which utilises BV° or FMN or FAD when reduced by NADH was found in *A. fischeri*[320-322]. A homogeneous protein reduced nitrite (K_m 50–80 μM) and hydroxylamine (K_m 5–8 mM) to ammonia stoichiometrically. Nitrite inhibited reduction of hydroxylamine which had no detectable effect on nitrite reduction. Carbon monoxide inhibited, oxygen repressed and nitrate and nitrite induced activity. *Azotobacter agile* preparations purified fourfold reduced nitrite with NAD (P)H and flavin stoichiometrically to ammonia[323]. Hydroxylamine also disappeared in the presence of NADH and manganese but no ammonia or nitrite were detected. Nitrite and hydroxylamine reductase activities which yield ammonia occur in *Nitrosomonas* and *Nitrobacter*[324]. Manganese stimulated both activities which required NAD(P)H and FMN in preference to FAD but BV° was most active. The K_m for nitrite was 480 μM and for hydroxylamine 720 μM. Hydroxylamine was suggested as an intermediate product of nitrite reduction but this was not shown and the enzymes were not separated.

There are two nitrite reductase systems in *E. coli*, one specific for NADH and unable to reduce sulphite and the other specific for NADPH and able to reduce nitrite, hydroxylamine and sulphite. NADH nitrite reductase obtained from BN and K12 strains[325-327] appears to be a physiological nitrite reductase (K_m 10 μM) which reduces hydroxylamine (K_m 1.5 μM) but not sulphite[326] which is a competitive inhibitor with nitrite (K_i 30 μM). Production of ammonia, nitrite or hydroxylamine loss, and NADH oxidation were stoichiometric regardless of nitrite concentration. Hydroxylamine was considered not to be an intermediate[326] but to react at the same site with mutual competition related to K_m values. Other experiments[327] showed an unexpected stoichiometry of 4 mol NADH oxidised under argon per mole of nitrite reduced with a different K_m (2.5 μM). A c type cytochrome of unknown function which was oxidised by nitrite and hydroxylamine was also present and was possibly part of the system described below. NAD^+ may be a regulator[421].

NADPH-specific nitrite-sulphite reductase[159, 328] and hydroxylamine reductase[329] is a complex flavin, haem and non-haem iron protein[330, 331] and resembles that found in *Saccharomyces*[316-319] with the characteristically high mol. wt. (7×10^5 daltons) for this class. The complex comprised 4 mol each FAD and FMN in sequence, about 12 labile sulphide and non-haem iron atoms and 2 mol of an unusual chlorin type haem with a possible soret peak between 387 and 410 nm and a chromophore at 587 nm. This reacted directly with MV° and sulphite (K_m 7.4 μM), nitrite (K_m 400 μM) or hydroxylamine and also with carbon monoxide. The flavins probably formed semiquinone-reduced flavin redox couples[330]. Copper was absent. A common mechanism for reduction of sulphite or nitrite by one protein with bound intermediates and transfer of six electrons[159] was accepted as appropriate for sulphite reduction.[330] Failure to detect labelled hydroxylamine from 15N nitrite[159] argued against hydroxylamine as an intermediate. E.S.R. studies of the sulphite-complexed enzyme were interpreted[330] to suggest that electrons pass into the complex without formal valency change by the iron, all reducing equivalents being transferred directly to sulphite.

The homogeneous wild type enzyme from *Salmonella typhimurum* had a mol. wt. of 6.74×10^5 daltons and consisted probably of eight subunits of 8.3×10^4, and reduced nitrite, sulphite and hydroxylamine with NADPH or MV° as electron donors[332]. Relative to all eight subunits there were 4 mol each of FAD and FMN, 14 atoms of iron, 12 of labile sulphide and probably 2 mol of a haem similar to that in the *E. coli*[330, 331] sulphite reductase systems. Strong light absorption occurred at 390 and 580 nm with a shoulder at about 470 nm. One mutant reduced sulphite, nitrite and hydroxylamine with MV° but not with NADPH. Some mutants reduced cytochrome c with NADPH but could not reduce sulphite with NADPH or MV°. Mutants unable to reduce sulphite with NADPH contained flavoproteins (mol. wt. about 4.6×10^5) but no non-haem iron or labile sulphide. The MV° site and the non-haem iron, labile sulphide and haem probably resided in one polypeptide and the FAD and FMN and NADPH-cytochrome c reductase resided in another polypeptide. *A. chroococcum* has a NADH–FAD enzyme (6.7×10^4 daltons)[422].

6.3.2.2 Dissimilatory nitrite reduction

(a) *Copper proteins*—The copper protein from *Achromobacter cycloclastes* reduced nitrite (K_m 500 μM) principally to nitric oxide with phenazine methosulphate reduced by ascorbate as donor[333]. The mol. wt. was 6.9×10^4 daltons for two copper atoms. Light absorption peaks at 283, 466 (shoulder), 590 and 700 nm were characteristic of many copper proteins. Flavins were absent. Carbon monoxide inhibited irreversibly. Nitrous oxide was produced with hydroxylamine as reductant. The copper protein in *Pseudomonas denitrificans*[334-336] was considered to be similar to that of *A. cycloclastes*. The reduction of nitrite by hydroxylamine to yield nitrous oxide was considered characteristic of copper proteins unlike the c type cytochromes[337]. In other experiments[338] *P. denitrificans* nitrite reductase reduced nitrite to nitric oxide but did not convert nitrite to nitrous oxide with hydroxylamine. It was considered[333] to differ from that described above. Nitrite reductase from *Nitrosomonas* produced nitric oxide as the initial product but produced nitrous oxide in the presence of hydroxylamine[339, 340]. This would seem to be very similar to the enzyme from *A. cycloclastes*. The hydroxylamine-nitrite reductase system is thus found in nitrifying and denitrifying bacteria.

(b) *Iron proteins with or without copper*—*Pseudomonas aeruginosa* nitrite reductase (K_m 31 μM) produced nitric oxide with NADH as donor[341, 342]. Radioactively labelled copper and iron present in the growth medium both accumulated in protein with increased specific activity. The enzyme contained FAD. A c type cytochrome (with bands at 520 and 550 nm) was reduced by $FADH_2$ or NADH and oxidised by nitrite. Light absorption between 630 and 635 nm was characteristic of copper proteins and disappeared with $FADH_2$ and was restored by nitrite. The ratio of iron: copper: FAD was approximately 10:1:1 in the purified yellow-green protein. A non-haem iron component seems possible and consistent with a peak at 457 nm. *Alcaligenes faecalis* nitrite reductase[337, 343] reduced nitrite to nitric oxide and had a mol. wt. of 9×10^4 daltons. The absorption spectrum had peaks at 640, 553–556, 524, 460 (shoulder) and 418 nm. A double cd haem complex was deduced from iron analysis (2 atom/mol) but a copper component seems likely.

Nitrite-inducible cytochrome c oxidase systems, with inseparable nitrite reductase activity have been obtained from *Ps. aeruginosa* (mol. wt. 9.4×10^4 daltons)[344-346] and (8.5×10^4)[347] and from *M. denitrificans* (mol. wt. 1.22×10^5)[347, 348]. Cytochrome c reduced nitrite to nitric oxide anaerobically. In both organisms the complex yellow-green proteins had two haem moieties, the reduced cytochrome c having light absorption at 418, 521 and 625 nm. The *M. denitrificans* cytochrome a_2 showed bands at 435 and 460 nm (oxidised or reduced) and 547, 553 and 655 nm (reduced) and at 702 nm (oxidised), possibly associated with a chlorin structure (haem d)[347]. The *Ps. aeruginosa* a_2 cytochrome had bands at 460 and 655 nm (reduced) at pH 7.6. Copper was necessary for formation of the *Ps. aeruginosa* haem protein[342, 344] but was not a component[344]. Copper was thought responsible for absorption at 630–635 nm[342] although the isolated haem a_2 also absorbed strongly at 620–635 nm[345] and at 702 nm[347] so that interpretation is confused. Carbon monoxide inhibited oxygen uptake but not nitrite reduction with cytochrome c. After removal of haem a_2 with acid acetone the protein was insoluble at pH 7 but was soluble when reconstituted with the haem a_2[344, 347].

6.3.3 Algae

Iron is essential for nitrite (but not nitrate) reduction in algae[90, 100]. Direct activation of the enzyme with BV° instead of ferredoxin[100] and incorporation of ^{59}Fe into purified enzyme[22] were shown for *C. fusca*. The homogeneous protein obtained from *C. fusca*[11, 349] contains two atoms of iron per mol. wt. of 6.3×10^4 daltons. Ferredoxin, or flavodoxin[350] (reduced by chloroplasts) from *Chlorella*, and MV° and BV° are electron donors; NAD(P)H and reduced flavins are inactive[349]. Electrophoresis showed twin iso enzyme bands. Light absorption maxima appeared at 278, 384 (0.34 of 278 nm), 573, 635 and 692 nm (weak), and recall those of yeast and *E. coli* sulphite-nitrite reductases (Sections 6.3.1, 6.3.2) and plant nitrite reductase but differ from plant sulphite reductase (Section 6.3.4.2). Dithionite decreased absorption at 573, 635 and 692 nm and produced weak bands at 555 and 585 nm. Nitrite restored only the 573 nm band but so did oxygen and the enzyme may be autoxidisable. No pyridine haemochromogen was obtained with HCl and butanone released a red iron containing pigment. Ammonia was the stoichiometric product with maximal specific activity of 51.7 μmol nitrite reduced min^{-1} mg^{-1} protein using dithionite-reduced MV° (turnover no.: 3.4×10^3 mol min^{-1}). Hydroxylamine was reduced at 1/6th of this rate but sulphite was not reduced. Amino acid analysis indicated 600 residues of which Asp., Glu., Gly, and Ala. comprised 40% in nearly equal amounts and 10 Cys were possibly involved in binding the iron. Cyanide and carbon monoxide inhibited (reversibly by light[11]) but *o*-phenanthroline, *a,a*-dipyridyl and oxine were ineffective as found for plants[64, 276].

Nitrite reductase in *Dunaliella tertiolecta*[351] utilised ferredoxin and dithionite-reduced MV° or BV° as donors. NAD(P)H and NADPH reduced-BV° were inactive but $FMNH_2$ or $FADH_2$ were appreciably active contrary to *Chlorella*[349] but similar to occasional results with plants[352]. A redox effect on activity as found for plants[352] was inferred. Ammonia was produced stoichiometrically from nitrite (K_m 110 μM), probably by a single protein (mol. wt. 7×10^4 daltons). Activity with hydroxylamine or sulphite was not reported. The *Anabaena cylindrica* enzyme[69, 353, 354] functioned with ferredoxin from spinach or *Anabaena* and MV°, BV° and diquat reduced by chloroplasts or by dithionite but NAD(P)H, $FADH_2$ and $FMNH_2$ were again inactive. Ferredoxin reduced by an NADPH system was effective but the redox effect[351, 352] was seen in rapid loss of activity as NADPH was appreciably reoxidised. The importance of low potential single electron donors was noted. The purified enzyme reduced nitrite (K_m 50 μM) stoichiometrically to ammonia with ferredoxin (K_m 5 μM) but was unable to reduce hydroxylamine or sulphite. The *Anacystis nidulans* enzyme utilised ferredoxin reduced by dithionite or chloroplasts as a reductant. The flavoprotein phytoflavin from this alga also functioned when reduced with chloroplasts but not with dithionite[355]. However, phytoflavin is a two-electron donor and has a higher potential (about −0.28 V) than ferredoxin (−0.41 V). The analogy between phytoflavin and flavodoxin reduced by chloroplasts which was effective with *C. fusca*[349] was noted. These flavoproteins probably behave also as low redox potential (—0.46 V) single electron carriers represented by the reduced semi-quinone couples which do not freely equilibrate, see Ref. 356, and might explain the need for lower photochemical reduction potentials. Nitrite reduction in *Ankistrodesmus braunii* appears to require high energy phosphate supply in light or dark systems and *in vitro*[104, 357]. Nitrite reduction in light (500 lux) was inhibited by uncoupling reagents including dinitrophenol[358], pentachlorophenol-carbonyl-cyanide, n-chlorophenylhydrazine and arsenate[358-360]. These were not inhibitory in the dark or light in the presence of hydrogen, which mediated nitrite reduction via hydrogenase[361] or under saturating light intensity[357], and limiting redox effects, which can be overcome by ATP, may be involved.

6.3.4 Higher plants

6.3.4.1 Electron donors

Nitrite reductases in plants were obscured by ignorance regarding electron donors. Reports for soya bean[308] regarding ammonia production from nitrite with NAD(P)H and manganese could not be repeated in other plants[63]. A manganese and co-factor dependent oxidation of NAD(P)H in the presence of nitrite or hydroxylamine which yielded no recognisable products[362] was attributed[63] to a peroxidation mechanism[363]. The first nitrite reductase obtained from spinach[364] was confused with a flavo protein[365] but the absorption spectrum of one component inspired the prediction[366] that the physiological donor should be PPNR, i.e. ferredoxin. Enzymes from maize, *C. pepo* and spinach were found to reduce nitrite stoichiometrically to ammonia using BV° [63,64,367] or MV° [368,369] as electron donors for which ferredoxin was shown to be a physiological alternative[368-372] with a K_m about 10 μM[369, 373] in chloroplast or dithionite systems.

Inability to utilise NAD(P)H with or without flavins is generally observed[63, 64, 352, 367, 369, 374] but $FMNH_2$ functions unpredictably[352]. NADP severely inhibits nitrite reductase when ferredoxin and an illuminated chloroplast system is used until all NADP is reduced[375,376]. Plant (and algal) nitrite reductases appear to require one e^- donors of low standard potential and are dependent on minimal redox values in the system with BV°[64], probably with ferredoxin[351,352, 375,377,378] and possibly with semiquinone/reduced couples of phytoflavin[355] and flavodoxin[349] which could provide low E_o one e^- donors[356]. Unpredictable behaviour with $FMNH_2$[352] might have a similar basis. Non-chlorophyllous tissues possibly have donors which behave like MV° or ferredoxin[379] or may require ATP[380, 381]. Reduced ferredoxin without enzyme reduced nitrite at 5 to 15% of the enzymic rate[379, 382] but the reaction was negligible in other experiments[352, 375] and was increasingly rapid with pH decrease below 7.8[378] with defective yield of ammonia. A comparable reaction occurred with BV° [352].

6.3.4.2 Properties

The mol. wts. (10^{-4} daltons) are similar for spinach leaf (6.4)[375, 383] (6.3; 4.9S)[384], *C. pepo* leaf 6.0–6.3[375, 383,385], and maize scutellum iso enzymes 6.1–6.3[379]. Specific activities of highly purified (970–1300-fold) or homogeneous preparations vary with donor systems[352,375] according to the redox effect. Maximal values (μmol nitrite reduced min^{-1} mg^{-1} protein) using ferredoxin reduced by chloroplasts and light[352,375] were 57 for spinach and 48 for *C. pepo* and a turnover number of about 3.5×10^3 mol min^{-1} or 2.1×10^4 e^- min^{-1}. Iron deficiency depressed activity in *C. pepo*[64]. Carbon monoxide inhibited irreversibly[275, 276], cyanide, bathophenanthroline sulphonate and bathocuproine sulphonate inhibited the BV° system whereas the unsulphonated derivatives, cuprizone, 2,2-biquinolyl, *a*,*a*-dipyridyl, azide, oxine and *o*-phenantholine inhibited insignificantly[64,276] as found in other nitrite reductases (Section 6.3.4.1). Radioactive iron was incorporated into the *C. pepo* enzyme during growth and by exchange into homogeneous protein *in vitro*[384]. The spinach and *C. pepo* enzymes contain 2 atoms iron mol^{-1} and no copper[385, 386, 423] like *C. fusca*. Light absorption maxima occur at 278, 380 (or 385) and 570 nm[384-386, 423] like *C. fusca* and the terminal moieties of the sulphite-nitrite reductases of yeast[316,319], *E. coli*[330, 331] and *Salmonella*[332] which have non-haem iron and labile sulphide. Spinach sulphite specific reductase[387] absorbs at 404 (385 shoulder) and 589 nm (mol. wt. 8.4 × 10^4 daltons). Nitrite reductase has labile sulphide[423] and is dimeric[424].

6.3.4.3 Substrates, products and possible intermediates

Pure plant and algal nitrite reductases will not reduce sulphite[352, 358] (or vice versa[387]) but show variable weak (1–15%) hydroxylamine reductase activity[349, 352, 375] which functions with NADPH and $FMNH_2$ in addition to BV° and ferredoxin[352, 375, 383, 388] whereas nitrite reductase does not. The K_m values for ferredoxin differ. (10 μM for nitrite and 3 μM for hydroxylamine) in the *same* system with respective V_{max} ratios < 2:1[373]. Both are reduced stoichiometrically to ammonia regardless of electron donor, rate or degree of

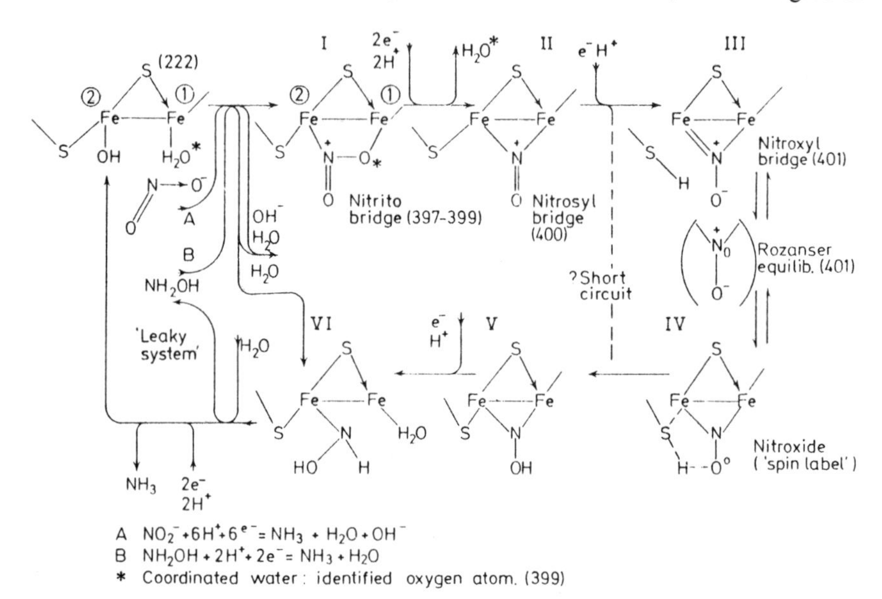

Figure 6.3 Tentative mechanism for nitrite reductase in plants and algae (References in parenthesis)

purification, or origin[63, 64, 349, 352, 367, 369, 373-375, 379]. Nitric K_m values are variable (3–200 μM) depending on conditions even in one species[36, 64, 352, 369, 373-375, 379, 382, 389]. Discrepancies between different experiments and substrate inhibition when using ferredoxin are attributed to inhibition of ferredoxin function probably by the nitrosonium ion NO^+ [378]. With abundant chlorophyll and saturating light, or dithionite, and pH > 7.5, K_m values are ⩾ 100 μM[36, 369, 375, 382]. Hydroxylamine K_m values are variable because additional (haem protein) hydroxylamine reductases occur[275, 276, 352, 376, 383, 388, 390]. However, the lowest values are 5–10 times and often 20 times greater than for nitrite which severely inhibits hydroxylamine reduction by both nitrite reductase and the haem proteins[64, 276, 352, 375].

Nitric oxide is not reduced by and does not inhibit nitrite reductase, and does not react with ferredoxin when rigorous precautions are used to exclude oxygen[378, 391] and prevent nitrosation by NO_2[221]. Reported nitric oxide uptake by crude plant homogenates and NADH[392] needs re-examination. Nitrous oxide, hyponitrite and oxyhyponitrite do not inhibit or react with plant nitrite reductase[352,378,393]. Rapid decomposition of oxyhyponitrite (nitrohydroxylamine) to nitrite at physiological pH[378,393,394] accounts for its use in fungal and plant growth[395]. Generalisations regarding the mechanism and intermediates in nitrite reduction for plants derived from studies with fungi[306,307,313] seem no longer justified.

6.3.5 Possible mechanism for assimilatory nitrite reductase (plants and algae)

Based on analysis and absorption spectra[349, 385, 386] and redox effects, a non-haem two atom iron sulphur prosthetic structure of low standard potential similar to models either for ferredoxin or rubredoxin is suggested[396]. The first step is postulated as nitrito bridge formation (I)[397-399] with expulsion of coordinated water and oxygen exchange (Ref. 399, p. 272) at Fe 1 and displacement of OH as OH^- ions[159, 375] from Fe 2. The two iron atoms, 1,2, are visualised in slightly different ligand fields and the sulphur atoms are labile sulphide or cysteine[396]. The site is 'open sided'[219] and combination of the oxygen with the iron atom changes this to a stable low spin Fe complex which may transfer single electrons sequentially to the oxygen[219]. Initial $2e^-$ reduction yields a polynuclear nitrosyl bridge chelate (II)[400] where sulphur coordination is often a feature[222]. Electron donation at the sulphur atom would yield the functional free SH[64] and a nitroxyl bridge (III)[401]. The equilibrium between its different forms[401] including nitroxide ('spin label') radical might allow reduction by the nearby —SH to the substituted hydroximic acid stage (V)[401]. Nitroxide reduction by —SH compounds[402] and MV°-pyridine *N* oxide reductase[403] in *E. coli* are known. Electron donation at the next stage would rupture the Fe—N band, yield a hydroxamate (VI) and expose Fe 1 to coordinate water. A final $2e^-$ donation would yield ammonia and the original configuration with Fe 2 OH. Once nitrite combines covalently with the enzyme hydroxylamine cannot equilibrate with intermediate stages. It may combine initially by expulsion of water at Fe 1 and equilibration at VI may be difficult. This might explain the low V_{max} and high K_m for hydroxylamine and the severe competition by nitrite. The reduction of hydroxylamine or the hydroxamate intermediate would yield ammonia by the same reaction and a $2e^-$ donor $(FMNH_2)$[352] might also function at this stage.

Disparity in K_m values, inhibition of hydroxylamine reduction by nitrite, and different relationships between rates and electron donor for each substrate[64, 373, 375] and transfer of six electrons by one protein with obligatory one e^- steps are compatible with this model. Iso-electronic nitrito and carbon monoxide structures and dinitrosyl bridges also occur[400] which account for carbon monoxide inhibition and possibly nitrogen dimerisation (N_2O) in denitrifying systems. Sulphite probably forms analogous ligands to nitrite[404].

Acknowledgements

I am most grateful to Dr. C. D. Garner (University of Manchester) and Dr. P. C. H. Mitchell (University of Reading) for their prompt and kindly assistance in acquainting me with new references concerning nitrato and molybdenum complexes. I much appreciate the valuable bibliographical assistance given by Mr. R. Fido during preparation of this review and thank Miss Alethea Goddard and Mrs. Carol McIntosh for their intensive typographical work.

References

1. Forget, P. (1971). *Eur. J. Biochem.*, **18,** 442
2. Van't Riet, J., Stouthamer, A. H. and Planta, R. J. (1968). *J. Bacteriol.*, **96,** 1455
3. Van't Riet, J. and Planta, R. J. (1969). *FEBS Lett.*, **5,** 249
4. Van't Riet, J. (1970). *Thesis. Nitrate Reductase in Aerobacter Aerogenes.* Free University, Amsterdam
5. Garrett, R. H. and Nason, A. (1969). *J. Biol. Chem.*, **244,** 2870
6. Cove, D. J. and Coddington, A. (1965). *Biochim. Biophys. Acta*, **110,** 312
7. MacDonald, D. W. (1969). Thesis for Ph.D. Univ. of East Anglia. Nitrate and Cytochrome-c reductases from wild type and mutant strains of *Aspergillus nidulans.*
8. Downey, R. J. (1971). *J. Bacteriol.*, **105,** 759
9. Zumft, W. G., Paneque, A., Aparicio, P. J. and Losada, M. (1969). *Biochem. Biophys. Res. Commun.*, **36,** 980
10. Zumft, W. G., Aparicio, D. J., Paneque, A. and Losada, M. (1970). *FEBS Lett.*, **9,** 157
11. Zumft, W. G. (1970). *Ber. Deutsch. Bot. Ges.*, **53,** 221
12. Le Claire, J. A. and Grant, B. R. (1972). *Plant Cell Physiol.*, **13,** 899
13. Anacker, W. F. and Stoy, V. (1958). *Biochem. Z.*, **330,** 141
14. Wray, J. L. and Filner, P. (1970). *Biochem. J.*, **119,** 715
15. Notton, B. A., Hewitt, E. J. and Fielding, A. H. (1972). *Phytochem.*, **11,** 2447
16. Zielke, H. R. and Filner, P. (1971). *J. Biol. Chem.*, **246,** 1772
17. Relimpio, A. Ma., Aparicio, P. J., Paneque, A. and Losada, M. (1971). *FEBS Lett.*, **17,** 226

17a. Hageman, R. H. and Hucklesby, D. P. (1971). *Methods in Enzymology*, **23,** 491 (A. San Pietro, editor) (New York and London: Academic Press)

18. Kannangara, C. G. and Woolhouse, H. W. (1968). *New Phytol.*, **67,** 533
19. Sims, A. P., Folkes, B. F. and Bussey, A. H. (1967). 1st Long Ashton Symposium 1967. *Recent Aspects of Nitrogen Metabolism in Plants. 91.* (E. J. Hewitt & C. V. Cutting, editors) Long Ashton, Bristol. (London and New York: Academic Press) (1968).
20. Taniguchi, S. and Itagaki, E. (1960). *Biochim. Biophys. Acta*, **44,** 263
21. Showe, M. K. and DeMoss, J. A. (1968). *J. Bacteriol.*, **95,** 1305
22. Aparicio, P. J., Cardenas, J., Zumft, W. G., Vega, J. Ma., Herrera, J., Paneque, A. and Losada, M. (1971). *Phytochem.*, **10,** 1487
23. Nicholas, D. J. D. and Nason, A. (1954). *J. Biol. Chem.*, **207,** 353
24. Forget, P. and Dervartanian, D. V. (1972). *Biochim. Biophys. Acta*, **256,** 600
25. Azoulay, E. and Puig, J. (1968). *Biochem. Biophys. Res. Commun.*, **33,** 1019
26. Pichinoty, F. (1969). *Archiv. Mickrobiol.*, **68,** 51
27. Radcliffe, B. C. and Nicholas, D. J. D. (1970). *Biochim. Biophys. Acta*, **205,** 273
28. Fewson, C. A. and Nicholas, D. J. D. (1961). *Biochim. Biophys. Acta*, **49,** 335
29. MacDonald, D. W. and Coddington, A. (1968). *Biochem. J.*, **106,** 52P
30. Solomonson, L. P. and Vennesland, B. (1972). *Plant Physiol. Lancaster*, **50,** 421
31. Vega, J. Ma., Herrera, J., Relimpio, A. Ma. and Aparicio, P. J. (1972). *Physiol. Végétàle*, **10,** 637
32. Rigano, C. (1970). *Archiv. Mikrobiol.*, **70,** 147
33. Lam, Y. and Nicholas, D. J. D. (1969). *Biochim. Biophys. Acta*, **178,** 225

34. Faull, K. F., Wallace, W. and Nicholas, D. J. D. (1969). *Biochem. J.*, **113,** 449
35. Schrader, L. E., Ritenour, G. L., Eilrich, G. L. and Hageman, R. H. (1968). *Plant Physiol. Lancaster*, **43,** 930
36. Eaglesham, A. R. J. and Hewitt, E. J. (1970). *Ann. Rep. Long Ashton Res. Sta.*, **1969,** 52
37. Pichinoty, F. (1964). *Compt. Rend. Acad. Sci. Paris*, **259,** 3868
38. Pichinoty, F. (1964). *Biochim. Biophys. Acta*, **89,** 378
39. Pichinoty, F. (1964). *Compt. Rend. Soc. Biol. Française*, **158,** 1122
40. Pichinoty, F. (1965). *Bull. Soc. Chim. Biol.*, **47,** 1526
41. Pichinoty, F. (1966). *Bull. Soc. Française, Physiol. Veg.*, **12,** 97
42. Pichinoty, F. (1969). *Archiv. Mikrobiol.*, **68,** 65
43. Piechaud, M., Puig, J., Pichinoty, F., Azoulay, E. and Le Minor, L. (1967). *Ann. Inst. Pasteur*, **112,** 24
44. Pichinoty, F. and Piechaud, M. (1968). *Ann. Inst. Pasteur*, **114,** 77
45. Pichinoty, F., Chippaux, M., Bigliardi-Rouvier, Ja. and Rimassa, M. R. (1969). *Ann. Inst. Pasteur*, **117,** 145
45a. Chippaux, M. and Pichinoty, F. (1970). *Archivs. Mikrobiol.*, **71,** 361
46. Azoulay, E., Mutaftschier, S. and Martins-Rosado de Sousa, M. L. (1971). *Biochim. Biophys. Acta*, **237,** 579
46a. Nason, A. and Evans, H. J. (1953). *J. Biol. Chem.*, **202,** 655
47. Beevers, L., Schrader, L. E., Flesher, D. and Hageman, R. H. (1965). *Plant Physiol. (Lancaster)*, **40,** 691
48. Rigano, C. (1971). *Archiv. Mikrobiol.*, **76,** 265
49. Rigano, C. and Violante, U. (1972). *Biochem. Biophys. Res. Commun.*, **47,** 372
50. Silver, W. S. (1957). *J. Bacteriol.*, **73,** 241
51. Evans, H. J. and Nason, A. (1953). *Plant Physiol. Lancaster*, **28,** 233
52. Hatton, A. and Myers, J. (1967). *Plant Cell Physiol.*, **8,** 327
53. Lowe, R. H. and Evans, H. J. (1964). *Biochim. Biophys. Acta*, **85,** 377
54. Gauthier, D. K., Clark-Walker, G. D., Garrard, W. T. Jr. and Lascelles J. (1970.) *J. Bacteriol.*, **102,** 797
55. Nicholas, D. J. D. and Nason, A. (1954). *Archiv. Biochem. Biophys.*, **51,** 311
56. Nicholas, D. J. D. and Nason, A. (1954). *J. Biol. Chem.*, **211,** 183
57. Paneque, A., Del Campo, F. F., Ramirez, J. M. and Losada, M. (1965). *Biochim. Biophys. Acta*, **109,** 79
58. Losada, M., Ramirez, J. M., Paneque, A. and Del Campo, F. F. (1965). *Biochim. Biophys. Acta*, **109,** 86
59. Stoy, V. (1955). *Physiol. Plantarum*, **8,** 986
60. Stoy, V. (1956). *Biochim. Biophys. Acta*, **21,** 395
61. Oji, Y. and Izawa, G. (1969). *Plant Cell Physiol.*, **10,** 743
62. Paneque, A., Aparicio, P. and Losada, M. (1968). Atti. Symp. Int. Agrochim., **7,** 119
63. Hageman, R. H., Cresswell, C. F. and Hewitt, E. J. (1962). *Nature Lond.*, **193,** 247
64. Cresswell, C. F., Hageman, R. H., Hewitt, E. J. and Hucklesby, D. P. (1965). *Biochem. J.*, **94,** 40
65. Ramirez, J. M., Del Campo, F. F., Paneque, A. and Losada, M. (1964). *Biochem. Biophys. Res. Commun.*, **15,** 297
66. Sadana, J. C. and McElroy, W. D. (1957). *Archiv. Biochem. Biophys.*, **67,** 16
67. Pichinoty, F. and Metenier, G. (1966). *Ann. Inst. Pasteur*, **111,** 282
68. Rigano, C. and Violante, U. (1972). *Biochim. Biophys. Acta*, **256,** 524
69. Hattori, A. and Uesugi, I. (1967). *Proc. Comparative Biochemistry and Biophysics of Photosynthesis*, 201 (K. Shibata, A. Takamya, A. T. Jagendorf and R. C. Fuller, editors) Univ. Tokyo Press (Tokyo and Univ. Park Press, Pennsylvania:) (1968)
70. Nicholas, D. J. D. and Wilson, P. J. (1964). *Biochim. Biophys. Acta*, **86,** 466
71. Walker, G. C. and Nicholas, D. J. D. (1961). *Nature (London)*, **189,** 141
72. Del Campo, F. F., Paneque, A., Ramirez, J. N. and Losada, M. (1963). *Biochim. Biophys. Acta*, **66,** 450
73. Eaglesham, A. R. J. and Hewitt, E. J. (1972). *Ann. Rep. Long Ashton Res. Sta.*, **1971,** 54
74. Ware, D. A. (1972). *Biochem. J.*, **130,** 301
75. Adams, C. A., Warnes, G. M. and Nicholas, D. J. D. (1971). *Biochim. Biophys. Acta*, **235,** 398
76. Kessler, D. L. and Rajagopalan, K. V. (1972). *J. Biol. Chem.*, **247,** 6566
77. Cohen, H. J. and Fridovich, I. (1971). *J, Biol. Chem.*, **246,** 359

78. Cohen, H. J. and Fridovich, I. (1971). *J. Biol. Chem.*, **246,** 367
79. Cohen, H. J., Fridovich, I. and Rajagopalan, K. V. (1971). *J. Biol. Chem.*, **246,** 374
80. Candela, M. I., Hewitt, E. J. and Stevens, H. M. (1956). *Anal. Chim. Acta*, **14,** 66
81. Nicholas, D. J. D. and Stevens, H. M. (1955). *Nature, London*, **176,** 1066
82. Nicholas, D. J. D. and Stevens, H. M. (1956). *Inorganic Nitrogen Metabolism*, 178 (W. D. McElroy and B. Glass, editors) (Baltimore: Johns Hopkins Press)
83. Nicholas, D. J. D. and Nason, A. (1955). *Plant Physiol. Lancaster*, **30,** 135
84. Mahler, H. R., Mackler, B., Green, D. E. and Bock, R. M. (1954). *J. Biol. Chem.*, **210,** 465
85. Mackler, B., Mahler, H. R. and Green, D. E. (1954). *J. Biol. Chem.*, **210,** 149
86. Losada, M., Aparicio, P. J. and Paneque, A. (1969). *Progress in Photosynthesis Research*, **3,** 1504. *Proc. Symp. Tübingen.* (H. Mezner, editor) Tübingen: H. Jampp. Jr.
87. Garrett, R. H. and Nason, A. (1967). *Proc. Nat. Acad. Sci. U.S.A.*, **58,** 1603
88. Cheniae, G. and Evans, H. J. (1959). *Biochim. Biophys. Acta*, **35,** 140
89. Vennesland, B. and Jetschmann, C. (1971). *Biochim. Biophys. Acta*, **227,** 554
90. Solomonson, L. P. and Vennesland, B. (1972). *Biochim. Biophys. Acta*, **267,** 544
91. Sadana, J. C., Rao, R. R. and Joshi, M. D. (1963). *Biochim. Biophys. Acta*, **67,** 340
92. Peive, Ya. V. and Ivanova, N. N. (1970). *Dokl. Akad. Nauk S.S.S.R.*, **195,** 1456
93. Lam, Y. and Nicholas, D. J. D. (1969). *Biochim. Biophys. Acta*, **172,** 450
94. Fewson, C. A. and Nicholas, D. J. D. (1961). *Biochim. Biophys. Acta*, **48,** 208
95. Taniguchi, S. (1961). *Z. Allg. Mikrobiol.*, **1,** 341
96. Ruiz-Herrera, J. and De Moss, J. A. (1969). *J. Bacteriol.*, **99,** 720
97. Itagaki, E., Fujita, T. and Sato, R. (1961). *Biochim. Biophys. Acta*, **51,** 392
98. Itagaki, E., Fujita, T. and Sato, R. (1962). *J. Biochem. Tokyo*, **52,** 131
99. Kessler, E. and Czygan, F. C. (1968). *Archiv. Mikrobiol.*, **60,** 282
100. Cardenas, J., Rivas, J., Paneque, A. and Losada, M. (1972). *Archiv. Mikrobiol.*, **81,** 260
101. Vega, J. Ma., Herrera, J., Aparicio, P. J.. Paneque, A. and Losada, M. (1971). *Plant Physiol.* (*Lancaster*), **48,** 294
102. Kaplan, F., Setlow, P. and Kaplan, N. O. (1969). *Archiv. Biochem. Biophys.*, **132,** 91
103. Vennesland, B. and Solomonson, L. P. (1972). *Plant Physiol.* (*Lancaster*), **49,** 1029
104. Czygan, F. C. (1963). *Planta* (*Berlin*), **60,** 225
104a. Zumft, W. G., Spiller, H. and Yeboah-Smith, I. (1972). *Planta* (*Berlin*), **102,** 228
105. Nicholas, D. J. D. and Nason, A. (1955). *J. Bacteriol.*, **69,** 580
106. Spencer, D. (1959). *Austral. J. Biol. Sci.*, **12,** 181
107. Maretzki, A. and De La Cruz, A. (1967). *Plant Cell, Physiol.* 7, 605
108. Wainwright, S. D. (1955). *Biochim. Biophys. Acta*, **18,** 583
109. Itagaki, E. and Taniguchi, S. (1959). *J. Biochem. Tokyo*, **46,** 1419
110. Medina, A. and De Heredia, C. F. (1958). *Biochim. Biophys. Acta*, **28,** 452
111. Heredia, C. F. and Medina, A. (1960). *Biochem. J.*, **77,** 24
112. Hewitt, E. J. and Nicholas, D. J. D. (1964). *Modern Methods of Plant Analysis*, **7,** 67. (H. F. Linskens, B. D. Sanwal and M. V. Tracey, editors) (Berlin: Springer)
113. Iida, K. and Taniguchi, S. (1959). *J. Biochem. Tokyo*, **46,** 1041
114. Cole, J. A. and Wimpenny, J. W. T. (1968). *Biochim. Biophys. Acta*, **162,** 39
115. Wimpenny, J. W. T. and Cole, J. A. (1967). *Biochim. Biophys. Acta*, **148,** 233
116. Ruiz-Herrera, J., Showe, M. K. and De Moss, J. A. (1969). *J. Bacteriol.*, **97,** 1291
117. Guest, J. R. (1969). *Mol. Gen. Genet.*, **105,** 285
118. Murray, E. D. and Sanwal, B. D. (1963). *Canad. J. Microbiol.*, **9,** 781
119. Azoulay, E., Puig, J. and Pichinoty, F. (1967). *Biochem. Biophys. Res. Commun.*, **27,** 270
120. Schnaitman, C. A. (1969). *Biochem. Biophys. Res. Commun.*, **37,** 1
121. O'Hara, J., Gray, C. T., Puig, J. and Pichinoty, F. (1967). *Biochem. Biophys. Res. Commun.*, **28,** 951
122. Pichinoty, F. (1963). *Colloque Internationaux du Centre National de la Recherche Scientifique No. 124.* Marseilles, July 1963, Paris CNRS (1965).
123. Pichinoty, F. and D'Oranano, L. (1961). *Nature* (*London*), **191,** 879
123a. Wimpenny, J. W. T. (1969). *Microbiol. Growth*, 161. Sympos. Soc. General Microbiology. No. 19 (S. J. Pirt and P. Meadow, editors)
124. Sapshead, L. M. and Wimpenny, J. W. T. (1972). *Biochim. Biophys. Acta*, **267,** 388
125. Lester, R. L. and De Moss, J. A. (1971). *J. Bacteriol.*, **105,** 1006
126. Pinsent, J. (1954). *Biochem. J.*, **57,** 10

127. Schulp, J. A. and Stouthamer, A. H. (1972). *J. Gen. Microbiol.*, **73,** 95
128. Schulp, J. A. and Stouthamer, A. H. (1970). *J. Gen. Microbiol.*, **64,** 195
129. Van't Riet, J., Knook, D. L. and Planta, R. J. (1972). *FEBS Lett.*, **23,** 44
130. De Croot, G. N. (1971). Regulation of Reductase Formation in *Proteus mirabilis.* Thesis, Free University of Amsterdam, Amsterdam, 1971
131. De Groot, G. N. and Stouthamer, A. H. (1970). *Biochim. Biophys. Acta*, **208,** 414
132. Enoch, H. G. and Lester, R. L. (1972). *J. Bacteriol.*, **110,** 1032
133. De Groot, G. N. and Stouthamer, A. H. (1970). *Archiv. Mikrobiol.*, **74,** 340
134. De Groot, G. N. and Stouthamer, A. H. (1970). *Archiv. Mikrobiol.*, **74,** 326
135. Azoulay, E., Puig, J. and Couchoud-Beaumont, P. (1969). *Biochim. Biophys. Acta*, **171,** 238
136. Azoulay, E., Puig, J. and Martins, M. L. (1969). *Ann. Inst. Pasteur*, **117,** 474
137. Hewitt, E. J. (1957). *Nature, Lond.*, **180,** 1020
138. Hewitt, E. J. and Afridi, M. M. R. K. (1959). *Nature, Lond.*, **183,** 57
139. Afridi, M. M. R. K. and Hewitt, E. J. (1962). *Life Sciences*, **1,** 287
140. Afridi, M. M. R. K. and Hewitt, E. J. (1964). *J. Exp. Bot.*, **15,** 251
141. Afridi, M. M. R. K. and Hewitt, E. J. (1955). *J. Exp. Bot.*, **16,** 628
142. Hewitt, E. J. and Notton, B. A. (1967). *Phytochem.*, **6,** 1329
143. Hewitt, E. J., Notton, B. A. and Afridi, M. M. R. K. (1967). *Plant Cell Physiol.*, **8,** 385
144. Notton, B. A. and Hewitt, E. J. (1971). *Plant Cell Physiol.*, **12,** 465
145. Notton, B. A. and Hewitt, E. J. (1971). *Biochem. Biophys. Res. Commun.*, **44,** 702
146. Subramanian, K. N. and Sorger, G. J. (1972). *Biochim. Biophys. Acta*, **256,** 533
147. Pateman, J. A., Cove, D. J., Rever, B. M. and Roberts, D. B. (1964). *Nature, London.*, **201,** 58
148. Arst, H. N. Jr., MacDonald, D. W. and Cove, D. J. (1970). *Molec. Gen. Genet.*, **108,** 129
149. Pateman, J. A., Rever, B. M. and Cove, D. J. (1967). *Biochem. J.*, **104,** 103
150. Arst, H. N. Jr. and Cove, D. J. (1970). *Molec. Gen. Genet.*, **108,** 146
151. Cove, D. J., Arst, H. N. Jr. and Scazzocchio, C. (1974). *Adv. Molec. Genetics*, **1**
152. Glaser, J. H. and De Moss, J. A. (1971). *J. Bacteriol.*, **108,** 854
153. Nicholas, D. J. D., Nason, A. and McElroy, W. D. (1954). *J. Biol. Chem.*, **207,** 341
154. McKenna, C. E., Benemann, J. R. and Traylor, T. G. (1970). *Biochim. Biophys. Res. Commun.*, **41,** 1507
155. Benemann, J. R. McKenna, C. E., Lie, R. F., Traylor, T. G. and Kamen, M. D. (1972). *Biochim. Biophys. Acta*, **264,** 25
156. Fukuyama, T. and Ordal, E. J. (1965). *J. Bacteriol.*, **90,** 673
157. Levine, V. E. (1925). *J. Bacteriol.*, **10,** 217
158. Wilson, L. G. and Bandurski, R. S. (1958). *J. Biol. Chem.*, **233,** 975
159. Kemp, J. D., Atkinson, D. E., Ehret, A. and Lazzarini, R. A. (1963). *J. Biol. Chem.*, **238,** 3466
160. Shum, A. C. and Murphy, J. C. (1972). *J. Bacteriol.*, **110,** 447
161. Tsibris, J. C. M., Namtvedt, M. J. and Gunsalus, I. C. (1968). *Biochem. Biophys. Res. Commun.*, **30,** 323
162. Fee, J. A. and Palmer, G. (1971). *Biochim. Biophys. Acta*, **245,** 175
163. Fee, J. A., Mayhew, S. G. and Palmer, G. (1971). *Biochim. Biophys. Acta*, **245,** 196
164. Takahashi, H. and Nason, A. (1957). *Biochim. Biophys. Acta*, **23,** 433
165. Keeler, R. F., Bulen, W. A. and Varner, J. E. (1956). *J. Bacteriol.*, **72,** 394
166. Keeler, R. F. (1957). *J. Bacteriol.*, **73,** 582
167. Keeler, R. F. and Varner, J. E. (1957). *Arch. Biochem. Biophys.*, **70,** 585
168. Keeler, R. F. and Varner, J. E. (1958). In *Trace Elements*, 297. (C. A. Lamb, O. C. Bentley and J. M. Beattie, editors) (New York and London: Academic Press)
169. Benemann, J. R., Smith, G. M., Kostel, P. J. and McKenna, C. E. (1973). *FEBS Lett.*, **29,** 219
170. Jensen, H. L. (1947). *Linnean Soc. N.S.Wales Proc.*, **72,** 299
171. Commoner, B. and Lippincott, B. B. (1958). *Proc. Nat. Acad. Sci. U.S.A.*, **44,** 1110
172. Becking, J. H. (1962). *Plant and Soil*, **16,** 171
173. Jensen, H. G. and Betty, R. C. (1943). *Linnean Soc. N.S.Wales Proc.*, **68,** 1
174. Frisell, W. R. and McKenzie, C. G. (1959). *Proc. Nat. Acad. Sci. U.S.A.*, **45,** 1568
175. Bortels, H. (1940). *Arch. Mikrobiol.*, **11,** 155
176. Jensen, H. L. and Spencer, D. (1947). *Linnean Soc. N.S.Wales Proc.*, **72,** 73

177. Bortels, H. (1939). *Zbl. Bakter.*, **100,** 373
178. Paul, K. G. (1963). *The Enzymes*, Vol. 8, 264 (P. D. Boyer, H. Lardy and K. Myrbäck, editors) (New York and London: Academic Press)
179. Burns, R. C. and Hardy, R. W. F. (1971). *Biochem. Biophys. Res. Commun.*, **42,** 353
180. Mitidieri, E. and Affonso, O. R. (1965). *Biochim. Biophys. Acta*, **105,** 371
181. Higgins, E. S., Richert, D. A. and Westerfield, W. W. (1956). *Proc. Soc. Exp. Biol. Med.*, **92,** 509
182. Hewitt, E. J. and Hallas, D. G. (1951). *Plant and Soil*, **3,** 366
183. Paneque, A., Vega, J. Ma., Cárdenas, J., Herrera, J., Aparicco, P. J. and Losada, M. (1972). *Plant Cell Physiol.*, **13,** 175
184. Arnon, D. I. and Wessel, G. (1953). *Nature, London*, **172,** 1039
185. Arnon, D. I. (1958). *Trace Elements* (C. A. Lamb, O. C. Bentley and J. M. Beattie, editors) (New York and London: Academic Press)
186. Heimer, Y. M., Wray, J. L. and Filner, P. (1969). *Plant Physiol.* (*Lancaster*), **44,** 1197
187. Notton, B. A., Fido, R. J. and Hewitt, E. J. (1973). *Ann. Rep. Long Ashton Res. Sta.*, 1972, 66
188. Heimer, Y. M. and Filner, P. (1971). *Biochim. Biophys. Acta*, **230,** 362
189. Notton, B. A. and Hewitt, E. J. (1972). *Biochim. Biophys. Acta*, **275,** 355
190. Agarwala, S. C. (1952). *Nature, London*, **169,** 1099
191. Agarwala, S. C. and Hewitt, E. J. (1955). *J. Hort. Sci.*, **30,** 163
192. Hewitt, E. J. (1957). *J. Sci. Fd. Agr.*, **8,** Suppl. 6
193. Hewitt, E. J. and McCready, C. C. (1956). *J. Hort. Sci.*, **31,** 284
194. Hewitt, E. J. (1963). *Plant Physiology*, Vol. 3, 137. (F. C. Steward, editor) (New York and London: Academic Press)
195. Hewitt, E. J., Argarwala, S. C. and Williams, A. H. (1957). *J. Hort. Sci.*, **32,** 34
196. Ichioka, P. S. and Arnon, D. I. (1955). *Physiol. Plantarum*, **8,** 552
197. Hewitt, E. J. (1956). *Soil Sci.*, **81,** 159
198. Hewitt, E. J. and Agarwala, S. C. (1951). *Nature, London*, **167,** 733
199. Hewitt, E. J. (1959). *Biol. Rev.*, **34,** 333
200. Hewitt, E. J. and Gundry, C. S. (1970). *J. Hort. Sci.*, **45,** 351
201. Morris, C. J. and Thompson, J. F. (1956). *J. Amer. Chem. Soc.*, **78,** 1605
202. Synge, R. L. M. and Wood, J. C. (1956). *Biochem. J.*, **64,** 252
203. Notton, B. A., Thompson, J. F. and Hewitt, E. J. Unpublished work.
204. Arnold, W. N., Morris, C. J. and Thompson, J. F. (1960). *Nature, London*, **186,** 1051
205. Gundry, C. S. and Hewitt, E. J. (1973). *Ann. Rep. Long Ashton Res. Stat.*, **1972,** 68
206. Notton, B. A., Fido, R. J. and Hewitt, E. J. (1973). *Ann. Rep. Long Ashton Res. Sta.*, **1972,** 68
207. Peive, Ya. V. and Ivanova, N. N. (1968). Translated Doklady Akademii Nauk. SSSR, **184** (No. 5), 1224
208. Notton, B. A. and Hewitt, E. J. (1971). *FEBS Lett.*, **18,** 19
208a. Garrett, R. H. and Greenbaum, P. (1973). *Biochim. Biophys. Acta*, **302,** 24
209. Williams, R. J. P. (1961). *Advances in the Chemistry of coordination Compounds*, 66. Proc. VI Sympos. Internal Conf. Coordination Chemistry (S. Kirschrer, editor). Detroit August 1961. (New York: MacMillan), 1961
209a. Mitchell, P. C. H. (1966). *Coord. Chem. Rev.*, **1,** 315
210. Cotton, F. A. and Wilkinson, G. (1966). *Advanced Inorganic Chemistry*, 930, 2nd edn., New York: John Wiley Interscience
211. Eaglesham, A. R. J. and Hewitt, E. J. (1971). *Biochem. J.*, **122,** 18P
212. Benesch, R. and Benesch, R. E. (1952). *Archiv. Biochim. Biophys.*, **38,** 425
213. Kay, A. and Mitchell, P. C. H. (1968). *Nature, London*, **219,** 267
214. Meriwether, L. S., Marzluff, W. F. and Hodgson, W. G. (1966). *Nature, London*, **212,** 465
215. Mitchell, P. C. H. and Williams, R. J. P. (1964). *Biochim. Biophys. Acta*, **86,** 39
216. Spence, J. T. (1970). *Arch. Biochem. Biophys.*, **137,** 287
217. Colovos, G. and Spence, J. T. (1972). *Biochemistry*, **11,** 2542
218. Schranzer, G. N. and Doemeny, A. P. A. (1971). *J. Amer. Chem. Soc.*, **93,** 1608
219. Williams, R. J. P. (1973). *Biochem. Soc.* (*U.K.*) *Trans.*, **1,** 1
219a. Hewitt, E. J. and Fido, R. J. (unpublished work)
220. Guymon, E. P. and Spence, J. T. (1966). *J. Phys. Chem.*, **70,** 1964

221. Gray, P. (1958). *Royal Institute of Chemistry* (*London*) *Lectures, Monographs and Reports*, No. 4, 1
222. Addison, C. C. and Lewis, J. (1955). *Quart. Rev. Chem. Soc.*, **9**, 115
223. Bray, R. C. and Vängärd, (1969). *Biochem. J.*, **114**, 725
224. Hemmerich, P. and Spence, J. W. T. (1966). In *Flavins and Flavoproteins* 1st Conference, Amsterdam, July 1965, 82 (E. C. Slater, editor) (Amsterdam: Elsevier)
225. Spence, J. T., Heydaneck, M. and Hemmerich, P. (1967). In *Magnetic Resonance in Biological Systems*, 269 (A. Eherenberg, B. G. Malmström and T. Vängärd, editors) (Oxford: Pergamon Press)
226. Palmer, G. and Massey, V. (1969). *J. Biol. Chem.*, **244**, 2614
227. Massey, V. and Edmundson, D. (1970). *J. Biol. Chem.*, **245**, 6595
228. Swann, J. C. and Bray, R. C. (1972). *Eur. J. Biochem.*, **26**, 407
229. Bray, R. C. and Swann, J. C. (1972). *Structure and Bonding*, **11**, 107
230. Addison, C. C., Logan, N., Wallwork, S. C. and Garner, C. D. (1971). *Quart. Rev. Chem. Soc. Lond.*, **25**, 289
231. Cotton, F. A. and Bergman, J. G. (1964). *J. Amer. Chem. Soc.*, **86**, 2941
232. Spence, J. T. and Lee, J. Y. (1965). *Inorganic Chem.*, **4**, 385
233. Melby, L. R. (1969). *Inorganic Chem.*, **8**, 1539
234. Kay, A. and Mitchell, P. C. H. (1970). *J. Chem. Soc.*, 1970, 2421
235. Bray, R. C. and Meriwether, L. S. (1966). *Nature, London*, **212**, 467
236. Silver, W. S. and McElroy, W. D. (1954). *Archiv. Biochem. Biophys.*, **51**, 379
237. Sorger, G. J. (1963). *Biochem. Biophys. Res. Commun.*, **12**, 395
238. Sorger, G. J. (1964). *Nature, London*, **204**, 575
239. Sorger, G. J. (1965). *Biochim. Biophys. Acta*, **99**, 234
240. Sorger, G. J. and Giles, N. H. (1965). *Genetics*, **52**, 777
241. Sorger, G. J. (1966). *Biochim. Biophys. Acta*, **118**, 484
242. Sorger, G. J. and Davies, J. (1973). *Biochem. J.*, **134**, 673
243. Nason, A., Antoine, A. D., Ketchum, P. A., Frazier, W. A. III and Lee, D. K. (1970). *Proc. Nat. Acad. Sci. U.S.A.*, **65**, 137
244. Cove, D. J. and Pateman, J. A. (1963). *Nature, London*, 198, 262
245. Cove, D. J., Pateman, J. A. and Rever, B. M. (1964). *Heredity*, **19**, 529
246. Cove, D. J. (1966). *Biochim. Biophys. Acta*, **113**, 51
247. Cove, D. J. (1967). *Biochem. J.*, **104**, 1033
248. Pateman, J. A. and Cove, D. J. (1967). *Nature, London*, **215**, 1234
249. Cove, D. J. and Pateman, J. A. (1969). *J. Bacteriol.*, **97**, 1374
250. Cove, D. J. (1970). *Proc. Roy. Soc. Lond.*, **B176**, 267
251. Kinsky, S. C. and McElroy, W. D. (1958). *Archiv. Biochem. Biophys.*, **73**, 466
252. MacGregor, C. H. and Schnaitman, C. A. (1971). *J. Bacteriol.*, **108**, 564
253. Venables, W. A., Wimpenny, J. W. T. and Cole, J. A. (1968). *Archiv. Mikrobiol.*, **63**, 117
254. Venables, W. A. (1972). *Molec. Gen. Genet.*, **114**, 223
255. Azoulay, E. and Marty, B. (1970). *Europ. J. Biochem.*, **13**, 186
256. Riviere, C. and Azoulay, E. (1971). *Biochem. Biophys. Res. Commun.*, **45**, 1608
257. Azoulay, E., Couchoud-Beaumont, P. and Le Beault, J. M. (1972). *Biochim. Biophys. Acta*, **256**, 670
258. Puig, J. and Azoulay, E. (1967). *C.R. Acad. Sci. Paris*, **264**, 1916
259. Casse, F. (1970). *Biochem. Biophys. Res. Comm.*, **39**, 429
260. Marcot, J. and Azoulay, E. (1971). *FEBS Lett.*, **13**, 137
261. Ketchum, P. A., Cambier, H. Y., Frazier, W. A., Madansky, C. H. and Nason, A. (1970). *Proc. Nat. Acad. Sci. U.S.A.*, **66**, 1016
262. Nason, A., Lee, K-Y., Pan, S-S., Ketchum, P. A., Lamberti, A. and De Vries, J. (1971). *Proc. Nat. Acad. Sci. U.S.A.*, **68**, 3242
263. MacGregor, C. H. and Schnaitman, C. A. (1972). *J. Bacteriol.*, **112**, 388
264. Dolney, R. J. (1971). *Biochem. Biophys. Res. Commun.*, **50**, 920
265. Morris, I. and Syrett, P. J. (1963). *Archiv. Mikrobiol.*, **47**, 32
266. Syrett, P. J. and Morris, I. (1963). *Biochim. Biophys. Acta*, **67**, 566
267. Morris, I. and Syrett, P. J. (1963). *Biochim. Biophys. Acta*, **77**, 649
268. Schrader, L. E. and Hageman, R. H. (1967). *Plant Physiol.* (*Lancaster*), **42**, 1750
269. Eaglesham, A. R. J. and Hewitt, E. J. (1971). *FEBS Lett.*, **16**, 315
270. Chang, T. J., Wang, J. C. and Tang, J. W. (1965). *Acta Physiol. Sinica*, **2,** 1

271. Nelson, N. and Ilan, I. (1969). *Plant Cell Physiol.*, **10**, 143
272. Vunkora, R. (1971). *Compt. Rend. Acad. Bulg. Sci.*, **24**, 263
273. Nicholas, D. J. D. and Scawin, J. H. (1956). *Nature, London*, **178**, 1474
274. Vennesland, B. and Jetschmann, C. (1971). *Archives Biochem. Biophys.* **144**, 428
275. Hewitt, E. J., Hucklesby, D. P. and James, D. M. (1969). *Ann. Rep. Long Ashton Res. Sta.*, **1968**, 33
276. Hucklesby, D. P., Hewitt, E. J. and James, D. M. (1970). *Biochem. J.*, **117**, 30P
277. Jetschmann, K., Solomonson, L. P. and Vennesland, B. (1972). *Biochim. Biophys. Acta*, **275**, 276
278. Solomonson, L. P., Jetschmann, K. and Vennesland, B. (1973). *Biochim. Biophys. Acta*, **309**, 32
279. Jetschmann, K. and Vennesland, B. (1973). *Abst. Internat. Biochem. Congress, Stockholm*, July 1973
280. Solomonson, L. P. (1973). *Abst. Internat. Biochem. Congress, Stockholm*, July 1973
281. Losada, M., Paneque, A., Aparicio, P. J., Vega, J. Ma., Cardenas, J. and Herrera, J. (1970). *Biochem. Biophys. Res. Commun.*, **38**, 1009
282. Moreno, C. G., Aparicio, P. J., Palacian, E. and Losada, M. (1972). *FEBS Lett.*, **26**, 11
282a. Maldonado, J. M., Herrera, J., Paneque, A. and Losada, M. (1973). *Biochem. Biophys. Res. Commun.*, **51**, 27
283. Thacker, A. and Syrett, P. J. (1972). *New Phytol.*, **71**, 423
284. Thacker, A. and Syrett, P. J. (1972). *New Phytol.*, **71**, 435
285. Holder, M., Morgenthaler, J-J., Eichenberger, W. and Grob, E. C. (1972). *FEBS Lett.*, **28**, 19
286. Herrera, J., Paneque, A., Maldonado, J. Ma., Barea, J. L. and Losada, M. (1972). *Biochem. Biophys. Res. Commun.*, **48**, 996
287. Losada, M., Herrera, J., Maldonado, J. Ma. and Paneque, A. (1973). *Plant Science Lett.*, **1**, 31
288. Subramanian, K. N. and Sorger, G. J. (1972). *J. Bacteriol.*, **110**, 538
289. Subramanian, K. N. and Sorger, G. J. (1972). *J. Bacteriol.*, **110**, 547
290. Downey, R. J. and Cove, D. J. (1971). *J. Bacteriol.*, **106**, 1047
291. Smith, F. W. and Thompson, J. F. (1971). *Plant Physiol. (Lancaster)*, **48**, 219
292. Bayley, J. M., King, J. and Gamborg, O. L. (1972). *Planta (Berlin)*, **105**, 15
293. Joy, K. (1969). *Plant Physiol. (Lancaster)*, **44**, 849
294. Filner, P. (1966). *Biochim. Biophys. Acta*, **118**, 299
295. Kelke, H. C. and Filner, P. (1971). *Biochim. Biophys. Acta*, **252**, 69
296. Ingle, J., Joy, K. W. and Hageman, R. H. (1966). *Biochem. J.*, **100**, 577
297. Ferrari, T. E. and Varner, J. E. (1969). *Plant Physiol. (Lancaster)*, **44**, 85
298. Schrader, L. E., Beevers, L. and Hageman, R. H. (1967). *Biochem. Biophys. Res. Commun.*, **26**, 14
299. Stewart, G. R. (1968). *Phytochem.*, **7**, 1139
300. Maranville, G. W. (1970). *Plant. Physiol. (Lancaster)*, **45**, 591
301. Nicholas, D. J. D. (1963). *Biol. Rev.*, **38**, 530
302. Fewson, C. A. and Nicholas, D. J. D. (1961). *Nature, London*, **190**, 2
303. Medina, A. and Nicholas, D. J. D. (1957). *Biochim. Biophys. Acta*, **25**, 138
304. Nicholas, D. J. D., Medina, A. and Jones, O. T. G. (1960). *Biochim. Biophys. Acta*, **37**, 468
305. Cook, K. A. and Sorger, G. J. (1969). *Biochim. Biophys. Acta*, **177**, 412
306. Nicholas, D. J. D. (1957). *4th Internat. Congress. Biochem., Vienna, Colloquia*, **13**, 307 (London, New York , Paris, Los Angeles: Pergamon Press) (1958)
307. Nicholas, D. J. D. (1958). *Utilisation of Nitrogen and its Compounds by Plants*, 1. Sympos. Soc. Exper. Biol. No. **13**, Sept. 1958, Univ. Reading, (H. K. Porter, editor) Cambridge: University Press (1959)
308. Nason, A., Abraham, R. C. and Averbach, B. C. (1954). *Biochim. Biophys. Acta*, **15**, 160
309. Zucker, M. and Nason, A. (1955). *J. Biol. Chem.*, **213**, 463
310. Leinweber, F-J., Siegel, L. M. and Monty, K. J. (1965). *J. Biol. Chem.*, **240**, 2699
311. Siegel, L. M., Leinweber, F-J. and Monty, K. J. (1965). *J. Biol. Chem.*, **240**, 2705
312. Medina, A. and Nicholas, D. J. D. (1957). *Nature, London*, **179**, 533
313. Nicholas, D. J. D. (1957). *Ann. Bot. (Lond.), N.S.*, **21**, 587
314. Yoshimoto, A., Nakamura, T. and Sato, R. (1967). *J. Biochem. (Tokyo)*, **62**, 756

315. Prabhakararao, K. and Nicholas, D. J. D. (1970). *Biochim. Biophys. Acta*, **216,** 122
316. Yoshimoto, A. and Sato, R. (1968). *Biochim. Biophys. Acta*, **153,** 555
317. Yoshimoto, A. and Sato, R. (1968). *Biochim. Biophys. Acta*, **153,** 576
318. Yoshimoto, A. and Sato, R. (1970). *Biochim. Biophys. Acta*, **220,** 190
319. Yoshimoto, A., Naiki, N. and Sato, R. (1971). *Methods in Enzymology*, **27B,** 520 (H. Tabor and C. W. Tabor, editors) (New York and London: Academic Press) (1971)
320. Prakash, O., Rao, R. R. and Sadana, J. C. (1966). *Biochim. Biophys. Acta*, **118,** 426
321. Prakash. O. and Sadana, J. C. (1972). *Archiv. Biochem. Biophys.*, **148,** 614
322. Husain, M. and Sadana, J. C. (1972). *Analyt. Biochem.*, **45,** 316
323. Spencer, D., Takahashi, H. and Nason, A. (1957). *J. Bacteriol.*, **73,** 533
324. Wallace, W. and Nicholas, D. J. D. (1968). *Biochem. J.*, **109,** 763
325. Zarowny, D. P. and Sanwal, B. D. (1963). *Canad. J. Microbiol.*, **9,** 531
326. Kemp, J. D. and Atkinson, D. E. (1966). *J. Bacteriol.*, **92,** 628
327. Cole, J. A. (1968). *Biochim. Biophys. Acta*, **162,** 356
328. Lazzarini, R. A. and Atkinson, D. E. (1961). *J. Biol. Chem.*, **236,** 3330
329. Mager, J. (1960). *Biochim. Biophys. Acta*, **41,** 553
330. Siegel, L. M. and Kamin, H. (1967). *Flavins and Flavoproteins*, 15, 2nd Conference, Magoya 1967, (K. Yagi, editor) Tokyo, Baltimore and Manchester, Univ. Tokyo Press and Univ. Park Press (1968)
331. Siegel, L. M. and Kamin, H. (1971). *Methods in Enzymology*, **17B,** 539. (H. Tabor and C. W. Tabor, editors) (New York and London: Academic Press)
332. Siegel, L. M., Kamin, H., Rueger, D. C., Presswood, R. P. and Gibson, Q. H. (1968). *Flavins and Flavoproteins*, 523. 3rd Internat. Sympos., Durham, Nth. Carolina (H Kamin, editor) Baltimore and London, University Park Press and Butterworths (1969)
333. Iwasaki, H. and Matsubara, T. (1972). *J. Biochem. (Tokyo)*, **71,** 645
334. Iwasaki, H., Shidara, S., Suzuki, H. and Mori, T. (1963). *J. Biochem. Tokyo*, **53,** 299
335. Miyata, M. and Mori, T. (1969). *J. Biochem. (Tokyo)*, **66,** 463
336. Matsubara, T. (1970). *J. Biochem. (Tokyo)*, **67,** 133
337. Matsubara, T. and Iwasaki, H. (1971). *J. Biochem. (Tokyo)*, **69,** 859
338. Radcliffe, B. C. and Nicholas, D. J. D. (1968). *Biochim. Biophys. Acta*, **153,** 545
339. Hooper, A. B. (1968). *Biochim. Biophys. Acta*, **162,** 49
340. Ritchie, G. A. F. and Nicholas, D. J. D. (1972). *Biochem. J.*, **126,** 1181
341. Walker, G. C. and Nicholas, D. J. D. (1960). *Biochem. J.*, **77,** 4P
342. Walker, G. C. and Nicholas, D. J. D. (1961). *Biochim. Biophys. Acta*, **49,** 350
343. Iwasaki, H. and Matsubara, T. (1971). *J. Biochem. (Tokyo)*, **69,** 847
344. Yamanaka, T. (1964). *Nature, Lond.*, **204,** 253
345. Horio, T., Higashi, T., Yamanaka, T., Matsubara, H. and Okunuki, K. (1961). *J. Biol. Chem.*, **236,** 944
346. Yamanaka, T., Ota, A. and Okunuki, K. (1960). *Biochim. Biophys. Acta*, **44,** 397
347. Newton, N. (1969). *Biochim. Biophys. Acta*, **185,** 316
348. Lam, Y. and Nicholas, D. J. D. (1969). *Biochim. Biophys. Acta*, **180,** 459
349. Zumft, W. G. (1972). *Biochim. Biophys. Acta*, **276,** 363
350. Zumft, W. G. and Spiller, H. (1971). *Biochem. Biophys. Res. Commun.*, **45,** 112
351. Grant, B. R. (1970). *Plant Cell Physiol.*, **11,** 55
352. Hucklesby, D. P. and Hewitt, E. J. (1970). *Biochem. J.*, **119,** 615
353. Hattori, A. and Myers, J. (1966). *Plant Physiol. (Lancaster)*, **41,** 1031
354. Hattori, A. and Uesugi, I. (1968). *Plant Cell Physiol.*, **9,** 689
355. Bothe, H. (1969). *Progress in Photosynthesis Research*, **3,** 1483 (H. Metzner, editor) Tubingen: H. Laupp Jr.
356. Yoch, D. C. (1972). *Biochem. Biophys. Res. Commun.*, **49,** 335
357. Kessler, E. (1957). *Planta (Berlin)*, **49,** 505
358. Ahmad, J. and Morris, I. (1967). *Archiv. Mikrobiol.*, **56,** 219
359. Kessler, E., Hofmann, A. and Zumft, W. G. (1970). *Archiv. Mikrobiol.*, **72,** 23
360. Hoffmann, A. (1972). *Planta (Berlin)*, **102,** 72
361. Kessler, E. (1957). *Archiv. Mikrobiol.*, **27,** 166
362. Roussos, G. G. and Nason, A. (1960). *J. Biol. Chem.*, **235,** 2997
363. Cresswell, C. F. and Hewitt, E. J. (1960). *Biochem. Biophys. Res. Commun.*, **3,** 544
364. Huzisige, H. and Satoh, K. (1961). *Botan. Mag. Tokyo*, **74,** 178

365. Huzisige, H., Satoh, K., Tanaka, K. and Hayasida, T. (1963) *Plant Cell Physiol.*, **4,** 307
366. Nason, A. (1962). *Bacteriol. Rev.*, **26,** 16
367. Cresswell, C. F., Hageman, R. H. and Hewitt, E. J. (1962). *Biochem. J.*, **83,** 38P
368. Paneque, A., Ramirez, J. M., Del Campo, F. F. and Losada, M. (1964). *J. Biol. Chem.*, **239,** 1737
369. Ramirez, J. M., Del Campo, F. F., Paneque, A. and Losada, M. (1966). *Biochim. Biophys. Acta*, **118,** 58
370. Hewitt, E. J. and Betts, G. F. (1963). *Biochem. J.*, **89,** 20P
371. Losada, M., Paneque, A., Ramirez, J. M. and Del Campo, F. F. (1963). *Biochem. Biophys. Res. Commun.*, **10,** 298
372. Paneque, A., Del Campo, F. F. and Losada, M. (1963). *Nature, London*, **198,** 90
373. Betts, G. F. and Hewitt, E. J. (1966). *Nature, Lond.*, **210,** 1327
374. Sanderson, G. W. and Cocking, E. C. (1964). *Plant Physiol. Lancaster*, **39,** 423
375. Hewitt, E. J., Hucklesby, D. P. and Betts, G. F. (1967). *Recent Aspects of Nitrogen Metabolism in Plants*, 47. Sympos. Long Ashton Res. Sta. April 1967 (E. J. Hewitt and C. F. Cutting, editors) (New York and London: Academic Press) (1968)
376. Shin, M. and Oda, Y. (1966). *Plant Cell Physiol.*, **7,** 643
377. Ratcliffe, S. J. and Hewitt, E. J. (1971). *Ann. Rep. Long Ashton Res. Sta.*, 1970, 58
378. Pickard, M. and Hewitt, E. J. (1973). *Ann. Rep. Long Ashton Res., Sta.*, 1972, 70
379. Hucklesby, D. P., Dalling, M. J. and Hageman, R. H. (1972). *Planta (Berlin)*, **104,** 220
380. Bourne, W. F. and Miflin, B. J. (1970). *Biochem. Biophys. Res. Commun.*, **40,** 1305
381. Ferrari, T. E. and Varner, J. E. (1971). *Plant Physiol. (Lancaster)*, **47,** 790
382. Joy, K. W. and Hageman, R. H. (1966). *Biochem. J.*, **100,** 263
383. Hewitt, E. J. and Hucklesby, D. P. (1966). *Biochem. Biophys. Res. Commun.*, **25,** 689
384. Hucklesby, D. P., James, D. M. and Hewitt, E. J. (1973). *Ann. Rep. Long Ashton Res. Sta.*, 1972
385. Cardenas, J., Barea, J. L., Rivas, J. and Moreno, C. G. (1972). *FEBS Lett.*, **23,** 131
386. Cardenas, J., Rivas, J. and Barea, J. L. (1972). *Pub. Rev. Real. Acad. Cienc. Exact. Fisic. Nat. Madrid*, **66,** 565
387. Asada, K., Tamura, G. and Bandurski, R. S. (1969). *J. Biol. Chem.*, **244,** 4904
388. Hewitt, E. J., Hucklesby, D. P. and Betts, G. F. (1966). *Biochem. J.*, **100,** 54P
389. Sanderson, G. W. and Cocking, E. C. (1963). *Biochem. J.*, **87,** 28P
390. Hucklesby, D. P. and Hewitt, E. J. (1972). *Ann. Rep. Long Ashton Res. Sta.*, 1971, 57
391. Wiskich, D. and Hewitt, E. J. (1971). *Ann. Rep. Long Ashton Res. Sta.*, 1970, 53
392. Fewson, C. A. and Nicholas, D. J. D. (1960). *Nature (London)*, **188,** 794
393. Wiskich, D., Notton, B. A. and Hewitt, E. J. (1971). *Ann. Rep. Long Ashton Res. Sta.*, 1970, 54
394. Addison, C. C., Gamlen, G. A. and Thompson, R. (1952). *J. Chem. Soc. London*, 1952, 338
395. Steinberg, R. A. (1955). *Inorganic Nitrogen Metabolism*, 153. Sympos. McCollum Pratt Inst., June 1955 (W. D. McElroy and B. Glass, editors) Baltimore: Johns Hopkins Press
396. Neilands, J. B. (1972). *Structure and Bonding*, **11,** 145
397. Goodgame, D. M. L. and Hitchman, M. A. (1965). *Inorg. Chem.*, **4,** 721
398. Drew, M. G. Ba., Goodgame, D. M. L., Hitchman, M. A. and Rogers, D. (1965). *Chem. Commun.*, 1965, 477
399. Griffith, W. P. (1966). *Developments in Inorganic Nitrogen Chemistry*, **1,** 241 (C. B. Colburn, editor) (Amsterdam, London and New York: Elsevier)
400. King, R. B. and Bisnette, M. B. (1964). *Inorg. Chem.*, **3,** 791
401. Rozantsev, E. G. (1970). *Free Nitrosyl Radicals*, **16,** (Translated by B. J. Hazzard, H. Ulrich, editor) (New York and London: Plenum Press)
402. Giotta, G. J. and Wang, H. W. (1972). *Biochem. Biophys. Res. Commun.*, **46,** 1576
403. Kester, M. and Norton, S. J. (1972). *Biochim. Biophys. Acta*, **258,** 709
404. Burmeister, J. L. (1968). *Co-ordin. Chem. Rev.*, **3,** 225
405. Guerrero, M. G., Vega, J. Ma., Leadbetter, E. and Losada, M. (1973). *Archiv. Mikrobiol.*, **91,** 287
406. Ivanova, N. N. and Peive, Ya. V. (1973). *FEBS Lett.*, **31,** 229
407. Notton, B. A. and Hewitt, E. J. (1973). In: *Proc. 2nd Int. Conf. on Chemistry and uses of molybdenum*. Univ. Reading Sept. (1973). *J. Rare Metals* (in press)

408. Stiefel, E. I. (1973). *Proc. Nat. Acad. Sci. U.S.A.*, **70,** 988
409. Bray, R. C. (1973). In: *Proc. 2nd Int. Conf. on Chemistry and uses of molybdenum.* Univ. Reading Sept. (1973). *J. Rare Metals* (in press)
410. Ketchum, P. A. and Swarin, R. S. (1973). *Biochem. Biophys. Res. Commun*, **52,** 1450
411. Nason, A., Lee, K-Y, Pan, S-S and Erickson, R. H. (1973). In: *Proc. 2nd Int. Conf. on Chemistry and uses of molybdenum.* Univ. Reading Sept. (1973). *J. Rare Metals* (in press)
412. Schloemer, R. H. and Garrett, R. H. (1973). *Plant Physiol. (Lancaster)*, **51,** 591
413. Wallace, W. (1973). *Plant Physiol. (Lancaster)*, **52,** 197
414. Borris, Von H. (1967). *Wiss. Zeit. Univ.*, Rostock, (Math-Naturwiss) **16,** 629
415. Lips, S. H. and Roth-Bejerano, N. (1969). *Science*, **166,** 109
416. Kende, H., Hahn, H. and Kays, S. E. (1971). *Plant Physiol. (Lancaster)*, **48,** 702
417. Parkash, V. (1972). *Planta (Berlin)*, **102,** 372
418. Hirschberg, K., Hübner, G. and Borriss, H. (1972). *Planta (Berlin)*, **108,** 333
419. Knypl, J. S. (1973). *Z. pflanzenphysiol.*, **70,** 1
420. Rivas, J., Guerrero, M. G., Paneque, A. and Losada, M. (1973). *Plant Sci. Lett.*, **1,** 105
421. Cornish-Bowden, A. J., Ward, F. B. and Cole, J. A. (1973). *J. Gen. Microbiol.*, **75** (proc xi)
422. Vega, J. M., Guerrero, M. G., Leadbetter, E. and Losada, M. (1973). *Biochem. J.*, **133,** 701
423. Hucklesby, D. P., James, D. M. and Hewitt, E. J. (1974). *Biochem. Soc. (U.K.) Trans.* **2,** (in the press)
424. Ida, S. and Morita, Y. (1973). *Plant Cell Physiol.*, **14,** 661

7
Enzymological Aspects of Flavonoid and Lignin Biosynthesis and Degradation in Plants

G. H. N. TOWERS
University of British Columbia

7.1 INTRODUCTION

The last 10 years has seen a gradual unfolding of our understanding of the enzymology associated with the metabolism of cinnamic acid in plants. Pioneer tracer studies by the schools of Neish[1], Freudenberg[1] and Grisebach[2] provided much of the basic groundwork necessary to attack problems of flavonoid and lignin biosynthesis at the enzymological and regulatory levels. With the discovery of the enzymes catalysing the non-oxidative deamination of phenylalanine and tyrosine to cinnamic and *p*-coumaric acids[3,4] the way was opened for an intelligent approach to the problems.

In this review I shall discuss the enzymes leading from phenylalanine and tyrosine to the C-6–C-3–C-6 class of compounds, namely the plant flavonoids, as well as the coumarins, and the phenylpropanoid polymers of plants known as lignins. Enzymes concerned with flavonoid breakdown will also be discussed. Other reviews dealing in part with this subject are those by Higuchi[5], Yoshida[6], and Conn[7]. Enzymes of the shikimic acid pathway will not be included here.

7.2 GENERAL ASPECTS OF PHENYLPROPANOID METABOLISM

For the reader unfamiliar with this large area of plant metabolism a brief orientation is necessary. Cinnamic acid, which is derived from phenylalanine via non-oxidative deamination, is similar in certain respects to mevalonic and acetic acids; as shown in Figure 7.1 a large number of biochemical pathways have evolved in plants whereby this phenylpropanoid molecule can be employed in the production of other molecules.

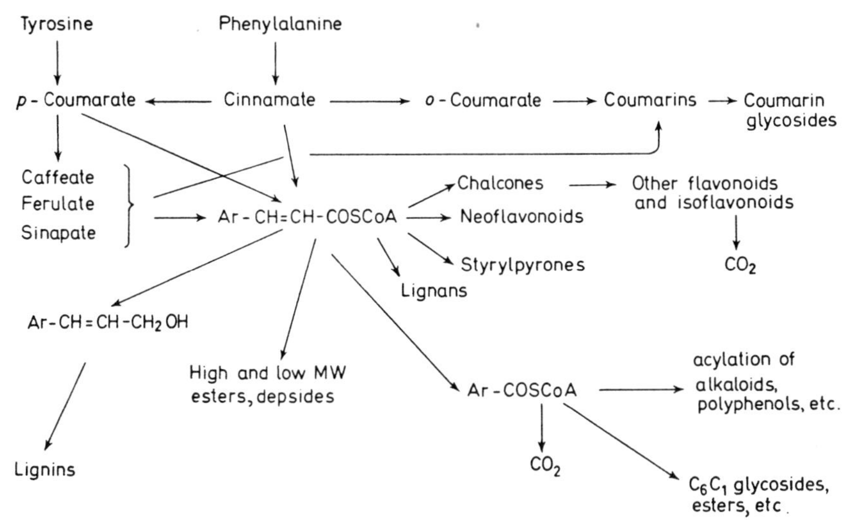

Figure 7.1 Metabolism of cinnamic acids in plants

Many basidiomycetous fungi have the ability to synthesise cinnamic and *p*-coumaric acids, but as far as is known, the variety of cinnamyl derivatives produced by them is more restricted[8]. This is even more so with *Streptomyces*, species of which have been shown to possess phenylalanine ammonia lyase[9].

7.2.1 Enzymes of phenylpropanoid metabolism

7.2.1.1 Phenylalanine and tyrosine ammonia lyases

As far as is known there is only one biosynthetic route leading to cinnamic acid and that is through the non-oxidative deamination of phenylalanine. The enzyme, phenylalanine ammonia lyase (PAL) (E.C. 4.3.1.5), has been studied extensively in plants and fungi not only because the product is the precursor of so many different types of phenolics but also because the enzyme, which is stable and readily assayed, fluctuates in amount, sometimes quite dramatically, in a given tissue in response to a variety of stimuli. PAL is the subject of a recent review[10] covering the literature up to 1972, and including particularly the effects of age, light, phytochrome, wounding, infection and growth modifiers on enzyme levels. The reader is also directed to a detailed discussion of the effect of light on this enzyme by Zucker[11] and to a critical account of the mechanism and properties of PAL from higher plants by Hanson and Havir[12].

The reaction catalysed by PAL is the non-oxidative deamination of L-phenylalanine to yield *trans*-cinnamic acid and ammonia. Pyridoxal phosphate is not a co-factor but the active site is believed to contain a dehydroalanyl residue present as a Schiff's base[13]. It is suggested that the amino group of phenylalanine adds to the β-position of the dehydroalanyl double bond. If this intermediate undergoes a prototropic shift, a conjugated system ($O{=}C{-}C^{\alpha}{=}C^{\beta}{-}N{-}$) may be formed which makes for a more facile elimination of the amino group of phenylalanine. Glycine is a competitive inhibitor[14] which lends support to the idea that the alanine sidechain of phenylalanine is closely associated with the β-carbon of dehydroalanine. Evidence has been presented, that with highly purified enzymes, the reaction proceeds via an enzyme ammonia intermediate[13, 14]:

$$\text{Enz} + \text{Phe} \rightleftharpoons \{\text{Enz-Phe} \rightleftharpoons \text{Enz-NH}_3\text{-Cin}\}$$
$$\{\text{Enz-Phe} \rightleftharpoons \text{Enz-NH}_3\text{-Cin}\} \rightleftharpoons \text{Enz-NH}_3 + \text{Cin}$$
$$\text{Enz-NH}_3 \rightleftharpoons \text{Enz} + \text{NH}_3$$

The enzyme has essential sulphydryl group(s) which may aid in the abstraction of a proton or protons from the substrate molecule[15].

Phenylalanine, stereospecifically labelled with isotopic hydrogen at C-3 has been used to establish that the pro-S proton from C-3 of L-phenylalanine, together with ammonia, is eliminated in an antiperiplanar fashion from C-3 to generate *trans*-cinnamic acid[16, 17].

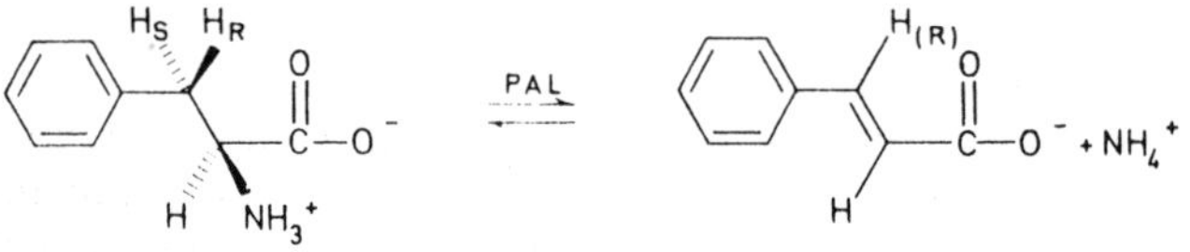

Preparations from many plant sources, particularly grasses, and some fungi also catalyse the deamination of L-tyrosine to *trans-p*-coumaric acid and ammonia, although always to a lesser extent. There is increasing evidence that both phenylalanine (PAL) and tyrosine-ammonia lyase (TAL) activities reside in the same enzyme. The evidence may be summarised as follows: (a) TAL, free of PAL activity has never been reported from any source although many PAL preparations are totally lacking in activity towards tyrosine, e.g. *Ustilago hordei* PAL[18]. (b) the two enzyme activities are inseparable in preparations from the fungus, *Rhodotorula*[19] (c) TAL activity accompanied PAL activity throughout a 450-fold purification of PAL from the fungus, *Sporobolomyces pararoseus*[20] (d) a constant ratio of PAL/TAL was found in the purification of PAL from *Zea mays*[21] and both activities were lost at the same rate on treatment of the enzyme with $NaBH_4$. Moreover, the activities with both substrates are enhanced by treating the plant with gibberellic acid and both activities decrease rapidly at the same rate when tissue is incubated in a moist atmosphere, and this treatment can be slowed by treatment with cycloheximide[22]. The two activities could not be separated by various purification steps including isoelectric focusing.

More recent studies indicate that there are multiple forms of PAL and that these are specifically compartmentalised within cells[23-25]. In *Quercus* one form of PAL is located in the microsomal fraction and a second in the mitochondrial fraction. The product of microsomal PAL is further metabolised to hydroxycinnamic acids and possibly flavonoids; cinnamate produced in mitochondria is channelled into the production of C-6–C-1 compounds[23]. From sweet potato tissue[26] and from tissue of *Quercus*[27] two forms of PAL are separable which differ in their sensitivities to phenolic inhibitors. PAL and TAL activity are separable in sweet potato[26]. Not much is known yet concerning the intracellular compartmentalisation of PAL in fungi. In *Polyporus hispidus*, however, there is an increase in PAL activity on exposure to light of dark grown cells without a concomitant increase in TAL activity[28].

Although they differ in several respects, including amino acid composition the enzyme[29] from corn leaves and that from light exposed potato tuber tissues each consists of four identical subunits with molecular weights close to 83 000. Evidence, based on ^{14}C-nitromethane labelling, indicates that there are two active sites per tetramer. PAL from wheat leaves[30], however, is reported to have a mol. wt. of 325 000 and to be composed of two subunits of mol. wt. 75 000 and two of mol. wt. 85 000. If this is correct, then at least two genes must be involved in PAL synthesis.

7.2.1.2 *Cinnamic acid-4-hydroxylase*

This enzyme was first described from pea seedlings[31] (*Pisum sativum*, var. Alaska) and has since been found in buckwheat[32], asparagus shoots[33], *Sorghum*[34, 35], potato tuber tissue[36] and in the fungus, *Polyporus hispidus*[37]. It is probably present in all plant tissues because it appears to be the main route to *p*-coumaric acid in most plants. It is only in grasses and some fungi[1, 37] that there appears to be an appreciable synthesis of *p*-coumarate from tyrosine. Cinnamic acid-4-hydroxylase (CAH) is a monoxygenase or 'mixed function oxidase' and molecular oxygen and NADPH are required in the reaction:

$$C_6H_5{-}CH{=}CH{-}CO_2H + O_2 + NADPH + H^+ \longrightarrow HO{-}C_6H_4{-}CH{=}CH{-}CO_2H + H_2O + NADP^+$$

The enzyme from asparagus shoots has a requirement for tetrahydrofolic acid and that from *Polyporus* requires FAD.

In all tissues examined so far the enzyme has been found to be associated with the microsomal fraction except for dormant potato tuber tissues[38] in which 84% was found in the soluble fraction and 14% in the microsomal. If discs, prepared from potato tissue, were aged for 18 h in light most of the activity was found to be in the microsomes.

The enzyme has been purified from Alaska pea seedlings[39] and from *Sorghum*[35]. The pea seedling enzyme does not catalyse the hydroxylation of phenylalanine or of *p*-coumaric acid but it is not known whether benzoic or phenylacetic acids or cinnamyl alcohol may serve as substrates. Benzoate-4-hydroxylase activity is separable from cinnamate-4-hydroxylase activity in *Polyporus*[37]. From work with animal systems there is evidence that similar types of oxidases consist of a multienzyme complex in which reduced cytochrome P-450 is the component responsible for the binding and activation of molecular oxygen. Russell[39] presents evidence for the involvement of cytochrome P-450 in the hydroxylation of cinnamic acid, e.g. light reversible CO inhibition. Similarly, Potts[35] has indicated that the enzyme from *Sorghum* displays a pattern of behaviour which is typical of cytochrome P-450 hydroxylases, i.e. CO, azide, *p*-CMB and quinones are effective inhibitors but the catalysis is indifferent to cyanide. The enzyme from *Sorghum* is associated with particles having a density of 1.120–1.145, microsomes or membrane fragments of the EPR. By differential spectrophotometry cytochromes b_5 and P-450 are found to be associated with these particles and, as in the case of the pea enzyme, the inhibition by CO is light reversible. The light sensitivity of this release of inhibition varies as a function of the wavelength of the light in a manner similar to the absorbance of the complex of ferrous P-450 and CO. The possibility of involvement of radicals[35] as obligatory intermediates is indicated by stimulation of hydroxylation by added catalase or inhibition by added peroxidase, catechol or glucose oxidase plus glucose.

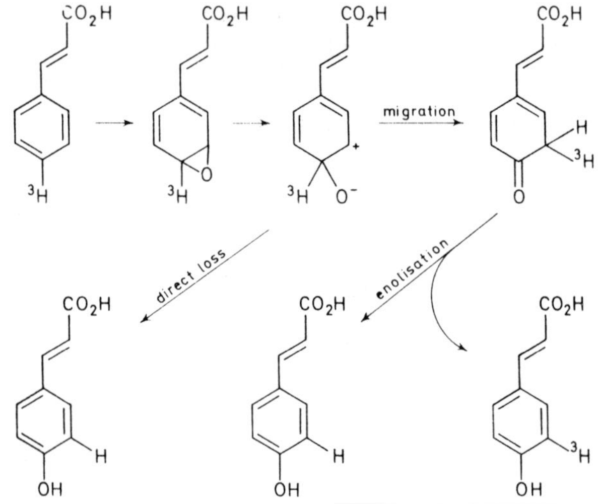

Figure 7.2 NIH shift in hydroxylation of 4-^{3}H-cinnamic acid with cinnamic acid-4-hydroxylase (after Reed *et al.*[44])

The enzyme from peas[39] has a high affinity for cinnamate ($K_m = 1.7 \times 10^{-5}$ M) and is inhibited non-competitively by low concentrations of the product. A sigmoid curve is obtained if $1/V_m$ is plotted against inhibitor (*p*-coumarate) indicating that the product exerts a stringent control over the activity of the enzyme. The control mechanism is one in which there is increasing cooperativity in inhibition with increasing concentration of the product.

It was shown[40] that when 4-^{3}H-cinnamic acid was fed to young *Catalpa hybrida* leaf discs there was an 85.3% retention of tritium in *p*-coumaric acid isolated from the tissues. A 93% retention of tritium was also shown with a microsomal preparation of CAH from *peas*[41]. This retention and migration of tritium in aromatic hydroxylations, known as the NIH shift[42,43] is believed to be due to the formation of labile arene oxides which oxidise to phenols with a concomitant migration of the tritium. According to Reed *et al.*[44], the isomerisation of the arene oxide intermediates proceeds via the keto-tautomer of the phenolic product as shown above (Figure 7.2).

The amount of enzyme in green tissues of pea seedlings varied according to the age of the tissues, being highest in the apical bud and youngest leaf[39]. Only 5–10% of this activity was found in the first leaf and none in the second leaf. Irradiation of etiolated seedlings for 10 min with a fluorescent light induced a fivefold increase in activity from apical tissues harvested about 12 h after returning the seedlings to darkness. This effect of light has also been shown with excised, etiolated buckwheat hypocotyls[32, 45]. In these tissues there is an increase in PAL and CAH which reaches a peak in 10–12 h. Similar results have been obtained with parsley cell cultures[46, 47]. In potato tuber tissue, however, although CAH activity was increased 10–30 times by wounding and ageing (18 h) it was unaffected by light in contrast to PAL[36]. This enzyme in *Polyporus* shows an increase in activity when cultures are exposed to light[37].

Ethylene, which has been shown to affect levels of PAL activity in many tissues (see Reference 10) causes a tenfold increase in CAH levels in the plumular hook of etiolated Alaska pea seedlings[48]. There is a lag period of 14 h followed by an increase which reaches a plateau at about 30 h. A similar pattern was shown by PAL except that the development required a shorter induction period and preceded the development of CAH by 8–10 h. The optimal concentration of ethylene for CAH was 50 p.p.m. for PAL it was about 20 p.p.m. Cycloheximide (5 $\mu g\ ml^{-1}$) or actinomycin D (50 $\mu g\ ml^{-1}$) strongly inhibited this increase in CAH caused by ethylene[48].

7.2.1.3 Ortho hydroxylation of cinnamic acid

Coumarin and its hydroxylated, methoxylated and otherwise modified derivatives are common constituents of plants but the nature of the enzymes involved in *ortho*-hydroxylation and lactonisation remain uncharacterised. The chloroplasts of *Saxifraga stolonifera* were found to convert *cis*-caffeic acid to esculetin. The reaction was shown to be enzymic and the enzyme is believed to be a phenolase (*ortho*-diphenol: O_2 reductase[49]). According to Sato[49] the *ortho*-quinone produced from *cis*-caffeic acid may convert spontaneously to esculetin as shown in Figure 7.3:

Using fractionation procedures involving sucrose density gradient centrifugation of preparations from *Hydrangea macrophylla*, Kindl[50] showed that

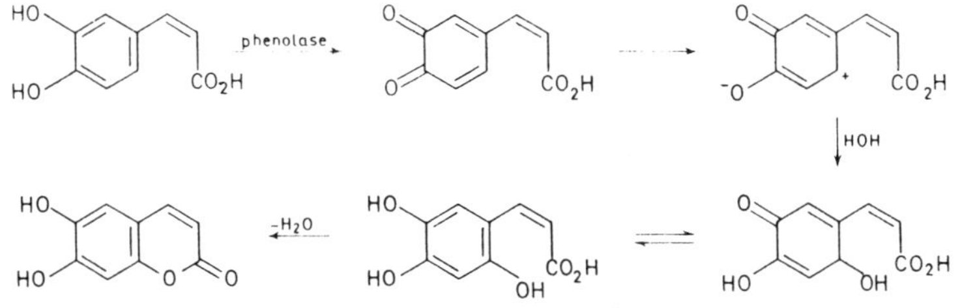

Figure 7.3 Suggested mode of synthesis of esculetin by the action of chloroplast prenolase on *cis*-caffeic acid (After Sato[54])

chloroplast fragments and chloroplasts had the highest activity for ortho hydroxylation in contrast to the 100 000 × **g** pellet which had most of the activity for para hydroxylation of cinnamate. In addition, these chloroplast preparations catalysed the hydroxylaton of *p*-coumaric acid to give umbelliferone (7-hydroxycoumarin), ferulic acid to give scopoletin (6-methoxy, 7-hydroxycoumarin) and, to a minor extent, benzoic acid was hydroxylated to give salicyclic acid. The reaction rates were enhanced by the addition of NADPH and 2-amino-4-hydroxy-6,7-dimethyl-5,6,7,8-tetrahydropteri dine.

7.2.1.4 Hydroxylation of p-coumaric acid

Very little is known about the hydroxylating enzyme that produces caffeic acid from *p*-coumaric acid. With a phenolase preparation from spinach beet[51] there was further oxidation of the product by the catechol oxidase activity of the enzyme. With dimethyltetrahydropteridine as electron donor, oxygen uptake was exactly equivalent to the caffeic acid produced, provided that *p*-coumaric acid was in excess[52]. It has been suggested[175] that the catechol oxidase activity of these phenolases may be suppressed in cells by rapid transfer of products such as caffeic acid and its esters to the vacuole or possibly by the maintenance of high levels of *p*-coumarate and tetrahydropteridines as reductants.

Sorghum contains at least three enzymes exhibiting phenoloxidase activity[53]. One of these, found in first internodes but absent from green leaves, catalyses the hydroxylation of *p*-coumaric acid to caffeic acid.

This low mol. wt. enzyme is found in the soluble fraction, after centrifugation at 100 000 × **g**, together with PAL and TAL. There appears to be a discrepancy, however, between these results and the suggestion (and results)[24] that there is a particulate complex in *Sorghum* tissues which catalyses the sequence:

Phenylalanine ⟶ cinnamate ⟶ *p*-coumarate ⟶ caffeate

With leaf extracts of *Beta vulgaris* phenoloxidase activity towards L-dopa, 4-methylcatechol and *p*-coumaric acid (hydroxylase activity) was found to be present in the chlorophyll-rich chloroplast membranes[34]. Dopa and 4-methylcatechol activity were associated with mitochondria whereas *p*-coumaric hydroxylase was restricted to the chloroplast and the supernatant fractions. These results are in agreement with the earlier work of Sato[54] who showed that chloroplasts of a variety of gymnosperms and angiosperms are able to effect this hydroxylation, This, however cannot be the only source of a *p*-coumarate hydroxylase because non-chlorophyllous tissues, e.g. roots and other storage tissues also synthesise caffeic acid and its derivatives. A further point, which requires examination, is the specificity of these hydroxylation enzymes. It has been shown, for example, that chlorogenic acid is formed from 3-0-*p*-coumaroyl-quinic acid by enzyme preparations of potato tuber[55]. It is not known whether this is the same phenolase which has been purified to homogeneity from potato tuber[56].

7.2.1.5 Prenylation

A large number of prenylated coumarins, flavonoids and other phenolic compounds have been identified in plants. The prenylation of umbelliferone in the 6-position has been demonstrated with extracts of *Ruta graveolens* cell cultures with dimethylallyl pyrophosphate serving as the alkylating

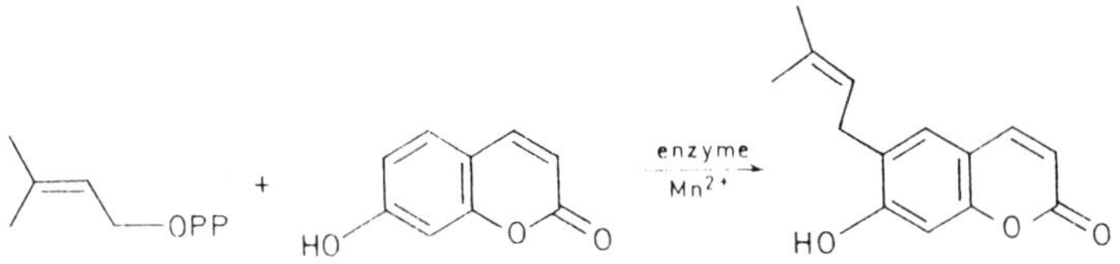

Figure 7.4 Prenylation of umbelliferone with enzyme preparation (From Ellis and Brown[57], personal communication)

agent[57] (Figure 7.4). The enzyme, which has been purified tenfold, requires Mn^{2+} (Mg^{2+} has no effect).

A similar type of prenylation of tryptophan or of a derivative has been demonstrated in *Claviceps sp.*[187], *Asperigillus amstelodami*[58] and in the ergot fungus.

7.2.1.6 O-Methyltransferases

In addition to the methylation of hydroxycinnamic and benzoic acids, coumarins and cinnamyl alcohols to give guaiacyl (3-methoxy-4-hydroxyphenyl) or syringyl (3,5-dimethoxy-4-hydroxyphenyl) nuclei, various positions on either the A or B ring of flavonoids are frequently *O*-methylated. Furthermore, there exists a very large number of alkaloids derived from phenylalanine, tyrosine or tryptophan which bear methoxyl groups. In spite of the availability of *S*-adenosylmethionine (methyl-^{14}C) very few attempts have been made to determine how many *O*-methyltransferases are involved in these reactions and it is not even known whether separate enzymes occur for *O*-, *N*- and *C*- methylations in plants. In animal tissues multiple forms of histamine *N*-methyltransferase and catechol *O*-methyltransferase occur in tissues within a given species as well as among different species[59] and undoubtedly the same situation prevails with plants.

Some of the questions that may be asked regarding these methylation reactions are:

(1) Are there distinct *para*- and *meta*-methylating enzymes?

(2) Are the enzymes methylating flavonoids distinct from those methylating hydroxy cinnamic and benzoic acids and alcohols and phenylethylamines?

(3) Is the origin of the syringyl nucleus a result of *O*-methylation of a 5-hydroxy guaiacyl nucleus?

The workers with alkaloids do not seem to be aware of the interest of those working with flavonoids and vice versa. Studies of specificity are usually restricted to one class of compounds. For example, a preparation from *Lophophora williamsii*[60], which has been purified 20-fold by chromatography on Sephadex G-100 and G-200, displayed the following relative activity towards a series of phenylethylamines:

HO, HO –R > MeO, HO, HO –R > MeO, HO, MeO –R > HO, MeO –R >

MeO, HO –R > MeO, MeO, HO –R where R = $—CH_2—CH_2NH_2$

None of the tetrahydroisoquinoline alkaloids of the cactus served as substrates. It would have been of interest to know if indeed this preparation was specific for hydroxyphenylethylamines or whether caffeate or 5-hydroxyferulate were equally effective as substrates. The enzyme from *Lophophora* had a pH optimum of 8.3 and a K_m for dopamine of 1.75×10^{-4} M. It did not require divalent cations nor was it affected by EDTA, cyanide or thiourea, in contrast to a preparation from *Nerine*[61] which was active with certain other hydroxylated alkaloids.

O-Methyltransferase activity for dihydric phenols has been reported from petals of *Impatiens balsamina*[62], wheat seedlings[63], *Petunia hybrida*[64], leaves of *Pinus thunbergii*[65], *Salix caprea*[65], pampas grass[66, 67], bamboo shoots[68], poplar[68] and *Gingko*[69]. In wheat seedlings there was a good correlation between changes in levels of *O*-methyltransferase activity for caffeic acid and ferulic acid accumulation up to 10 days after germination. Interestingly enough from day 40 to day 80 when there is a spectacular rise in lignification[70], i.e. production of guaiacylpropyl polymers, there are only very low levels of activity for this enzyme. This is a striking example of the lack of correlation between enzyme activity and rate of synthesis of product. In *Pinus thunbergii*, hypocotyls and roots have very much higher levels of *O*-methyltransferase activity than needles[65]. There is thus a good correlation between lignin formation and enzyme activity in this plant. Enzyme preparations from *Pinus* catalysed preferentially the methylation of caffeic acid to ferulic acid but scarcely methylated 5-hydroxyferulate to sinapate. The partially purified enzyme required Mg^{2+} for maximum formation of ferulate and Co, Zn, Ca and Ni as well as EDTA, PCMB and iodoacetate were strong inhibitors[71]. The enzyme was meta-specific, with a pH optimum of 7.5; of 16 phenolic compounds tested caffeic acid was the best.

The enzyme preparations isolated from bamboo shoots, on the other hand, catalysed the following methylations[5, 69, 72].

Caffeate ⟶ Ferulate

Chlorogenate ⟶ Ferulylquinate

5-Hydroxyferulate ⟶ Sinapate

3,4,5-Trihydroxycinnamate ⟶ 5-Hydroxyferulate + Sinapate

Isoferulate, and hydroxybenzoic acids and aldehydes were not methylated which is in contrast to the preparations obtained with *Petunia*[73] which could utilise hydroxybenzoic acids, hydroxybenzaldehydes as well as the dihydroxy coumarin, esculetin.

The ability of the bamboo enzyme to methylate 5-hydroxyferulic acid is lacking in the enzyme from *Pinus*; this is consistent with the ability of angiosperms to synthesise lignins of the syringyl type[74, 75, 76], in addition to those of the guaiacyl type.

Hess has examined eight different pure lines of *Petunia hybrida* and found that all these lines were able to methylate the same cinnamic acids and anthocyanins whether or not the genes for specific anthocyanin methylation were present[64]. These results argue against direct genetic control by means of methylating enzymes with distinct specificities and suggest an indirect genetic control of the methylation pattern.

With *Petunia* preparations maximum methylation was observed with cinnamic acids; caffeic and 5-hydroxyferulic acids were about 100 times more effective as substrates than cyanidin-3-glucoside or petunidin-3-glucoside. Hess[64] concluded that *O*-methylation of *Petunia* anthocyanins takes place at the level of the cinnamic acids for two reasons: (1) substituted cinnamic acids can be incorporated into the anthocyanins of *Petunia* (2) a specific cinnamic acid stimulates the synthesis of that anthocyanin with the same substitution pattern in the B ring.

An *O*-methyltransferase which catalyses the transfer of the methyl group of *S*-adenosylmethionine to the meta hydroxyl function of ortho-dihydric phenols has been partially purified from cell suspension cultures of parsley[77]. The enzyme, which has an estimated mol. wt. 48 000, has a pH optimum around 9.7, requires Mg^{2+} and is not inhibited by *p*-chloromercuribenzoate or iodoacetamide. Highest activities were obtained after illumination of the cells for 24 h with high intensity white light[46, 77].

Luteolin (5,7,3′,4′-tetrahydroxyflavone) and its 7-*O*-glucoside were the best substrates tested ($K_m = 4.6 \times 10^{-5}$ and 3.1×10^{-5} M respectively) whereas eriodictyol (5,7,3′,4′-tetrahydroxyflavanone ($K_m = 1.2 \times 10^{-3}$ M) and caffeic acid ($K_m = 1.6 \times 10^{-3}$ M) had much lower affinity for the enzyme. On ageing potato tuber slices in light for 24 h there is a twofold increase in the levels of an *O*-methyltransferase, which acts on caffeic acid[38] but it is not known whether this is a specific light effect. Over 90% of the enzyme activity is in the soluble fraction of this tissue with trace amounts in organelles[56].

As can be seen from the foregoing discussion of *O*-methyltransferase for dihydricphenols, no clear picture has as yet emerged as to the number of enzymes available in a given tissue nor to the absolute specificities of enzymes so far studied. Thus, virtually nothing can be said about the control of methylation of flavonoids and related compounds in plants.

7.2.1.7 Reduction of hydroxycinnamic acids to hydroxycinnamyl alcohols

Two enzymes, which reduce hydroxycinnamic acids to the corresponding aldehydes and alcohols, have been purified from *Neurospora crassa*[78-80]. Although this fungus neither synthesises cinnamic acids nor lignins these enzymes may be considered as models for what is believed to occur in plants and for which there is very little information.

The above enzymes are (1) an aryl-aldehyde oxidoreductase which has been purified 300-fold. It catalyses the reaction:

$$R\text{–}COOH + ATP + NADPH + H^{+} \rightarrow R\text{–}CHO + AMP + P\text{–}P + NADP^{+}$$

In the original study it was believed that ATP was hydrolysed to ADP and P_i but further work[81] showed that pyrophosphate and AMP are products. The enzyme uses the β-hydrogen atom at C-4 of NADPH and is therefore a 'β-type' enzyme. It does not work with NADH or CTP, GTP or UTP but exhibits broad specificity towards aromatic acids of C-6–C-1, C-6–C-2 and C-6–C-3 type. The enzyme is not a constitutive one but is induced by salicylate. (2) an aryl-alcohol oxidoreductase which has been purified 500-fold. This constitutive enzyme catalyses the reaction:

$$R\text{-}CHO + NADPH + H^{+} \rightleftharpoons R\text{-}CH_2OH + NADP^{+}$$

and is similar in its specificity toward NADP to the *m*-hydroxybenzyl alcohol dehydrogenase purified from *Penicillium urticae*[82] and from potato tuber tissue[83].

Potato tubers have been shown to contain at least three alcohol dehydrogenases[84], one active with NAD and aliphatic alcohols, one active with NADP and terpene alcohols and one active with NADP and aromatic alcohols. The third enzyme[83] utilises benzaldehyde, *p*-hydroxybenzaldehyde and cinnamaldehyde and from its broad specificity with a number of unnatural aromatic aldehydes there is every reason to suppose that it would catalyse the reduction of coniferaldehyde or sinapaldehyde to give the alcohols necessary for dehydrogenative polymerisation to form lignins.

Whether the reduction of hydroxycinnamic acids to hydroxycinnamyl alcohols proceeds via the corresponding aldehydes as suggested from tracer experiments[85] or whether it is through the coenzyme A ester of the hydroxycinnamic acid and a bound intermediate at the oxidation level of the aldehyde has yet to be determined. Preliminary experiments[86, 87] with plant extracts indicate that it is possible to reduce the acid to the alcohol using CoASH, ATP, Mg^{2+} and NADPH. Using ferulic acid as a substrate, coniferyl alcohol has been identified as the product. Some chromatographic evidence was obtained that coniferaldehyde is an intermediate in the reaction[87] so that the reactions involved would be:

Ferulic acid ⟶ ferulyl-CoA ⟶ coniferaldehyde ⟶ coniferyl alcohol

Confirmatory evidence for this scheme may be found in a recent report[88] which states that a protein fraction from *Salix alba* cambial cells was effective in catalysing the formation of coniferyl aldehyde from ferulyl-CoA in the presence of NADPH. With these preparations it was possible to demonstrate the reduction of ferulic acid to coniferyl alcohol. Details of enzyme specificities are not available.

7.2.1.8 *Cinnamyl CoA Ligase*

Active preparations of this enzyme have been obtained from cell suspension cultures of parsley leaf petioles[178], from cambial tissue of *Salix alba*[88] from aged disks of swede roots[188] and from leaf extracts of spinach beet[89]. In no case has work been carried out with purified enzymes and the types of preparations show somewhat different characteristics. The reaction is assumed to be:

$$\mathrm{ArCH{=}CH{-}CO_2H + ATP + CoASH \rightleftarrows ArCH{=}CH{-}COSCoA + AMP + P{-}P}$$

Methods of assay include a spectrophotometric one[89] based on the absorption of cinnamyl CoA at 311 nm and by the CoASH dependent formation of cinnamyl hydroxamate which reacts with $FeCl_3$ to give a product absorbing at 546 nm. The parsley preparations activate the cinnamic acids in the order *p*-coumarate > ferulate > *p*-methoxycinnamate > cinnamate. The swede root enzyme activates 4-hydroxycinnamic acids whereas spinach beet preparations activate cinnamic acid only. The latter type of preparation was also reported from leaves of young plants of pea, runner bean and spinach[89]. In contrast to acetyl CoA ligase in parsley cell cultures the levels of cinnamyl CoA ligase increase on illumination of these cultures. There is obviously much need for study of this enzyme which has a central place in flavonoid metabolism.

7.3 FLAVONOIDS

7.3.1 Interconversion of flavonoids

As a result of a long series of studies with tracers, Grisebach and co-workers[90] have indicated the metabolic relationships between certain of the flavonoid and isoflavonoid types. This is shown in Figure 7.5.

So far cell-free preparations have been obtained for only a few of these transformations and this represents a major area of future development in flavonoid biochemistry.

7.3.2 Enzymes of flavonoids synthesis and interconversion

7.3.2.1 *Chalcone synthesis*

The successful demonstration of chalcone synthesis with a cell-free preparation has been reported very recently[91]. Incubation of a relatively crude enzyme preparation of a light-treated parsley cell suspension culture with malonyl CoA, *p*-coumaroyl CoA and ATP yielded naringenin (4′,5,7-trihydroxyflavanone) in accordance with the following scheme:

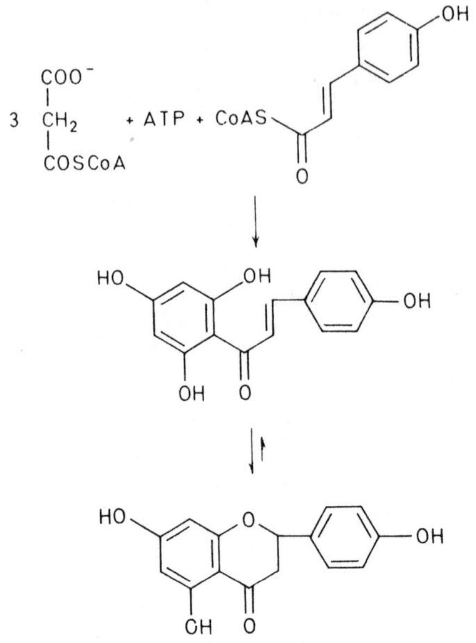

3 $CH_2(COO^-)COSCoA$ + ATP + CoAS–

Naringenin

The product was rigorously identified. This result is gratifying in view of the extensive tracer studies and theory which lay behind the experiment.

7.3.2.2 Chalcone—flavanone isomerase

An example of the reaction catalysed is the conversion of isoliquiritigenin to liquiritigenin[92]:

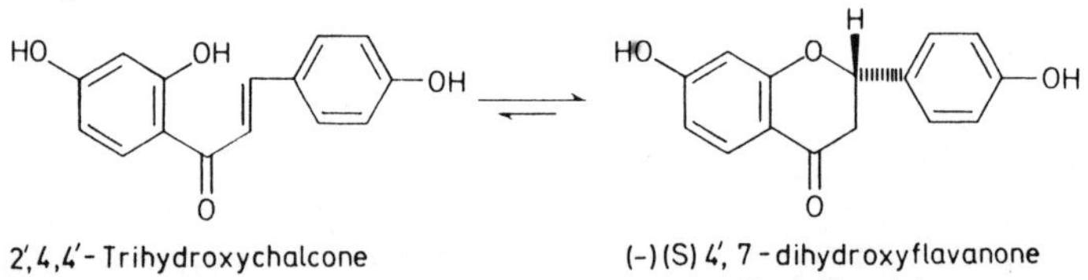

2′,4,4′-Trihydroxychalcone (isoliquiritigenin) ⇌ (–)(S) 4′, 7-dihydroxyflavanone (liquiritigenin)

Unlike the spontaneous isomerisation of most chalcones to the corresponding flavanones, the product of the enzyme catalysed reaction is optically active.

Cyclisation of 2′,4,4′-trihydroxychalcone, catalysed by isomerases from mung bean seedlings leads to the (—) (2S)-4′,7-dihydroxyflavanone[93]. The results on the stereochemical course of the reaction at C-3 of the flavanone with (^2H)-trihydroxychalcone in H_2O and non-deuterated trihydroxychalcone in ^2H_2O are complementary. Deuterium is found preferentially either in the equatorial or in the axial position at C-3 depending on the source of deuterium, i.e. deuterated chalcone or ^2H_2O. A mechanism consistent with these results is an acid-base catalysed reaction leading to a

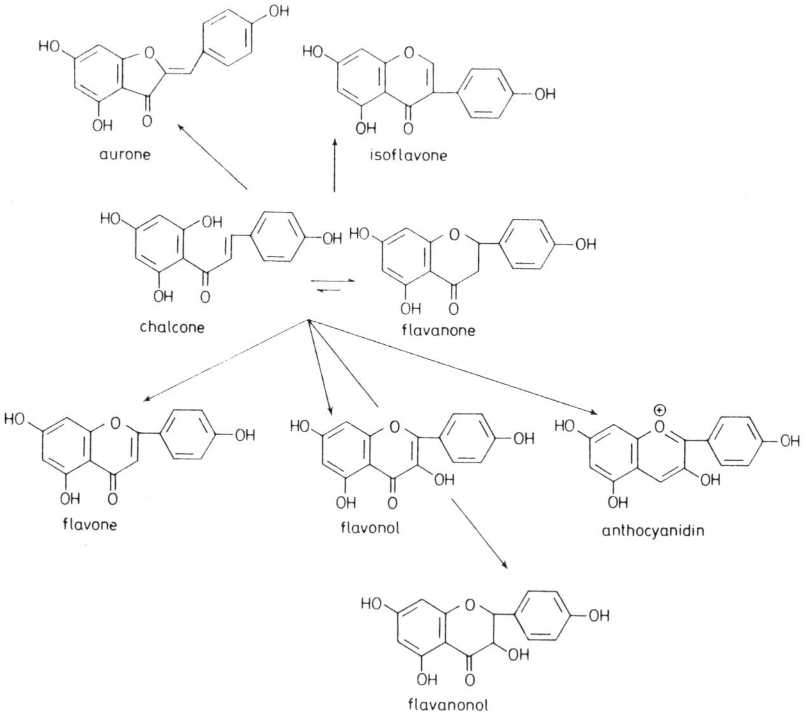

Figure 7.5 Relationships of flavonoids and isoflavonoids deduced from tracer studies

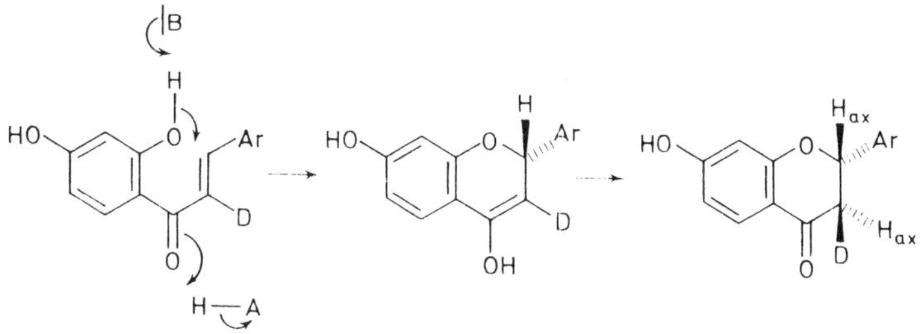

Figure 7.6 Mechanism postulated for enzyme catalysed chalcone ⇌ flavanone isomerism (After Hahlbrock *et al.*[93])

flav-3-en-4-ol which then undergoes a stereospecific proton transfer[93] (Figure 7.6). This enol intermediate would be enzyme bound.

The isomerase has been detected in lemon peel[94], *Soja hispida* seed[95], buckwheat seedlings[92], anthers of *Lilium* and *Tulipa*[96], Mung bean, garbanzo bean and parsley[97] and *Datisca cannabina*[98].

With day-old germinating soybean seed, a 150-fold purification of the enzyme was obtained by a procedure which included $(NH_4)_2SO_4$ fractionation, phosphate gel treatment, and Sephadex G-200 chromatography[95]. The pH optimum of the enzyme was 7.3–7.8 and it was only slightly inhibited by CN^-, azide, EDTA or diethyldithiocarbamate suggesting that it is not dependent on any of the metals chelated by these reagents. It was, however, strongly inhibited by low concentrations of *p*-hydroxymercuribenzoate indicating its dependence on a sulphydryl group. It also exhibited relatively low specificity with a requirement only for a 4′hydroxyl function in the substrate.

Further purification, with the inclusion of acrylamide gel electrophoresis, revealed two isozymes in mung bean preparations, three in garbanzo bean and at least five in parsley[97]. The two mung bean enzymes and that from garbanzo bean have K_ms in the range 7×10^{-6} to 2.6×10^{-4} mole l^{-1} for the chalcones investigated. These three enzymes had relatively low specificity. One of the parsley enzymes which was studied in detail was relatively specific reacting only with the chalcone possessing a 6′-hydroxy group. Only flavonoids with this substitution pattern in ring A occur in parsley. None of the enzymes utilises either 4′- or 6′-glucosides.

Enzyme preparations from anthers of *Lilium candidum* and a cultivar of *Tulipa* catalyse the isomerisation of 2′,4,4′,6′-tetrahydroxychalcone and are not active with 2′,4,4′-trihydroxychalcone[96,99]. As the anthers of *Tulipa* approach anthesis the increasing levels of enzyme fall off. Maximum activity occurs at a point when the concentration of chalcones is decreasing rapidly and the concentration of flavanols in increasing. Wierman[96] concludes that the isomerase may play an important role in flavonoid metabolism. In excised hypocotyls of 6-day old etiolated buckwheat seedlings, however, even though there is a five- to sixfold increase in PAL activity following exposure to light there is no corresponding effect on the chalcone-flavanone isomerase[92].

7.3.2.3 Glycosylation of flavonoids and other phenols

Naturally occurring phenolic compounds of higher plants usually occur as glycosides and phenols, when introduced into roots, stems, leaves or other tissues are readily glucosylated. This subject has been reviewed in detail[8,100,101]. The enzymes responsible for glycosylation use nucleotide sugars as donors, i.e.

$$\text{R-OH} + \text{NDPhexose} \longrightarrow \text{R-O-hexosyl} + \text{NDP (NDP = nucleoside diphosphate)}$$

They were first discovered by Cardini and Yamaha[102,103] using UDP-glucose or ADP-glucose and simple phenols such as hydroquinone. The glucosides formed are the *β*-D-anomers and the ability to carry out this glycosylation is ubiquitous in angiosperms and gymnosperms[104].

Most of the work on these glucosyltransferases has been carried out with relatively crude preparations and the number or specificity of the enzymes is not known. Miles and Hagen[105] have separated two glycosyltransferases from extracts of the flower petals of *Impatiens balsamina*. One of these glucosylates hydroquinone and requires a low molecular weight co-factor. The other glycosylates flavonols, including kaempferol, to give the 3-monoglucoside. The pH optima of the two enzymes differ significantly and there was some specificity difference in respect of the nucleotide sugar. UDP-glucose was an effective glucose donor with both but TDP-glucose was not effective in the hydroquinone glucosylation nor was ADP-glucose in the kaempferol glucosylation. Also the second enzyme did not require a co-factor.

Two glycosyltransferases have been separated from cell cultures of parsley, one of which transfers the D-glucosyl moiety of UDP-glucose to flavonoids to form 7-0-β-D-glucosides[106] and a second[107] catalyses the transfer of the apiosyl moiety of UDP-apiose to 7-0-(β-D-glucosyl)-apigenin to form apiin {7-0-(β,D-apiofuranosyl (1 ⟶ 2) (β,D-glucosyl)-apigenin}

The UDP glucosyltransferase is a soluble enzyme with a pH optimum of 7.5 and a mol. wt. estimated to be about 50 000. The apparent K_m value for UDP-glucose is 1.2×10^{-4} M and for TDP-glucose, which is also a glucosyl donor, it is 2.6×10^{-4} M. A number of flavones, flavanones and flavonols can function as glucosyl acceptors, whereas isoflavones, cyanidin, *p*-coumaric acid and some other phenols are inactive as acceptors. The best acceptors are luteolin, apigenin, chrysoeriol and naringenin, all of which occur in parsley and which are postulated to be biosynthetic intermediates in the flavone-glucoside pathway.

The apiosyl transferase has been purified 123-fold from illuminated cell cultures of parsley[107]. It is a soluble enzyme (pH optimum 7.0) with no co-factor requirements and is specific for UDP-apiose as glycosyl donor. 7-Glucosides of flavones, flavanones and isoflavones, apigenin-7-glucuronide and glucosides of *p*-substituted phenols can function as acceptors. Apigenin-7-0-β,D-glucoside and biochanin A are the best acceptors. No reaction takes place with flavonol-3-glucoside, flavanol-7-glucoside, apigenin-8-*C*-glucoside, aglycones of flavonoids or free glucose.

There is some evidence that the glucose esters of hydroxylated cinnamic acids, which are commonly found in plants, are synthesised via nucleotide sugars. The glucose esters of *p*-coumaric, caffeic, ferulic and sinapic acids were reported to be synthesised using UDP-glucose and acetone powders of *Geranium*[108]. No glucoside formation was detected. In contrast, the glucosylation of *o*-coumaric acid (trans-*o*-hydroxycinnamic acid) occurs with preparations of *Melilotus alba*[109], in the presence of UDP-glucose and β-mercaptoethanol. In this case there was no formation of the glucose ester of *o*-coumaric acid. Obviously much has to be learned about these enzymes.

7.3.2.4 Conversion of flavonols to 2,4-dihydroxyflavanones

Kaempferol and other flavonols are hydroxylated by crude acetone powders or extracts in all plants which have been examined[110, 111]. The reaction catalysed is as follows:

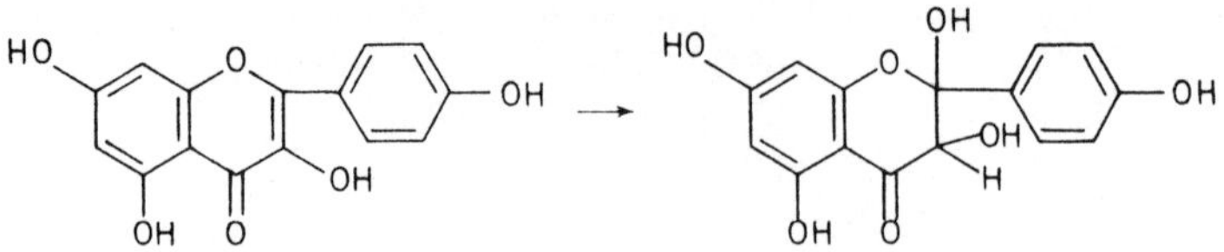

Kaempferol → 2,3,4′,5,7 - pentahydroxy flavanone

Flavanol-3-glycosides do not serve as substrates.

7.3.2.5 Conversion of chalcones to aurones (coumaranones)

The conversion of isoliquiritigenin to the corresponding aurone, hispidol, has been demonstrated with preparations from *Cosmos* and *Coreopsis* petals[112], *Soja hispida*[95] and *Phaseolus vulgaris* hypocotyls[113]. Crystalline horseradish peroxidase has also been shown to catalyse the conversion of isoliquiritigenin to the flavanone, garbanzol as well as to hispidol in the presence of hydrogen peroxide[113]. This is seen in Figure 7.7 where the α-hydroxy coumaranone is shown as an intermediate. This compound, 4′,6-dihydroxy-2-(α-hydroxybenzyl) coumaranone, is obtained from isoliquiritigenin in enzyme preparations from *Soja hispida*[103]. In this connection, the recent report of the natural occurrence of an aroylcoumaranone in flowers of *Helichrysum* spp. may be of interest[180].

Rathmell and Bendall were able to demonstrate similar reactions using preparations from hypocotyls of *Phaseolus vulgaris*[113]. They believe that it is

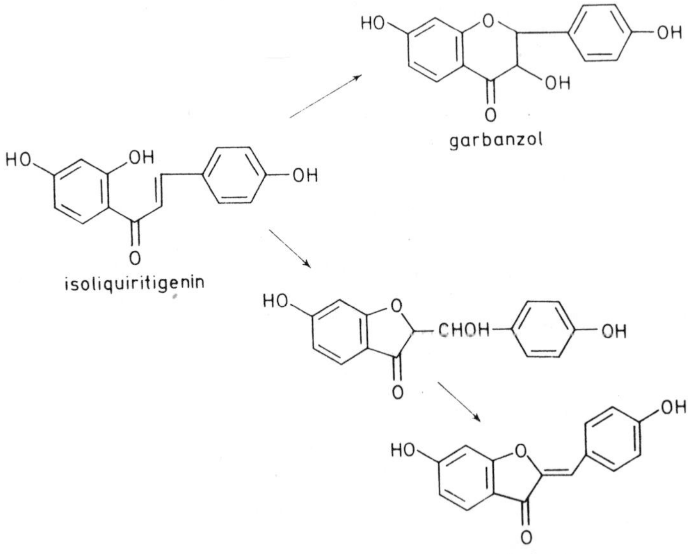

garbanzol

isoliquiritigenin

hispidol

Figure 7.7 Reactions catalysed by peroxidase

likely to be a free radical reaction and suggest in fact that many of the oxidative transformations of flavonoid and isoflavonoid compounds in plants are catalysed by an enzyme of low specificity, namely peroxidase.

7.3.2.6 Hydroxylation and O-methylation of flavonoids

The enzyme preparation from *Beta vulgaris* which catalyses the hydroxylation of *p*-coumaric acid to caffeic acid[51] also catalyses the hydroxylation of naringenin, dihydrokaempferol and kaempferol at the 3′-position to eriodictyol, dihydroquercetin and quercetin respectively[115, 116]. Substrate specificity of the enzyme is rather low, with various 4′-hydroxyflavanoids with different oxidation stages of the heterocyclic ring serving as substrates. The question remains open as to whether this enzyme is concerned in the biosynthesis of flavonoids with a 3′,4′-hydroxylation pattern. The hydroxylation of ring B is believed, by Hess to be determined at the cinnamic acid stage[117, 118].

That *O*-methylation may also be determined at the cinnamic acid stage is indicated by the incorporation of *p*-methoxycinnamate into acacetin (4′-methoxy-5,7-dihydroxyflavone) in leaves of *Robinia*[62].

7.3.2.7 Acylation of flavonoids

Many of the naturally occurring flavonoids are acylated, cinnamic and benzoic acids and their hydroxylated derivatives as well as acetic and malonic being the acids more commonly involved. One of the major flavonoids formed in parsley cell cultures is the flavone glycoside, apiin, bearing a malonyl residue in the sugar moiety of the glycoside. A crude enzyme preparation from illuminated cell suspension cultures catalyses the transfer of malonate from malonyl CoA to flavone glycosides and highest specific activities were observed about 24 h after the onset of illumination[119].

7.3.3. Cellular location of flavonoids

Flavonoids are found in all parts of plants and particular flavonoids may be restricted to specific tissues, cells and organelles[120]. Very often the epidermis and hypodermis are the sites of intense flavonoid synthesis, e.g. anthocyanins. Anthocyanins occur in solution but may also be deposited as crystals in vacuoles. Other flavonoids have been located in the chloroplasts of a number of species[121-123]. They have been found in isolated etioplasts of the leaves of etiolated *Avena sativa*[124]. These etioplasts were shown to contain all the flavonoids of the leaf although in different proportions. The presence of flavonoids could also be demonstrated in isolated prolamellar bodies from etioplasts. With increasing interest in the intracellular compartmentalisation of flavonoid enzymes it may become necessary to learn much more of the details of the intracellular distribution of flavonoids. For accounts of the chemistry and distribution of flavonoids in plants the general references by Harborne[181], Geissman[125] and Mabry *et al.*[126], are indispensable.

7.3.4 *Intracellular localisation of enzymes and regulation of flavonoid synthesis*

The microsomal fraction of *Quercus pedunculata* roots is reported to catalyse all the steps from phenylalanine ⟶ cinnamate ⟶ *p*-coumarate to caffeate[127] and, similarly, a particulate (100 000 × g) fraction from *Sorghum* has been shown to convert phenylalanine and tyrosine to the level of ferulic acid[24]. The microsomal fraction of *Sorghum* contains PAL, TAL and cinnamic acid hydroxylase activities[25] and these enzymes have been demonstrated in microsomal preparations of other plants including aged potato slices[38], *Quercus* roots[23] and pea seedlings[39]. The *O*-methylation of caffeate to give ferulate using *S*-adenosylmethionine, mercaptoethanol and a 100 000 × g fraction from *Sorghum* has also been reported[24].

Furthermore, two PAL isozymes have been found in *Quercus* tissues, one of which is cinnamate-sensitive and associated with the microsomal fraction and the other of which is benzoate-sensitive and is associated with a fraction consisting of mitochondria and microbodies[23]. A 'benzoate synthase' system[128], i.e. an enzyme complex responsible for the *β*-oxidation of cinnamic acids to benzoic acids, is confined to the fraction which includes microbodies. On the bases of these data Alibert *et al.*[23], have concluded that phenylpropanoid compounds are formed mainly in the microsomes whereas C-6–C-1 acids are formed in microbodies.

Their conclusions, however, are open to criticism. They have described PAL activity from an 'F 10 000' fraction (mitochondria and microbodies) and from a microsomal fraction but make no comment at all of soluble PAL, which is usually the major source of this enzyme in plant extracts. Again, although cinnamic acid-4-hydroxylase has been shown to be associated largely with the microsomal fraction, except in dormant potato tuber tissue[38], *p*-coumaric acid hydroxylase[53] and *O*-methyltransferase activity are usually associated with soluble fractions. In other words, the conversion of phenylalanine to ferulic acid could conceivably be demonstrated with the soluble fraction just as it can with microsomal preparations.

The activities of five enzymes related to the biosynthesis of apiin, (7-0 {*β*,D-apiofuranosyl (1 ⟶ 2) *β*,D-glucosyl}-5,7,4′-trihydroxyflavone) and to the corresponding glycoside of chrysoeriol, as well as the accumulation of these flavone glycosides, were studied during the growth of young parsley plants[129]. The enzymes were PAL, chalcone-flavone isomerase, UDP-apiose synthetase and a glucosyl as well as an apiosyl transferase. Enzyme levels showed a positive correlation with increase in glycoside formation in leaves.

Cell suspension cultures of parsley do not produce flavone glycosides in the dark but when exposed to high intensities of white light they start to produce apiin and graveobioside B, compounds which are normal constituents of parlsey plants[47]. Changes in the activities of nine enzymes directly related to the biosynthesis of these glycosides were measured over a period of 24 h after illumination of cell suspension cultures[46, 119]. All of these enzymes showed a dramatic increase, in contrast to enzymes such as acetate:CoA ligase and UDP-glucuronate carboxylyase which do not change upon illumination under these conditions. Moreover, the enzymes of flavone glycoside biosynthesis could be distinguished into two groups on the basis of their response to illumination. The first group comprising PAL, CAH and *p*-coumarate:CoA ligase, show an increase up to about 15 h followed by a rapid decline. The second group, consisting of chalcone-flavanone isomerase, UDP-glucose:apigenin 7-0-glucosyltransferase, UDP-apiose:apigenin 7-0-glucoside (1 ⟶ 2)-apiosyltransferase, UDP-apiose synthetase, *S*-adenosyl-methionine-luteolin 3′-0-methyltransferase and malonyl CoA:flavone glycoside malonyl-transferase[119] continue to rise even after 20 h. Thus those enzymes concerned strictly with phenylpropanoid metabolism appear to be under a different regulation from those concerned with flavonoid metabolism.

In the fungus, *Polyporus hispidus*, PAL, CAH and *p*-coumaric acid hydroxylase activity are stimulated by light and so is the synthesis of the styrylpyrone, hispidin[28].

7.4 LIGNINS

7.4.1 Constitution and distribution

Lignins are, next to carbohydrates, the most abundant of naturally occurring cell wall polymers. After more than 100 years of study the following generalisations may be made concerning their structure and distribution:

They are hetero-polymers of phenylpropane units, the substitution pattern of the phenyl moiety being of the *p*-hydroxyphenyl and guaiacyl (3-methoxy-4-hydroxyphenyl) type in gymnosperms with the addition of syringyl (3,5-dimethoxy-4-hydroxyphenyl) nuclei ain angiosperms. A variety of C—C and C—O linkages occur and primary and secondary alcohol as well as aldehyde functions are found on the side chains. Lignin has been defined[130] as a copolycondensate of the dehydrogenation products obtained from *p*-coumaryl, coniferyl and sinapyl alcohols. In addition, hydroxycinnamic acids are esterified to the main polymer which has a degree of polymerisation of up to several hundred and is highly branched in three dimensions. Lignins occur in close association with other cell wall carbohydrates and all evidence suggests that covalent linkages between lignin and carbohydrate are involved.

Tracer studies have shown clearly that phenylalanine (all plants) and tyrosine (grasses only) are efficient precursors (see reviews by Freudenberg and Neish[1] and Sarkanen and Ludwig[179] for details). Hydroxycinnamic acids[184] and coniferin, the phenyl-β,D-glucoside of coniferyl alcohol[185, 186] have also been shown to be efficiently incorporated.

7.4.2 Dehydrogenation of hydroxycinnamyl alcohols and polymerisation to form lignins

The enzymic dehydrogenation of the *p*-hydroxycinnamyl alcohols *in vitro* leads to the synthesis of artificial lignins. This was first demonstrated 30 years ago by Freudenberg and Richtzenhain[131] with coniferyl alcohol and a crude cell-free preparation from certain mushrooms. Freudenberg's school has pursued vigorously the problems of the nature of the products formed in this complex reaction. Japanese workers, on the other hand, have been more concerned with identifying exactly which enzymes are involved in the *in vitro* synthesis[132, 133].

According to Freudenberg[1], when coniferyl alcohol is dehydrogenated, it loses its phenolic hydrogen atom to form an aroxyl radical shown below (Figure 7.8) in its mesomeric forms. These radicals, which are detectable by electron paramagnetic spin resonance, combine to form quinone methides that become stabilised by intramolecular prototropy or condensation with other phenolic monomers or carbohydrates (when present). The products, in turn may be subjected to dehydrogenation to form free radicals and quinone methides and the process may continue until a relatively high molecular weight product is obtained. The intermediate dimers, trimers and oligomers are called lignols and 20 or 30 of them have been identified.

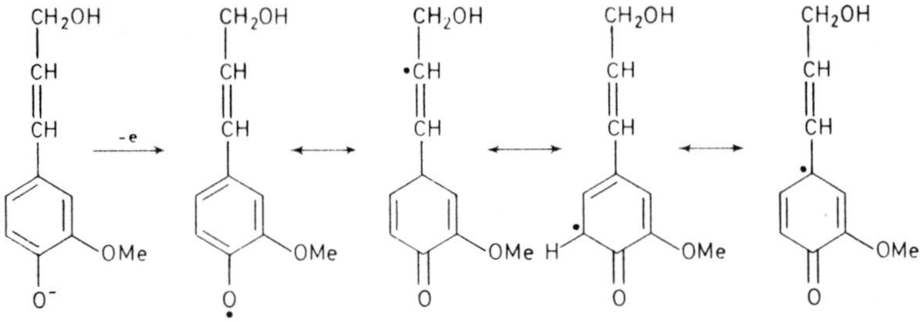

Figure 7.8 Coniferyl alcohol and its free radicals (a, b, c, d) which were produced on dehydrogenation

With coniferyl alcohol the overall reaction may be expressed in the following way:

$$C_9H_9O_2(OCH_3)_2 + H_2O_2 \longrightarrow 1.6H_2O + C_9H_7O_2\{H_2O\}_{0\cdot4}(OCH_3)_2$$

The formula indicates the removal of two atoms of hydrogen and the addition of 0.4 molecules of water in the dehydrogenation polymer (DHP lignin).

The enzyme dehydrogenates the phenolic group and therefore the products, including the oligolignols and the DHP lignin, are optically inactive. (This is in contrast to naturally occurring and closely related lignans which are optically active.)

The precise nature of the enzyme(s), mediating the dehydrogenative polymerisation, has been investigated by Nakamura[132]. Three enzymes were separated from the latex of the Chinese lacquer tree (*Rhus vernicifera*,) (a) an *o*-diphenol oxidase or phenolase (EC 1.10.3.1) (b) a *p*-diphenol oxidase or laccase (EC 1.10.3.2) and (c) a peroxidase (EC 1.11.17). Laccase was purified to an homogenous state and shown to be incapable of catalysing the dehydrogenation of coniferyl alcohol. The peroxidase was shown to catalyse the reaction in the presence of H_2O_2 and the phenolase was effective in the presence of air or O_2. Nakamura, however, believes that peroxidase is the main enzyme involved in lignin biosynthesis in plant tissues. Histochemical tests[144], employing syringaldazine or furoguaiacin, on freshly cut stems of various woody species support the conclusion that it is peroxidase rather than phenolase, laccase or cytochrome oxidase that is involved in the lignification process.

Purified bamboo shoot peroxidase[133] was shown to give a DHP lignin from coniferyl alcohol which resembled softwood lignin except for a lower mol. wt. (1000). Wheat germ peroxidase and horseradish peroxidase were also shown to be effective. The rate of DHP synthesis was dependent on the concentrations of enzyme, coniferyl alcohol and H_2O_2. The disappearance of coniferyl alcohol from the reaction mixture was inhibited by KCN but the polymerisation step was not. These results indicate that H_2O_2 and peroxidase are essential for the dehydrogenation of coniferyl alcohol and that the subsequent polymerisation is non-enyzmic. According to Nozu[133] the essential groups in the molecule of the substrate for dehydrogenation and polymerisation are a free phenolic hydroxyl group and a double bond in the side chain. Suitable substrates, in addition to coniferyl alcohol, were eugenol, isoeugenol and vinyl guaiacol. Ferulic acid, however, was not polymerised. The copolymerisation product of coniferyl and sinapyl alcohols resembled hard wood lignin.

7.5 DEGRADATION OF AROMATIC COMPOUNDS BY PLANTS

7.5.1 Demethylation and demethoxylation

There are a considerable number of reports indicating that methoxylated cinnamic and benzoic acids may undergo *O*-demethylation when administered to plant tissues[134, 135, 136, 137]. *O*-Demethylation of syringin[138] and other polyphenols by plants has also been recorded[139, 140]. *O*-Demethoxylation of ferulic acid to give *p*-coumaric acid[114, 141] or of sinapic to give caffeic acid[136, 142] or even *p*-coumaric acid[141] has also been found to occur. Because of considerable *O*-demethylation of precursor, difficulty was encountered in demonstrating the incorporation of *p*-methoxycinnamate (methyl-^{3}H) into the 4′-methoxyisoflavones, formononetin and biochanin A in leaves of *Robinia pseudacacia*[139]. In young leaves demethylation is less rapid and it was possible to demonstrate the incorporation of this acid into acacetin (4′-methoxy-5,7-dihydroxyflavone) without prior demethylation[143]. That *O*-demethylation activity resides in the plants themselves rather than in contaminating micro-organisms is indicated in experiments with sterile tissues. Sterile cultures of wheat seedlings[134] and cell suspension cultures of *Phaseolus aureus*[145] have been found to demethylate various methoxybenzoic acids such as anisic, veratric and 3,4,5-trimethoxybenzoic acids. *O*-Demethylation was shown to be specific for *para* methoxy groups.

O-Demethylating enzymes responsible for the demethylation of *para*- and *meta*- substituted methoxybenzoic acids, have been identified from species and strains of *Pseudomonas*[146-150]. A monoxygenase has been identified in a strain of *Pseudomonas putida*[146] growing on *p*-anisic acid. *p*-Anisic acid is *O*-demethylated to give *p*-hydroxybenzoic acid and formaldehyde. The enzyme system consists of a flavoprotein, an iron–sulphur protein and a terminal oxidase. The first two proteins act as an electron transport system for the reduction of the oxygen-activating protein. No enzymological work has been carried out with plants.

7.5.2 Flavonoid degradation

When 2′,4,4′-trihydroxychalcone-4′-glucoside $\{\beta\text{-}^{14}C\}$ was fed to red cabbage seedlings *p*-coumaric acid (—^{14}C) was isolated from the seedlings[151] The incorporation rate into the acid was about 0.1 %. The same kind of result was obtained in administering 2′,4,4′,6′-tetrahydroxychalcone-2′-glucoside-^{14}C to *Petunia hybrida*. These results indicate that flavonoids may be degraded in plants. The only enzymological work with higher plants however, is the demonstration, with crude extracts from the sap of apple spurs, of the hydrolysis of the dihydrochalcone, phloretin and its glucoside, phoridzin to phloroglucinol and phlorctic acid[152] (Figure 7.9).

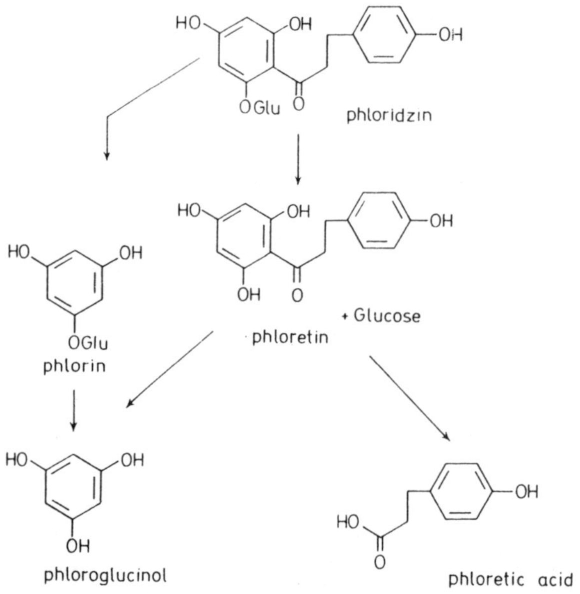

Figure 7.9 Plant and microbial degradation of phloridzin and phloretin

Of twelve phytopathogenic bacteria tested, only one, *Erwinia herbicola*, yielded an enzyme capable of hydrolysing phloretin to phloroglucinol and phloretic acid[153]. The enzyme which had a pH optimum of 6.7–6.8, was purified 142-fold. It was sensitive to Hg^{2+} and Cu^{2+} ions but insensitive to *p*-chloromercuribenzoate and iodoacetamide. Moreover, it did not react with phloridzin, naringin or naringenin. It appears to be different from the inducible hydrolase from *Aspergillus niger*[154] and other fungi[155], acting on carbon–carbon bonds, for phloridzin and other *C*-acylated phenols. The fungal enzyme, which was purified to homogeneity by polyacrylamide gel electrophoresis, has a pH optimum around 9.6 and, in addition to phloridzin, catalysed the hydrolysis of 3′-methylphloracetophenone, phloracetophenone and 2′,4,4′-trihydroxydihydrochalcone. The systematic name *C*-acylphenol acylhydrolase (EC group 3.7.1) has been proposed for this enzyme[154].

Crude enzyme preparations have been obtained from a number of plants, particularly *Fagopyrum vulgare*, which are able to degrade the flavonol glycoside, rutin, to protocatechuic acid and phloroglucinol[156]. This is similar to the fungal degradation of rutin and other flavonol glycosides which have been studied[157-159]. Phloroglucinol and protocatechuate account for 27 of the 28 carbons of the aglycone of rutin. The missing carbon was found to be released as CO and an enzyme named quercetinase[183] was obtained from fungal sources, which acts on flavonoids that possess a methyl or a phenyl group on C-2, a free hydroxyl on C-3, and a double bond between C-2 and C-3. A hydroxyl group on C-3 is required for the production of CO[160,161].

The transformation of flavonols to 2,3-dihydroxyflavanones by enzyme preparations from cell suspension cultures of various plants including parsley[162] has already been discussed. The 2,3-dihydroxyflavanones are further transformed enzymically. For example salicylic acid was produced as a degradation product of ring B of 2,2′,3,4,7,-pentahydroxyflavanone derived from datiscetin (Figure 7.10).

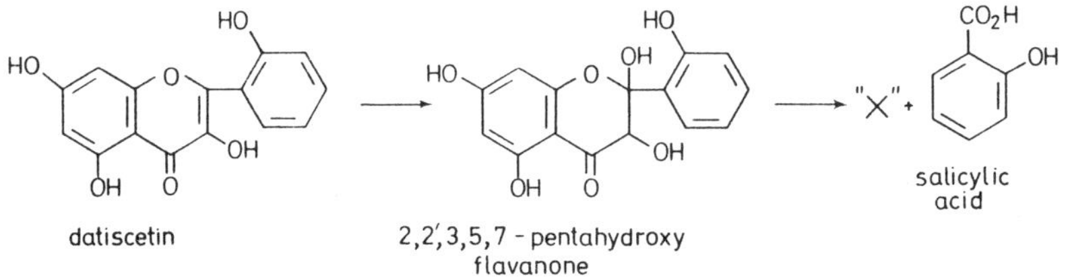

datiscetin — 2,2′,3,5,7 - pentahydroxy flavanone — "X" + salicylic acid

Figure 7.10 Enzymic degradation of datiscitin by crude preparations from sterile plant cell suspensions

Kaempferol gave *p*-hydroxybenzoic acid and quercetin gave protocatechuic acid. Neither phloroglucinol nor phloroglucinol carboxylic acid were observed as metabolites of ring A. It was suggested[162] that these transfor mations represent a route, in plants, leading to the degradation of flavonoids: phenylalanine ⟶ cinnamic acids ⟶ chalcones ⟶ flavonols ⟶ 2,3-dihydroxyflavanones ⟶ hydroxybenzoic acids ⟶ CO_2.

7.5.3 Lignin degradation

There is no evidence that lignins, once formed in the plant, are oxidised, depolymerised or otherwise degraded. Many fungi, particularly basidiomycetes, however, produce enzymes, such as laccase, which possibly function in lignin breakdown. Depolymerisation of lignin and the production of low molecular weight compounds with laccases have been observed. The reader is directed to a detailed discussion of this topic by Higuchi[5].

7.5.4 Ring cleavage in plants

Evidence continues to mount that aromatic compounds, including flavonoids, are far from being end-products of metabolism in plants. Not only do the structures of many naturally occurring compounds such as the betalains[163], certain cyanogenic glycosides[164,165] or amino acids[182] imply an origin from ring cleavage of DOPA but tracer studies also show that plants are capable of cleaving the ring of aromatic compounds[166-170]. Ring-labelled protocatechuic and *p*-coumaric acids gave particularly high yields of $^{14}CO_2$ when administered to cell suspension cultures of mung bean[166]. Until recently ring cleaving enzymes have been known only from higher animals[171], fungi and bacteria[172,173,174]. An enzyme which catalyses the aerobic oxidation of 2,3-dihydroxybenzoic acid to yield 2,6-dioxa-3,7-dioxobicyclo (3:3:0) octane-8-carboxylic acid has now been purified from young leaves of *Tecoma stans*[175]. This represents an intradiol oxygenative cleavage of 2,3-dihydroxybenzoic acid. In bacteria the cleavage is extradiol[176] and in fungi the acid is decarboxylated to catechol prior to ring cleavage[177]. The distribution of this enzyme in plants is not known.

References

1. Freudenberg, K. and Neish, A. C. (1968). *Constitution and biosynthesis of lignin* (Berlin: Springer-Verlag)
2. Grisebach, H. (1967). *Biosynthetic patterns in microorganisms and higher plants* (New York: J. Wiley & Sons Inc)
3. Koukol, J. and Conn, E. E. (1961). *J. Biol. Chem.*, **236**, 2692
4. Neish, A. C. (1961). *Phytochem.*, **1**, 1
5. Higuchi, T. (1971). *Advan. Enzymol.*, **34**, 207
6. Yoshida, S. (1969). *Ann. Rev. Plant Physiol.*, **20**, 41
7. Conn, E. E. (1964). *Biochemistry of Phenolic Compounds*, Chap. 10 (J. B. Harborne, editor) (New York: Academic Press)
8. Towers, G. H. N. (1969). *Perspectives in Phytochemistry*, p. 179 (J. B. Harborne and T. Swain, editors) (New York: Academic Press)
9. Bezanson, G. S., Desaty, D., Emes, A. V. and Vining, L. C. (1970). *Can. J. Microbiol.*, **16**, 147
10. Camm, E. L. and Towers, G. H. N. (1973). *Phytochem.*, **12**, 961
11. Zucker, M. (1965). *Plant Physiol.*, **40**, 779
12. Hanson, K. R. and Havir, E. A. (1972). *Recent Advances in Phytochemistry*, Vol. 4, 45 (V. C. Runeckles and J. E. Watkin, editors) (New York: Appleton-Century-Crofts)
13. Hanson, K. R. and Havir, E. A. (1970). *Arch. Biochem. Biophys.*, **141**, 1
14. Parkhurst, J. R. and Hodgins, D. S. (1972). *Arch. Biochem. Biophys.*, **152**, 597
15. Hodgins, D. S. (1972). *Arch. Biochem. Biophys.*, **149**, 91
16. Hanson, K. R., Wightman, R. H., Staunton, J., and Battersby, A. R. (1971). *Chem. Commun.*, 185
17. Ife, R. and Haslam, E. (1971). *Chem. Commun.*, **2818**
18. Subba Rao, P. V., Moore, K., and Towers, G. H. N. (1967). *Can. J. Biochem.*, **45**, 1863
19. Ogata, K., Uchiyama, K. snd Yamada, K. (1967). *Agr. Biol. Chem.*, **31**, 60
20. Parkhurst, J. R. and Hodgins, D. S. (1971). *Phytochem.*, **10**, 2997
21. Havir, E.A., Reid, P. D. and Marsh, H. Y. (1971). *Plant Physiol.*, **48**, 130
22. Reid, P. D., Havir, E. A. and Marsh, H. Y. (1972). *Plant Physiol.*, **50**, 480
23. Alibert, G., Ranjeva, R., and Boudet, A. (1972). *Biochem. Biophys. Acta*, **279**, 282

24. Stafford, H. A. and Baldy, R. (1970). *Plant Physiol.*, **45,** 215
25. Stafford, H. A. (1969). *Phtochem.*, **8,** 743
26. Minimikawa, T., and Uritani, I. (1965). *J. Biochem.* (*Tokyo*), **58,** 53
27. Boudet, A., Ranjeva, R., and Gadal, P. (1971). *Phytochem.*, **10,** 997
28. Nambudiri, A. M. D., Vance, C. P., and Towers, G. H. N. (1973). *Biochem. J.* **134,** 891
29. Havir, E. A. and Hanson, K. R. (1973). *Biochem.*, **12,** 1583
30. Nari, J., Mouttet, C., Pinna, M. H. and Ricard, J. (1972). *FEBS Letts.*, **23,** 220
31. Russell, D. W. and Conn, E. E. (1967). *Arch. Biochem. Biophys.*, **122,** 256
32. Amrhein, N. and Zenk, M. H. (1968). *Naturwissen schaften*, **55,** 394
33. Shimada, M., Yamazaki, R. and Higuchi, T. (1970). *Phytochem.*, **9,** 1
34. Parish, R. W. (1972). *Eur. J. Biochem.*, **31,** 446
35. Potts, J. R. M. (1972). 4-*Hydroxylation of cinnamic acid by Sorghum microsomes.* Ph.D. Dissertation, University of California, Davis
36. Camm, E. L. and Towers, G. H. N. (1973). *Can. J. Bot.*, **51,** 824
37. Vance, C. P., Nambudiri, A. M. D. and Towers, G. H. N. (1973). *Can. J. Biochem.*, **51,** 731
38. Camm, E. L. and Towers, G. H. N. (1973). *Phytochem.*, **12,** 1575
39. Russell, D. W. (1971). *J. Biol. Chem.*, **246,** 3870
40. Zenk, M. H. (1967). *Z. Pflanzenphysiol.*, **57,** 477
41. Russell, D. W., Conn, E. E., Sutter, A. and Grisebach, H. (1968). *Biochim. Biophys. Acta*, **170,** 210
42. Daly, J. W. and Jerina, D. M. (1970). *Biochim. Biophys. Acta*, **208,** 340
43. Guroff, G., Daly, J. W., Jerina, D. M., Renson, J., Witkop, B. and Udenfriend, S. (1967). *Science*, **157,** 1524
44. Reed, D. J., Vimmerstedt, J., Jerina, D. M. and Daly, J. W. (1973). *Arch. Biochem. Biophys.*, **154,** 642
45. Amrhein, N. and Zenk, M. H. (1970). *Naturwissenschaften*, **57,** 312
46. Hahlbrock, K., Ebel, I., Ortman, R., Sutter, A., Wellmann, E. and Grisebach, H. (1971). *Biochim. Biophys. Acta* **224,** 7
47. Hahlbrock, K. and Wellmann, E. (1970). *Planta*, **94,** 236
48. Hyodo, H. and Yang, S. F. (1971). *Arch. Biochem. Biophys.*, **143,** 338
49. Sato, M. (1967). *Phytochem.*, **6,** 1363
50. Kindl, H. (1971). *Hoppe-Seyler's Z. Physiol. Chem.*, **352,** 78
51. Vaughan, P. F. T. and Butt, V. S. (1969). *Biochem. J.*, **113,** 109
52. Vaughan, P. F. T. and Butt, V. S. (1972). *Biochem. J.*, **127,** 641
53. Stafford, H. A. and Dresler, S. (1972). *Plant Physiol.*, **49,** 590
54. Sato, M. (1966). *Phytochem.*, **5,** 385
55. Levy, C. C. and Zucker, M. (1960). *J. Biol. Chem.*, **235,** 2418
56. Abukharma, D. A. and Woolhouse, H. W. (1966). *New Phytol.*, **65,** 477
57. Ellis, B. E. and Brown, S. A. (1973). Personal communication.
58. Allen, C. M. (1972). *Biochem.*, **11,** 2154
59. Axelrod, J. and Vessell, E. S. (1970). *Molec. Pharmacol.*, **6,** 78
60. Basmadjian, G. P. and Paul, A. G. (1971). *Lloydia*, **34,** 91
61. Mann, J. D., Fales, H. M. and Mudd, S. H. (1963). *J. Biol. Chem.*, **238,** 3820
62. Mansell, R. L. and Seder, J. A. (1971). *Phytochem.*, **10,** 2043
63. Glass, A. D. M. and Bohm, B. A. (1972). *Phytochem.*, **11,** 2195
64. Hess, D. (1966). *Z. Pflanzenphysiol*, **55,** 374
65. Shimada, M., Fushiki, H. and Higuchi, T. (1973). *Mokuzai Gakkaishi*, **19,** 13
66. Finkle, B. J. and Masri, M. S. (1964). *Biochem. Biophys. Acta*, **85,** 167
67. Finkle, B. J. and Nelson, R. F. (1963). *Biochim. Biophys. Acta*, **78,** 747
68. Shimada, M., Ohashi, H. and Higuchi, T. (1970). *Phytochem.*, **9,** 2463
69. Higuchi, T. (1969). *Wood Research*, No. **48,** 1
70. Stone, J. E., Blundell, M. J. and Tanner, K. G. (1951). *Can. J. Chem.*, **29,** 734
71. Shimada, M., Fushiki, H., and Higuchi, T. (1972). *Phytochem.*, **11,** 2657
72. Higuchi, T., Shimada, M. and Ohashi, H. (1967). *Agr. Biol. Chem.*, **31,** 1459
73. Hess, D. (1965). *Z. Pflanzenphysiol.*, **53,** 1
74. Creighton, R. H. J., Gibbs, R. D. and Hibbert, H. (1944). *J. Amer. Chem. Soc.*, **66,** 32
75. Ibrahim, R. K., Towers, G. H. N. and Gibbs, R. D. (1963). *J. Linn. Soc.*, **58,** 223
76. Towers, G. H. N. and R. D. Gibbs, (1953). *Nature* (*London*), **172,** 25

77. Ebel, J., Hahlbrock, K. and Grisebach, H. (1972). *Biochim. Biophys. Acta*, **269,** 313
78. Gross, G. G., Bolkart, K. H. and Zenk, M. H. (1968). *Biochem. Biophys. Res. Commun.*, **32,** 173
79. Gross, G. G. and Zenk, M. H. (1969). *Eur. J. Biochem.*, **8,** 413
80. Gross, G. G. and Zenk, M. H. (1969). *Eur. J. Biochem.*, **8,** 420
81. Zenk, M. H. and Gross, G. G. (1972). *Recent Advances in Phytochemistry*, Vol. 4 (V. C. Runeckles and J. E. Watkin editors) (New York: Appleton-Century-Crofts)
82. Forrester, P. I. and Gaucher, G. M. (1972). *Biochem.*, **11,** 1108
83. Davies, D. D. Ugochukwu, E. N., Patil, K. D. and Towers, G. H. N. (1973). *Phytochem.*, **12,** 531
84. Davies, D. D., Patil, K. D., Ugochukwu, E. N. and Towers, G. H. N. (1973). *Phytochem* , **12,** 523
85. Higuchi, T. and Brown, S. A. (1963). *Can. J. Biochem. Physiol.*, **41,** 1621
86. Ebel, J. and Grisebach, H. (1973). *FEBS Letts.*, **30,** 141
87. Mansell, R. L., Stöckigt, J. and Zenk, M. H. (1972). *Z. Pflanzenphysiol.*, **68,** 286
88. Gross, G. G., Stöckigt, J., Mansell, R. L. and Zenk, M. H. (1973). *FEBS Letts.*, **31,** 283
89. Walton, E. and Butt, V. S. (1971). *Phytochem.*, **10,** 295
90. Grisebach, H. and Barz, W. (1969). *Naturwissenschaften*, **56,** 538
91. Kreuzaler, F. and Hahlbrock, H. (1972). *FEBS Letts.*, **28,** 69
92. Amrhein, N. and Zenk, M. H. (1971). *Z. Pflanzenphysiol.*, **64,** 145
93. Hahlbrock, K., Zilg, H. and Grisebach, H. (1970). *Eur. J. Biochem.*, **15,** 13
94. Shimokoriyama, M. (1957). *J. Amer. Chem. Soc.*, **79,** 4199
95. Moustafa, E. and Wong, E. (1967). *Phytochem.*, **6,** 625
96. Wiermann, K. (1972). *Planta*, **102,** 55
97. Hahlbrock, K., Wong, E., Schill, L. and Grisebach, H. (1970). *Phytochem.*, **9,** 949
98. Grambow, H. J. and Grisebach, H. (1971). *Phytochem.*, **10,** 789
99. Wiermann, R. (1973). *Planta*, **110,** 353
100. Hopkinson, S. M. (1969). *Quart. Rev. Chem. Soc.* (*London*), **23,** 98
101. Pridham, J. B. (1964). *Ann. Rev. Plant Physiol.*, **16,** 13
102. Cardini, C. E. and Yamaha, T. (1948). *Nature* (*London*), **182,** 1446
103. Yamaha, T. and Cardini, C. E. (1960). *Arch. Biochem. Biophys.*, **86,** 133
104. Pridham, J. B. (1964). *Phytochem.*, **3,** 493
105. Miles, C. D. and Hagen, C. W. (1968). *Plant Physiol.*, **43,** 1347
106. Sutter, A., Ortmann, R. and Grisebach, H. (1972). *Biochim. Biophys. Acta*, **258,** 71
107. Ortmann, R., Sutter, A. and Grisebach, H. (1972). *Biochim. Biophys. Acta*, **289,** 293
108. Corner, J. J. and Swain, T. (1965). *Nature* (*London*), **207,** 634
109. Kleinhofs, A., Haskins, F. A. and Gorz, H. J. (1967). *Phytochem.*, **6,** 1313
110. Hösel, W. and Barz, W. (1972). *Biochim. Biophys. Acta*, **261,** 294
111. Hösel, W., Frey, G., Teufel, E. and Barz, W. (1972). *Planta*, **103,** 74
112. Shimokoriyama, M. and Hattori, S. (1953). *J. Amer. Chem. Soc.*, **75,** 2277
113. Rathmell, W. G. and Bendall, D. S. (1972). *Biochem. J.*, **127,** 125
114. Shimada, M., Fushiki, H. and Higuchi, T. (1972). *Phytochem.*, **11,** 2247
115. Vaughan, P. F. T., Butt, V. S., Grisebach, H. and Schill, L. (1969). *Phytochem.*, **8,** 1373
116. Roberts, R. J. and Vaughan, P. F. T. (1971). *Phytochem.*, **10,** 2649
117. Hess, D. (1964). *Planta*, **50,** 568
118. Hess, D. (1968). *Biochemische Genetik*, p. 89 (Berlin: Springer-Verlag)
119. Hahlbrock, K. (1972). *FEBS Letts.*, **28,** 65
120. Blank, F. (1947). *Bot. Revs.*, **13,** 241
121. Zaprometov, M. N. and Kolankova, S. V. (1967). *Doklad. Akad. Nauk. S.S.R.*, **176,** 473
122. Monties, B. (1969). *Bull. Soc. Fr. Physiol. Veg.*, **15,** 29
123. Oettmeier, W. and Heupel, A. (1972). *Z. Naturforsch.*, **27b,** 177
124. Weissenbock, G., Fleing, I. and Ruppel, H. G. (1972). *Z. Naturforsch.*, **27b,** 1216
125. Geissman, T. A. (1962). *The chemistry of flavonoid compounds.* (T. Geissman, editor) (New York: MacMillan)
126. Mabry, T. J., Markham, K. R. and Thomas, M. B. (1970). *The systematic identification of flavonoids.* (Berlin: Springer-Verlag)
127. Alibert, G., Ranjeva, R. and Boudet, A. (1972). *Physiol. Plant.*, **27,** 240
128. Alibert, G. and Ranjeva, R. (1971). *FEBS Letts.*, **19,** 11

129. Hahlbrock, K., Sutter, A., Wellmann, E., Ortmann, R. and Grisebach, H. (1971). *Phytochem.*, **10**, 109
130. Freudenberg, K. (1965). *Science*, **148**, 595
131. Freudenberg, K. and Richtzenhain, H. (1943). *Ber. Deut. Chem. Ges.*, **76**, 997
132. Nakamura, W. (1967). *J. Biochem.*, **62**, 54
133. Nozu, Y. (1967). *J. Biochem.*, **62**, 519
134. Harms, H. and Priess, I. (1973). *Planta*, **109**, 307
135. Higuchi, T. and Brown, S. A. (1963). *Can. J. Biochem. Physiol.*, **41**, 613
136. Steiner, A. M. (1970). *Z. Pflanzenphysiol.*, **63**, 370
137. Zenk, M. H. (1966). *Proc. 2nd Meeting Fed. Europ. Biochem. Soc.*, Vol. 3 (Oxford: Pergamon)
138. Kratzl, K. (1960). *Tappi*, **43**, 650
139. Barz, W. and Grisebach, H. (1967). *Z. Naturforsch.*, **22b**, 627
140. Ebel, J., Achenbach, H., Barz, W. and Grisebach, H. (1970). *Biochim. Biophys. Acta*, **215**, 203
141. El-Basyouni, S. Z., Neish, A. C. and Towers, G. H. N. (1964). *Phytochem.*, **3**, 627
142. El-Basyouni, S. Z., Chen, D., Ibrahim, R. K., Neish, A. C. and Towers, G. H. N. (1964). *Phytochem.*, **3**, 485
143. Ebel, J., Barz, W. and Grisebach, H. (1970). *Phytochem.*, **9**, 1529
144. Harkin, J. M. and Obst, J. R. (1973). *Science*, **180**, 296
145. Harms, H., Haider, K., Berlin, J., Kiss, P. and Barz, W. (1972). *Planta*, **105**, 342
146. Bernhardt, F., Ruff, H. H. and Staudinger, H. (1971). *Hoppe-Seyler's Z. Physiol. Chem.*, **352**, 1091
147. Cartwright, N. J. and Buswell, J. A. (1967). *Biochem. J.*, **105**, 767
148. Cartwright, N. J. and Smith, A. R. W. (1967). *Biochem. J.*, **102**, 826
149. Ribbons, D. W. (1970). *FEBS Letts.*, **8**, 101
150. Ribbons, D. W. (1971). *FEBS Letts.*, **12**, 161
151. Patschke, L., Hess, D. and Grisebach, H. (1964). *Z. Naturforsch.*, **19b**, 1114
152. Grochowska, M. J. (1967). *Bull. Acad. Polon. Sci.*, **15**, 455
153. Chatterjee, A. K. and Gibbins, L. N. (1969). *J. Bact.*, **100**, 594
154. Minamikawa, T., Jayansankar, N. P., Bohm, B. A., Taylor, I. E. P. and Towers, G. H. N. (1970). *Biochem. J.*, **116**, 889
155. Jayasankar, N. P., Bandoni, R. J. and Towers, G. H. N. (1969). *Phytochem.*, **8**, 379
156. Noguchi, I. and Mori, S. (1969). *Arch. Biochem. Biophys.*, **132**, 352
157. Hattori, S. and Noguchi, I. (1958). *Bot. Mag. Tokyo*, **71**, 43
158. Hattori, S. and Noguchi, I. (1959). *Nature (London)*, **184**, 1145
159. Westlake, D. W. S., Talbot, G., Blakley, E. R., and Simpson, F. J. (1959). *Can. J. Microbiol.*, **5**, 621
160. Padron, J., Grist, K. L., Clark, J. B. and Wender, S. H. (1960). *Biochem. Biophys. Res. Commun.*, **3**, 412
161. Simpson, F. J., Narasimhachari, N. and Westlake, D. W. S. (1963). *Can. J. Microbiol.*, **9**, 15
162. Hosel, W., Shaw, P. D. and Barz, W. (1972). *Z. Naturforsch.*, **27b**, 946
163. Fischer, N. and Dreiding, A. S. (1972). *Helv. Chim. Acta*, **55**, 649
164. Ettlinger, M. and Eyjolfsson, R. (1972). *Chem. Commun.*, **572**
165. Sharples, D., Spring, M. S. and Stoker, J. R. (1972). *Phytochem.*, **11**, 3069
166. Berlin, J., Barz, W., Harms, H. and Haider, K. (1971). *FEBS Letts.*, **16**, 141
167. Bough, W. A. and Gander, J. E. (1971). *Phytochem.*, **10**, 67
168. Craigie, J. S., McLachlan, J. and Towers, G. H. N. (1965). *Can. J. Bot.*, **43**, 1589
169. Ellis, B. E. (1973). *Planta*, **111**, 113
170. Harms, H., Söchtig, H. and Haider, K. (1971). *Z. Pflanzenphysiol.*, **64**, 437
171. Meister, A. (1965). *Biochemistry of the amino acids*, Vol. 2, 884 2nd ed. (New York: Academic Press)
172. Dagley, S. (1970). *Soil Biochemistry* p. 287 (A. D. McLaren and G. H. Peterson, editors) (London: Edward Arnold)
173. Hayaishi, O. and Nozaki, M. (1969). *Science*, **164**, 389
174. Gibbons, D. W. (1965). *Ann. Repr. Prog. Chem. (Lond.)*, **62**, 445
175. Sharma, H. K., Jamalludin, M. and Vaidyanathan, C. S. (1972). *FEBS Letts.*, **28**, 41
176. Ribbons, D. W. (1966). *Biochem. J.*, **99**, 30P
177. Cain, R. B., Bilton, R. F. and Darrah, J. A. (1968). *Biochem. J.*, **108**, 797

178. Hahlbrock, K. and Grisebach, H. (1970). *FEBS Letts.*, **11,** 62
179. Sarkanen, K. V. and Ludwig, C. H. (1971). *Lignins: Occurrence, formation, structure and reactions.* (New York: Wiley-Interscience)
180. Hänsel, R. Rimpler, H. and Schwartz, R. (1965). *Tetrahedron Letts.*, 1545
181. Harborne, J. B. (1967). *Comparative Biochemistry of the Flavonoids* (New York: Academic Press)
182. Senoh, S., Imamoto, Y., Maeno, K., Yamashita, K., Matsui, M., Tokuyama, T., Sakan, S., Komamine, A. and Hattori, S. (1965). *Tetrahedron Letts.*, **46,** 3437
183. Simpson, F. J., Talbot, G. and Westlake, D. W. S. (1960). *Biochem. Biophys. Res. Commun.*, **2,** 15
184. Brown, S. A. and Neish, A. C. (1956). *Can. J. Biochem. Physiol.*, **34,** 769
185. Freudenberg, K., Reznik, H., Fuchs, W. and Reichert, M. (1955). *Naturwissen schaften*, **42,** 29
186. Kratzl, K., Billek, G., Klein, E. and Buchtela, K. (1957). *Monatsch. Chem.*, **88,** 721
187. Heinstein, P. F., Lee, S. I. and Floss, H. G. (1971). *Biochem. Biophys. Res. Commun.*, **44,** 1244
188. Rhodes, M. J. C. and Wooltorton, L. S. C. (1973). *Phytochem.*, **12,** 2381

Index